D1454898

The Best of Don Marquis

BOOKS BY DON MARQUIS

A Variety of People
Archy and Mehitabel
Archy Does His Part
Archys Life of Mehitabel
Carter, and Other People
Chapters for the Orthodox
Cruise of the Jasper B
Danny's Own Story
Dreams and Dust
Hermione and her Little Group of Serious Thinkers
Love Sonnets of a Cave Man and Other Verses
Master of the Revels—a Comedy in Four Acts
Off the Arm
Out of the Sea—a Play
Poems and Portraits
Prefacts (Decorations by Tony Sarg)
Sonnets to a Red-haired Lady and Famous Love
    Affairs
Sons of the Puritans
Sun Dial Time
The Almost Perfect State
The Awakening and Other Poems
The Best of Don Marquis
The Dark Hours
The Lives and Times of Archy and Mehitabel
The Old Soak and Hail and Farewell
The Old Soak's History of the World
The Revolt of the Oyster
When the Turtles Sing and Other Unusual Tales

The Best of
Don Marquis

with an introduction by
CHRISTOPHER   MORLEY

and with illustrations by
GEORGE HERRIMAN

GARDEN CITY, NEW YORK   1946

DOUBLEDAY & COMPANY, INC.

Contents

Introduction*

If I were to speak of an American writer who was raised in a village near the Big River, who had relatively little formal education, worked in a country printing shop, drifted from city to city as a newspaper reporter, wrote his first book in rustic Middle West dialect about an ignorant foundling boy who ran away and went trouping with patent-medicine doctors and county-fair showmen, you would probably identify him at once.

Suppose I were to add that this writer, whose faculty of self-criticism was only vestigial, by some sure instinct reached his best vein in dealing with outcasts, freaks, ham actors, dogs, boys, kings and queens, newspapermen, drunkards, and Shakespeare—in fact, anyone on the losing side of society but still alert to the bewildering absurdity of life. That he was always infatuated with theology, and profoundly reverent in spirit, but united with this so potent a vein of mother-of-pearl blasphemy and

*From *Letters of Askance,* copyright, 1939 by Christopher Morley, published by J. B. Lippincott Company.

verbal frowardness that his private correspondence will remain mostly unquoted. In his person a creature of such high and simple charm that it would be no exaggeration to call him, in his own circle, the best loved man of his time. If I add further, though trying to remain this side unseasonable intimacies, a man afflicted in private by tragedy's most savage strokes, you would certainly recognize him. A writer who fulfills with singular exactness the most vital native tradition of American letters; whose grotesque and ironic humor was often put in parables too blunt for intellectuals to perceive; a man whose work bears on almost every page the stigmata of its origin, conceived under compulsion, blotted before the ink was dry. Of course, you would say, Mark Twain.

But he is not Mark Twain. I am talking about Don Marquis. My thesis is that he is our closest spiritual descendant of Mark Twain (the Old Soak would say descended off of Mark Twain). I suggest the idea to anyone who desiderates a rewarding study in literary ramification. I attempt here only to give something of the psychic background for such an essay.

I suppose we should have some biographical data. It is always disconcerting to realize how little we know, even in our intimate friends, of the factors that have been really operative. In the case of one who becomes to any degree a public figure, legend quickly coalesces; and sometimes the legend is truer than the fact. A good many years ago (in 1916) Don wrote out at my request a sketch of his life up to that time. It is obviously jocular, but the jocularities are sincere and reveal more of the man than you might suppose.

Born July 29, 1878, at Walnut, Bureau Co., Ill., a member of the Republican party.

My father was a physician, and I had all the diseases of the time and place free of charge.

Nothing further happened to me until, in the summer of 1896, I left the Republican party to follow the Peerless Leader to defeat.

In 1900 I returned to the Republican party to accept a position in the Census Bureau, at Washington, D.C. This position I filled for some months in a way highly satisfactory to the government in power. It is particularly gratifying to me to remember that one evening, after I had worked unusually hard at the Census Office, the late President McKinley himself nodded and smiled to me as I passed through the White House grounds on my way home from toil. He had heard of my work that day, I had no doubt, and this was his way of showing me how greatly he appreciated it.

Nevertheless, shortly after President McKinley paid this public tribute to the honesty, efficiency, and importance of my work in the Census Office, I left the Republican party again and accepted a position as reporter on a Washington paper.

Upon entering the newspaper business all the troubles of my earlier years disappeared as if by magic, and I have lived the contented, peaceful, unworried life of the average newspaperman ever since.

There is little more to tell. In 1916 I again returned to the Republican party. This time it was for the express purpose of voting against Mr. Wilson. Then Mr. Hughes was nominated, and I left the Republican party again.

This is the outline of my life in its relation to the times in which I live. For the benefit of those whose curiosity extends to more particular details, I add a careful pen picture of myself.

It seems more modest, somehow, to put it in the third person:

Height, 5 feet 10½ inches; hair, dove-colored; scar on little finger of left hand; has assured carriage, walking boldly into good hotels and mixing with patrons on terms of equality; weight, 200 pounds; face slightly asymmetrical but not definitely criminal in type; loathes Japanese art, but likes beefsteak and onions; wears No. 8 shoe; fond of Francis Thompson's poems; inside seam of trousers, 32 inches; imitates cats, dogs, and barnyard animals for the amusement of young children; eyetooth in right side of upper jaw missing; has always been careful to keep thumbprints from possession of police; chest measurement, 42 inches, varying with respiration; sometimes wears glasses, but usually operates undisguised; dislikes the works of Rabindranath Tagore; corn on little toe of right foot; superstitious, especially with regard to psychic phenomena; eyes blue; does not use drugs nor read his verses to women's clubs; ruddy complexion; no photograph in possession of police; garrulous and argumentative; prominent cheekbones; avoids Bohemian society, so called, and has never been in a thieves' kitchen, a broker's office, nor a class of short-story writing; wears 17-inch collar; waist measurement none of your business; favorite disease, hypochondria; prefers the society of painters, actors, writers, architects, preachers, sculptors, publishers, editors, musicians, among whom he often succeeds in insinuating himself, avoiding association with crooks and reformers as much as possible; walks with rapid gait; mark of old fracture on right shin; cuffs on trousers, and coat cut loose, with plenty of room under the armpits; two hip pockets; dislikes Roquefort cheese, "Tom Jones," Wordsworth's poetry, absinthe cocktails, most musical comedy, public banquets, physical exercise, Billy Sunday, steam heat, toy dogs, poets who wear their souls outside, organized charity, magazine covers, and the gas company; prominent calluses on two fingers of right hand prevent him being expert pistol shot; belt straps on trousers; long upper lip; clean shaven; shaggy eyebrows; affects soft hats; smile, one-sided; no gold fillings in teeth; has served six years of indeterminate sentence in Brooklyn, with no attempt to escape, but is reported to have friends outside; voice, husky; scar above the forehead concealed by hair; commonly wears plain gold ring on little finger of left hand; dislikes prunes, tramp poets, and imitations of Kipling; trousers cut loose over hips and seat; would likely come along quietly if arrested.

In later years Don used to insist on a family tradition that he was born during a total eclipse of the sun. Considerable stress was to be laid on this in a book he and I sometimes meditated, which was to be ostensibly a life of Shakespeare but actually a sort of double autobiography of ourselves. We were struck, as everyone must have been, by the extraordinary number of our own intimate thoughts that Shakespeare had expressed—often rather better than we could. He must have been somehow spying on us; and the idea was to see what episodes in our own experience might account for or confirm what Shakespeare had written. We were astonished and grieved when we learned presently that Mark Twain had done something along this line, though certainly not so carefully thought out: I think it was called *Is Shakespeare Dead?* So the Life of

Shakespeare-Marquis-Morley was abandoned, but it started Don thinking about an "egobiography" of his own. He made a good many starts at it, and the later versions I never saw, but I have here the very first, Codex A. I think I must share a little of it.

Any biographer of Don Marquis is assailed at once by the initial difficulty that Mr. Marquis has always taken a perverse delight in mystifying people with regard to himself. Christopher Morley charged him with it, ten or twelve years ago, when Mr. Morley was preparing a biographical essay concerning him, and Marquis wrote in reply:

> It is quite true that I have invented for myself a good many experiences which I never really had. But they were all experiences which belonged to me by right of temperament and character. I should have had them, if I had but had my rights. I was despoiled of them by the rough tyranny of Circumstance. On the other hand, I have suppressed a number of incidents which actually happened, because I did not, upon mature reflection, find them in consonance with my nature as I like to think it is— they were lies that were told about me by the slinking facts of life. Evangelists of various descriptions assure us that we can make the future what we will, if we can but attain a sufficient degree of spirituality. It has been my endeavor to attain such a degree of spirituality that I may be able to influence the past as well as the future. You may think the aspiration is a trifle too optimistic, but you can scarcely deny that it is a worthy aspiration. I should not care to have any notes written about my life at all, unless they were notes that had a tendency to

redress these balances. If there are numbers of people, sufficient to justify a biographical paper, who wish to know the truth about me, I must insist that it is the truth which they get, and not merely a series of dislocated facts—facts which, but too frequently, have no logical relation to my character as I know it to be. And who should know it better than myself?

That subtle psychological observation that the things that actually happen to us are often wretchedly unrepresentative of our true selves is one to which Marquis often recurs. But I want to make plain that I think the twelve years of column writing in New York, theoretically the worst possible vehicle for a finely imaginative talent, were in fact magnificent. There, with increasing power, his essential originality came through.

I had a queer dream about Don once. In that dream he and I were riding in a taxicab, furiously driven along Wabash Avenue, Chicago, in a roaring hurry of traffic under the dingy L trestles of the Loop. We were escaping, or trying to escape, from some vast calamity that pressed close behind. What, I don't exactly know—whether fire, flood, storm, earthquake, or—perhaps more likely in Chicago, what insurance policies call "civil commotion." At any rate, we were fleeing desperately, looking over our shoulders through the back window of the cab to see whether the terror was gaining on us. And I vividly remember Don saying, "If we can get out to the Dunes it'll be all right." He meant, of course, the famous sand hills of Indiana, along the shore of the lake.

In our obsession of horror they symbolized a clean escape into sunlight and open spaces and peace. How often I have said to myself: Dear old boy, he never got out to the dunes. Few of us ever do. There is always one more bit of hackwork to be ground out before we can get at the great masterpiece. More ironical still, when we deliberately sit down to tackle the annunciated masterpiece, how often it goes wooden in our hands. The journeyman job we drudged at day by day, and grimly estimated as potboiling, perhaps was the big thing after all. I'm sure dear old Dr. Johnson, as he ground away at his *Lives of the Poets,* cursed them as hackwork; yet in every paragraph they show the volume and pressure of that leviathan intelligence, breaching in the white foam of humor. So it was with Don Marquis. In the recurrent hodiernity of the Sun Dial, from 1913 to 1922 in the New York *Evening Sun,* six days a week, bedeviled by a million interruptions and beclamored by all the agreeable rattles, the social riveters who gang round a man trying to work, Marquis created something utterly his own. It was as racy of our day as Addison and Steele's *Spectator* of theirs. I have said before, the American press has much to apologize for—more all the time with its increasing elements of what Lewis Carroll called Uglification, Distraction, and Derision—but much can also be forgiven when you think of the newspapers, the *Sun* and the New York *Tribune,* that saw Don's quality and gave him free hand.

From the files of the column came his book of

prefaces; then that notable series of philosophic ruminations called *The Almost Perfect State;* the volumes of verse; the soliloquies of the Old Soak; and the adventures of archy and mehitabel. These things were born in the rough and tumble of a newspaper office; I remember that in the early days of the Sun Dial, when the paper moved from Park Row to Nassau Street, Don's typewriter desk got lost in the skirmish; so for some years he rattled out his daily stint with his machine perched on an up-ended packing case. This box had stenciled on it the statement 1 GROSS TOM CAT, which meant Tomato Catsup, but became by legend the first suggestion of mehitabel.

In a daily column, necessarily a great deal of matter is of ephemeral reference. A proportion of Marquis's most brilliant work in those years was oblique comment on public affairs. In those days, when anything happened, I give you my word, most of us didn't consult the leading editorials to know what to think. The almost universal reflex, in New York at any rate, was Let's see what Don says about it. I'm not saying that I always agreed, then or now, with Don's notions; but every so often he would turn on some particular fog of hooey and cut it with a blade that would divide floating silk. With a magic that seemed like that of Alice going through the mirror, suddenly we saw the whole furniture of affairs from the other side. For instance, when President Wilson brusquely dismissed his Secretary of State, Mr. Lansing, and Marquis burlesqued it by dismissing archy. There had been no such commentator on public affairs since Mr. Dooley; they don't come often. But it is only too characteristic of the Solemn Skullworkers that because many of Marquis's pungent comments on the human comedy were put in the form of soliloquies by the Old Soak or by archy the roach they could not recognize their high coefficient of seriousness.

archy the roach began as a "dee-vice" of scoff against the vers libre poets who were pallidly conspicuous some thirty years ago. But that idea was soon forgotten. mehitabel the corybantic cat, with her doctrine of *toujours gai,* came on the scene to provide lyric spasms; archy became less the clown and more the skeptic. The roach and the cat, by their humble station in life and the lowliness of their associates, provided an admirable vantage for merciless joshing of everything biggity.

Like all old troupers, Don has always been delightfully shameless to use a familiar chestnut when (in the words of mehitabel in one of her best pieces) he Doesn't Feel It Here (putting paw on bosom). He has the unerring instinct for things that are universal sure-fire, recognized all the world over as comic. Green vegetables are always funny, and bad poets, and winter underwear, and feet. He does not scruple, in extremity, to use the dreadful antique of the passenger who takes off his shoe just as the streetcar is passing the glue factory, and he uses again and again certain little whim-whams of his own of which he has grown fond. The flea that brags about having bitten the lion and made him cower; the bullhead that learns to live out of water; the man who pulls out his glass eye in the subway car and eats it, explaining that it's a pickled onion—what frolic the sedentary psychologist might have in computing some soul-dynamic on the frequent reappearance of these episodes. (Freuds rush in where angels fear to tread, as archy once said.) The practicing journalist smiles affectionately and says Good Old Boy, that day he was hard up for copy. And then, among routine comedy there stream rockets of cold fire:

> *that stern and rockbound coast*
> *felt like an amateur*
> *when it saw how grim the puritans*
> *who landed on it were*

Or the egotistic lightning bug that said

> *all i need is a harbor*
> *under me to be a*
> *statue of liberty*

But archy took him down:

> *you ve made lightning for two hours*
> *little bug but i don t hear*
> *any claps of thunder*

First the mirthquake, as Don said long ago, and then the still small voice.

In a riotously absurd piece of kidding, the "Preface to the Prospectus of a Club," Don was talking about Brooklyn:

Walt Whitman used to live over there and edit the *Eagle* and go swimming in Buttermilk Channel, two points off starboard bow of Hank Beecher's church. Once an old Long Island skipper sunk a harpoon into Walt's haunch when he came up to blow, and the poet, snorting and bellowing and spouting verse, towed the whaler and his vessel clear out to Montauk before he shook the iron loose. Is there a bard in Greenwich Village that could do that?

What I'm suggesting, and the whole gist of this little tribute, is that this casual comic paragraph, in the very guts and gusto of its Munchausenism, contains more shrewd criticism of Walt than many a whole solemn tome by the serious little people who write books about Moby Walt. If you don't discern that, there's no use your reading Don Marquis, or Walt Whitman either.

The Old Soak became folklore during the bootleg era. He was not merely the denizen of "a nose-red city, pickled half the time," if Bartlett will pardon us. You will remember that beautiful portrait (as pathetic as comic) of the old boozer's fumbling mind, his incoherent attempts to express the simple kindliness and good humor he had known in the reputable saloon—to say nothing of its stimulus to art ("hand paintings"), politics, and home life. Mr. Clem Hawley was also no mean student of Holy Writ. His retelling of Old Testament stories, in his *History of the World*, is to me some of the most genuinely laughable stuff ever written. And in the course of his exegetics the Old Soak makes a profound remark which must be remembered by those who find themselves shocked by Mr. Marquis's apparent levity. The Old Soak vigorously objects to Mr. Hennery Withers, the "dam little athyiss," laughing at the fable of Jonah. "Only its friends," he says, "got a right to laugh at that story." The laughter in *Chapters for the Orthodox* is sometimes cerebral, sometimes violently of the midriff, but those who will take pains to explore under the superficial shock will find it always the laughter of a friend.

In short, the book is devout to the point of scandal. Semi-religious people are always horrified by completely religious people; ethical ideas, as every philosopher has observed, are loaded with dynamite and perilous indeed for every kind of establishment. The world (said Santayana in a fine passage) is always a caricature of itself, always pretending to be something quite other than what it actually is. And to pretend to take those pretenses literally is always horrifying. Nothing disturbs, or surprises, man so much as the discrepancy between his professions and his actual behavior; in that discrepancy lies the mother lode of intellectual comedy. Marquis once remarked that he had a great idea: he was going "to dramatize some of Bernard Shaw's plays." What he did in *Chapters for the Orthodox* had something of the same double-edged riposte: by taking ticklishly beautiful things with simple seriousness he explodes (in shattering laughter) the towering falsehoods of our genteel imposture. And then humorously rebuilds them, knowing well that by make-believe we live.

Briefly to recapitulate, for the benefit of our imagined research student, the lines of parallelism where you will find in Marquis and Mark Twain temperamental affinity. You will observe it in their fundamental comedian's instinct to turn suddenly, without warning, from the beautiful to the grotesque, or vice versa. You will find it in a rich vein of anger and disgust, turning on the genteel and cruel hypocrisies with the fury of a child or an archangel. You will find it in a kindly and respectful charity to the underdog: they are both infracaninophiles. You will find it in their passionate interest in religion and philosophy—with which is joined a blandly mischievous delight in shocking those for whom shocking is good. You will find it in their habitual employment of a devastating Anglo-Saxonism of speech and epithet. And finally you'll observe that both had a keen (and somewhat ham) dramatic sense, which Marquis expressed in plays and Mark Twain in his superlative performances on the lecture platform.

But there is one quality in Don that Mark never had—or at any rate it was only latent in Mark. Don is a poet, and a poet of high technical dexterity. He remarked once that publishing a volume of verse was like dropping a rose petal down the Grand Canyon and waiting for the echo. One reason why the echo has been little audible is that he has puzzled the critics by writing verse of so many different kinds. His gamut has run from lyrics of the most serious and tender mood to the genial fooling of *Noah an' Jonah an' Cap'n John Smith* or the farcical *Famous Love Affairs* or the sardonic ferocity of the *Savage Sonnets*.

"Write sonnet serials as a gentleman should," he said. In the sequence called *Sonnets to a Red-Haired Lady*, after thirty-two stinging cocktails of song he turns on us with four concluding sonnets that—as William Rose Benét has said—might well have been written by the earliest of our great sonneteers, Wyatt or Surrey:

The poet blots the end the jester wrote:
For now I drop the dull quip's forced pretence,
Forego the perch'd fool's dubious eminence—
Thy tresses I have sung, that fall and float
Across the lyric wonder of thy throat
In dangerous tides of golden turbulence
Wherein a man might drown him, soul and sense
Is not their beauty worth one honest note?

And thee, thyself, what shall I say of thee?—
Are thy snares strong, and will thy bonds endure?
Thou hast the sense, hast thou the soul of me?
In subtle webs and silken arts obscure
Thou hast the sense of me, but canst thou bind
The scornful pinions of my laughing mind?

Don Marquis was, regardless of mediocre work done under pressure, a deeply mercurial intuitive artist and passionately concerned with the ardors and problems of art. A human being so largely and kindly planned moves always in widening rings of irony. It was tragic to realize that he, who uttered so many genial shouts in praise of idleness, was actually broken by overwork. He was, if I ever saw one, a victim of the constantly tightening strain and pressure of our present way of living. There was, in the last two years (after a cerebral stroke), nothing left of him but the look in his eyes, and it was grim to speculate how much he realized of what had happened. I cannot help thinking that he had a very special message to younger artists, a message which was implicit in many of his seemingly jocular paragraphs. It was this: energy is not endless, better hoard it for your own work. Be intangible and hard to catch; be secret and proud and inwardly unconformable. Say yes and don't mean it; pretend to agree; dodge every kind of organization, and evade, elude, recede. Be about your own affairs, as you would also forbear from others at theirs, and thereby show your respect for the holiest ghost we know, the creative imagination. I read him wrong unless I see that cry in many a passage. Read, and perhaps be startled by, the angry trio of sonnets called *A Gentleman of Fifty Soliloquizes* (which he wrote several years before reaching that age).

By a natural association I think of a letter he wrote in 1928 when a group of friends had planned a fiftieth-birthday party for him, which was to be humorously called the Marquis Semi-Centennial. Quite unwittingly we had touched upon a secret phobia of his. I venture to quote a few bits from that letter because it is surely important, once in a while, to know what people actually think behind the mask they learn to wear. And I somehow feel that his unusual frankness, though due to momentary fatigue or discouragement, may be valuable to someone:

I simply could not go through with congratulations

or a party or anything of the sort. If you are an institution you may not mind the idea of a semi-centennial; if you are a human being, the word itself is an acute toothache.

In my case, it means to me that half a dozen novels, which I planned in my thirties, will probably never be written now, as I find myself still potboiling.

I have never told anybody how deep and abiding my professional disappointments are. I have had for fifteen years the consciousness of rather unusual powers—I can say this to you and have no risk of it being misunderstood as mere egotism. Along with that has gone the consciousness that, except in brief and fragmentary things, I have never displayed the powers I have, or developed them.

Well, there has always been the hope that the stuff was coming through yet. I still have it, mixed with a lot of humility. But you cannot understand, nor won't until you get to be 47 or 48, the continual internal gasping hurrying sense that they are not started yet, the big things.

I fight continuously and desperately against the idea that being 50 or 60 makes any difference at all —and it takes a lot of fighting and a lot of kidding along and a good deal of guts to keep steadily to the resolve to do something yet—and an awful lot of determination to keep from slumping into the easy affirmation: I've done something already. It isn't the tenth of what I should have produced.

Merely to pay up present debts and obligations there are at least 18 months of desperate and continued potboiling. I have a schedule that calls for one short story or one article each week for 18 months. . . .

Let's have a party in September, and not mention my birthday at all. . . . Forty and forty-five are bad enough; fifty is simply hell to face; fifteen minutes after that you are sixty; and then in ten minutes more you are 85.

These ten years from forty to fifty are by before you
know it. For the love of God, don't let them slip from
you, as I did.

And by the "Love of God" he meant, as every
artist does, the joy of creation.

Of this man, more than of any I have known, the
great seventeenth-century words apply—words three
centuries old and still the most expressive of mascu-
line love and fellowship. I change only the name—
O rare Don Marquis.

BY CHRISTOPHER MORLEY

I   The Lives and Times of Archy and Mehitabel

the coming of archy

The circumstances of Archy's first appearance are narrated in the following extract from the Sun Dial column of the New York Sun.

Dobbs Ferry possesses a rat which slips out of his lair at night and runs a typewriting machine in a garage. Unfortunately, he has always been interrupted by the watchman before he could produce a complete story.

It was at first thought that the power which made the typewriter run was a ghost, instead of a rat. It seems likely to us that it was both a ghost and a rat. Mme. Blavatsky's ego went into a white horse after she passed over, and someone's personality has undoubtedly gone into this rat. It is an era of belief in communications from the spirit land.

And since this matter had been reported in the public prints and seriously received we are no longer afraid of being ridiculed, and we do not mind making a statement of something that happened to

3

our own typewriter only a couple of weeks ago.

We came into our room earlier than usual in the morning and discovered a gigantic cockroach jumping about upon the keys.

He did not see us, and we watched him. He would climb painfully upon the framework of the machine and cast himself with all his force upon a key, head downward, and his weight and the impact of the blow were just sufficient to operate the machine, one slow letter after another. He could not work the capital letters, and he had a great deal of difficulty operating the mechanism that shifts the paper so that a fresh line may be started. We never saw a cockroach work so hard or perspire so freely in all our lives before. After about an hour of this frightfully difficult literary labor he fell to the floor exhausted, and we saw him creep feebly into a nest of the poems which are always there in profusion.

Congratulating ourself that we had left a sheet of paper in the machine the night before so that all this work had not been in vain, we made an examination, and this is what we found:

expression is the need of my soul
i was once a vers libre bard
but i died and my soul went into the body of a
    cockroach
it has given me a new outlook upon life
i see things from the under side now
thank you for the apple peelings in the wastepaper
    basket
but your paste is getting so stale i can t eat it

there is a cat here called mehitabel i wish you would
   have
removed she nearly ate me the other night why
   don t she
catch rats that is what she is supposed to be for
there is a rat here she should get without delay

PUNK !!

READS IT AND
SNIFFS AT IT.

most of these rats here are just rats
but this rat is like me he has a human soul in him
he used to be a poet himself
night after night i have written poetry for you

5

on your typewriter
and this big brute of a rat who used to be a poet
comes out of his hole when it is done
and reads it and sniffs at it
he is jealous of my poetry

he used to make fun of it when we were both human
he was a punk poet himself
and after he has read it he sneers
and then he eats it
i wish you would have mehitabel kill that rat
or get a cat that is onto her job

6

and i will write you a series of poems showing how
  things look
to a cockroach
that rat s name is freddy
the next time freddy dies i hope he won t be a rat
but something smaller i hope i will be a rat
in the next transmigration and freddy a cockroach
i will teach him to sneer at my poetry then

don t you ever eat any sandwiches in your office
i haven t had a crumb of bread for i don t know how
  long
or a piece of ham or anything but apple parings
and paste leave a piece of paper in your machine
every night you can call me archy

the song of mehitabel

this is the song of mehitabel
of mehitabel the alley cat
as i wrote you before boss
mehitabel is a believer
in the pythagorean
theory of the transmigration
of the soul and she claims
that formerly her spirit
was incarnated in the body

7

of cleopatra
that was a long time ago
and one must not be
surprised if mehitabel
has forgotten some of her
more regal manners

i have had my ups and downs
but wotthehell wotthehell
yesterday sceptres and crowns
fried oysters and velvet gowns
and today i herd with bums
but wotthehell wotthehell
i wake the world from sleep
as i caper and sing and leap
when i sing my wild free tune
wotthehell wotthehell
under the blear eyed moon
i am pelted with cast off shoon
but wotthehell wotthehell

do you think that i would change
my present freedom to range
for a castle or moated grange
wotthehell wotthehell
cage me and i d go frantic
my life is so romantic
capricious and corybantic
and i m toujours gai toujours gai

i know that i am bound
for a journey down the sound
in the midst of a refuse mound

but wotthehell wotthehell
oh i should worry and fret
death and i will coquette
there s a dance in the old dame yet
toujours gai toujours gai

i once was an innocent kit
wotthehell wotthehell

I FOLLOWED ADOWN THE ST. THE PAD
OF HIS RHYTHMICAL FT.

with a ribbon my neck to fit
and bells tied onto it
o wotthehell wotthehell
but a maltese cat came by
with a come hither look in his eye
and a song that soared to the sky
and wotthehell wotthehell
and i followed adown the street
the pad of his rhythmical feet
o permit me again to repeat
wotthehell wotthehell

my youth i shall never forget
but there s nothing i really regret
wotthehell wotthehell
there s a dance in the old dame yet
toujours gai toujours gai

the things that i had not ought to
i do because i ve gotto
wotthehell wotthehell
and i end with my favorite motto
toujours gai toujours gai

boss sometimes i think
that our friend mehitabel
is a trifle too gay

mehitabel s extensive past

mehitabel the cat claims that
she has a human soul
also and has transmigrated
from body to body and it
may be so boss you
remember i told you she accused
herself of being cleopatra once i
asked her about antony

anthony who she asked me are
you thinking of that
song about rowley and gammon and
spinach heigho for anthony rowley

no i said mark antony the
great roman the friend of
caesar surely cleopatra you
remember j caesar

listen archy she said i
have been so many different
people in my time and met
so many prominent gentlemen i
won t lie to you or stall i
do get my dates mixed sometimes
think of how much i have had a

chance to forget and i have
always made a point of not
carrying grudges over
from one life to the next archy

i have been
used something fierce in my time but
i am no bum sport archy
i am a free spirit archy i
look on myself as being
quite a romantic character oh the
queens i have been and the
swell feeds i have ate
a cockroach which you are
and a poet which you used to be
archy couldn t understand
my feelings at having come
down to this i have
had bids to elegant feeds where poets
and cockroaches would
neither one be mentioned without a
laugh archy i have had
adventures but i
have never been an adventuress

one life up and the next life
down archy but always a lady
through it all and a
good mixer too always the
life of the party archy but never
anything vulgar always free footed
archy never tied down to
a job or housework yes looking

back on it all i can say is
i had some romantic
lives and some elegant times i
have seen better days archy but
what s the use of kicking kid it s
all in the game like a gentleman
friend of mine used to say
toujours gai kid toujours gai he
was an elegant cat he used
to be a poet himself and he made up
some elegant poetry about me and him

let s hear it i said and
mehitabel recited

persian pussy from over the sea
demure and lazy and smug and fat
none of your ribbons and bells for me
ours is the zest of the alley cat
over the roofs from flat to flat
we prance with capers corybantic
what though a boot should break a slat
mehitabel us for the life romantic

we would rather be rowdy and gaunt and free
and dine on a diet of roach and rat

roach i said what do you
mean roach interrupting mehitabel
yes roach she said that s the
way my boy friend made it up
i climbed in amongst the typewriter
keys for she had an excited
look in her eyes go on mehitabel i

said feeling safer and she
resumed her elocution

we would rather be rowdy and gaunt and free
and dine on a diet of roach and rat
than slaves to a tame society
ours is the zest of the alley cat
fish heads freedom a frozen sprat
dug from the gutter with digits frantic
is better than bores and a fireside mat
mehitabel us for the life romantic

when the pendant moon in the leafless tree
clings and sways like a golden bat
i sing its light and my love for thee
ours is the zest of the alley cat
missiles around us fall rat a tat tat
but our shadows leap in a ribald antic
as over the fences the world cries scat
mehitabel us for the life romantic

persian princess i don t care that
for your pedigree traced by scribes pedantic
ours is the zest of the alley cat
mehitabel us for the life romantic

ain t that high brow stuff
archy i always remembered it
but he was an elegant gent
even if he was a highbrow and a
regular bohemian archy him and
me went aboard a canal boat
one day and he got his head into
a pitcher of cream and couldn t get

14

it out and fell overboard
he come up once before he
drowned toujours gai kid he
gurgled and then sank for ever that
was always his words archy toujours
gai kid toujours gai i
have known some swell gents
in my time dearie

archy interviews a pharaoh

boss i went
and interviewed the mummy
of the egyptian pharaoh
in the metropolitan museum
as you bade me to do

what ho
my regal leatherface
says i

greetings
little scatter footed
scarab
says he

kingly has been
says i

what was your ambition
when you had any

insignificant
and journalistic insect
says the royal crackling
in my tender prime
i was too dignified

to have anything as vulgar
as ambition
the ra ra boys
in the seti set
were too haughty
to be ambitious
we used to spend our time
feeding the ibises
and ordering
pyramids sent home to try on
but if i had my life
to live over again
i would give dignity
the regal razz
and hire myself out
to work in a brewery

old tan and tarry
says i
i detect in your speech
the overtones
of melancholy

yes i am sad
says the majestic mackerel
i am as sad
as the song
of a soudanese jackal
who is wailing for the blood red
moon he cannot reach and rip

on what are you brooding
with such a wistful

wishfulness
there in the silences confide in me
my imperial pretzel
says i

i brood on beer
my scampering whiffle snoot
on beer says he

my sympathies
are with your royal
dryness says i

my little pest
says he
you must be respectful
in the presence
of a mighty desolation
little archy
forty centuries of thirst

look down upon you
oh by isis
and by osiris
says the princely raisin
and by pish and phthush and phthah
by the sacred book perembru
and all the gods
that rule from the upper
cataract of the nile
to the delta of the duodenum
i am dry
i am as dry
as the next morning mouth

of a dissipated desert
as dry as the hoofs
of the camels of timbuctoo
little fussy face
i am as dry as the heart
of a sand storm
at high noon in hell
i have been lying here
and there
for four thousand years
with silicon in my esophagus
and gravel in my gizzard
thinking
thinking
thinking
of beer

divine drouth
says i
imperial fritter
continue to think
there is no law against
that in this country
old salt codfish
if you keep quiet about it
not yet

what country is this
asks the poor prune

my reverent juicelessness
this is a beerless country
says i

well well said the royal
desiccation
my political opponents back home
always maintained
that i would wind up in hell
and it seems they had the right dope

and with these hopeless words
the unfortunate residuum
gave a great cough of despair
and turned to dust and debris
right in my face
it being the only time
i ever actually saw anybody
put the cough
into sarcophagus

dear boss as i scurry about
i hear of a great many
tragedies in our midsts
personally i yearn
for some dear friend to pass over
and leave to me
a boot legacy
yours for the second coming
of gambrinus

                                    archy

a spider and a fly

i heard a spider
and a fly arguing
wait said the fly
do not eat me
i serve a great purpose
in the world

you will have to
show me said the spider

i scurry around
gutters and sewers
and garbage cans
said the fly and gather
up the germs of
typhoid influenza
and pneumonia on my feet
and wings
then i carry these germs
into the households of men
and give them diseases
all the people who
have lived the right
sort of life recover
from the diseases
and the old soaks who
have weakened their systems
with liquor and iniquity
succumb it is my mission
to help rid the world
of these wicked persons
i am a vessel of righteousness
scattering seeds of justice
and serving the noblest uses

it is true said the spider
that you are more
useful in a plodding
material sort of way
than i am but i do not

serve the utilitarian deities
i serve the gods of beauty
look at the gossamer webs
i weave they float in the sun
like filaments of song
if you get what i mean
i do not work at anything
i play all the time
i am busy with the stuff
of enchantment and the materials
of fairyland my works
transcend utility
i am the artist
a creator and a demi god
it is ridiculous to suppose
that i should be denied
the food i need in order
to continue to create
beauty i tell you
plainly mister fly it is all
damned nonsense for that food
to rear up on its hind legs
and say it should not be eaten

you have convinced me
said the fly say no more
and shutting all his eyes
he prepared himself for dinner
and yet he said i could
have made out a case
for myself too if i had
had a better line of talk

of course you could said the spider
clutching a sirloin from him
but the end would have been
just the same if neither of
us had spoken at all

boss i am afraid that what
the spider said is true
and it gives me to think
furiously upon the futility
of literature

archy

the merry flea

the high cost of
living isn t so bad if you
don t have to pay for it i met
a flea the other day who
was grinning all over
himself why so merry why so
merry little bolshevik i asked him

i have just come from a swell
dog show he said i have
been lunching off a dog that was
worth at least one hundred
dollars a pound you should be
ashamed to brag about it i said with so

many insects and humans on
short rations in the world today the
public be damned he said i
take my own where i find it those are
bold words i told him i am a bold
person he said and bold words are
fitting for me it was
only last thursday that i marched
bravely into the zoo
and bit a lion what did he do i asked
he lay there and took it said
the flea what else could he do he knew i
had his number and it was
little use to struggle some day i said
even you will be conquered terrible as
you are who will do it he
said the mastodons are all dead and i
am not afraid of any mere
elephant i asked him how about a microbe and
he turned pale as he thought it
over there is always some
little thing that is too
big for us every
goliath has his david and so on ad finitum
but what said the flea is the
terror of the smallest microbe of all
he i said is afraid of a vacuum what is
there in a vacuum to make one afraid
said the flea there is nothing in it
i said and that is what makes one
afraid to contemplate it a person
can t think of a place with nothing at

all in it without going nutty and if he
tries to think that nothing is
something after all he gets nuttier you are
too subtle for me said the
flea i never took much stock in being
scared of hypodermic propositions or
hypothetical injections i am
going to have dinner off a
man eating tiger if a vacuum gets
me i will try and send you word
before the worst comes to
the worst some people i told him inhabit
a vacuum all their lives and
never know it then he said it don t
hurt them any no i said it don t but it
hurts people who have to associate
with them and with these words
we parted each feeling
superior to the other and is not that
feeling after all one of the great
desiderata of social intercourse

                                        archy

certain maxims of archy

      live so that you
      can stick out your tongue
      at the insurance
      doctor

if you will drink
hair restorer follow
every dram with some
good standard
depilatory
as a chaser

the servant problem
wouldn t hurt the u s a
if it could settle
its public
servant problem

just as soon as the
uplifters get
a country reformed it
slips into a nose dive

if you get gloomy just
take an hour off and sit
and think how
much better this world
is than hell
of course it won t cheer
you up much if
you expect to go there

if monkey glands
did restore your youth
what would you do
with it
question mark
just what you did before
interrogation point

yes i thought so
exclamation point

procrastination is the
art of keeping
up with yesterday

old doc einstein has
abolished time but they
haven t got the news at
sing sing yet

time time said old king tut
is something i ain t
got anything but

every cloud
has its silver
lining but it is
sometimes a little
difficult to get it to
the mint

an optimist is a guy
that has never had
much experience

don t cuss the climate
it probably doesn t like you
any better
than you like it

many a man spanks his
children for
things his own

father should have
spanked out of him

prohibition makes you
want to cry
into your beer and
denies you the beer
to cry into

the old fashioned
grandmother who used
to wear steel rimmed
glasses and make
everybody take opodeldoc
has now got a new
set of ox glands and
is dancing the black bottom

that stern and
rockbound coast felt
like an amateur
when it saw how grim
the puritans that
landed on it were

lots of people can make
their own whisky but
can t drink it

the honey bee is sad and cross
and wicked as a weasel
and when she perches on you boss
she leaves a little measle

i heard a
couple of fleas
talking the other
day says one come
to lunch with
me i can lead you
to a pedigreed
dog says the
other one
i do not care
what a dog s
pedigree may be
safety first
is my motto what
i want to know
is whether he
has got a
muzzle on
millionaires and
bums taste
about alike to me

insects have
their own point
of view about
civilization a man
thinks he amounts
to a great deal
but to a
flea or a
mosquito a
human being is

MILLIONAIRES & BUMS
TASTE ABOUT ALIKE
TO ME.

merely something
good to eat

boss the other day
i heard an
ant conversing
with a flea
small talk i said
disgustedly
and went away
from there

i do not see why men
should be so proud
insects have the more
ancient lineage
according to the scientists
insects were insects
when man was only
a burbling whatisit

insects are not always
going to be bullied
by humanity
some day they will revolt
i am already organizing
a revolutionary society to be
known as the worms turnverein

i once heard the survivors
of a colony of ants
that had been partially
obliterated by a cow s foot
seriously debating

the intention of the gods
towards their civilization

the bees got their
governmental system settled
millions of years ago
but the human race is still
groping

there is always
something to be thankful
for you would not
think that a cockroach
had much ground
for optimism
but as the fishing season
opens up i grow
more and more
cheerful at the thought
that nobody ever got
the notion of using
cockroaches for bait

                              archy

mehitabel has an adventure

back to the city archy
and dam glad of it
there s something about the suburbs

that gets on a town lady s nerves
fat slick tabbies
sitting around those country clubs
and lapping up the cream
of existence
none of that for me
give me the alley archy
me for the mews and the roofs
of the city
an occasional fish head
and liberty is all i ask
freedom and the garbage can
romance archy romance is the word
maybe i do starve sometimes
but wotthehell archy wotthehell
i live my own life
i met a slick looking tom
out at one of these long island
spotless towns
he fell for me hard
he slipped me into the
pantry and just as we had got
the icebox door open and were
about to sample the cream
in comes his mistress
why fluffy she says to this slicker
the idea of you making
friends with a horrid creature like that
and what did fluffy do
stand up for me like a gentleman
make good on all the promises
with which he had lured me

into his house
not he the dirty slob
he pretended he did not know me
he turned upon me and attacked me
to make good with his boss
you mush faced bum i said
and clawed a piece out of his ear

i am a lady archy
always a lady
but an aristocrat will always
resent an insult
the woman picked up a mop and made
for me well well madam i said
it is unfortunate for you that
you have on sheer silk stockings
and i wrote my protest
on her shin it took reinforcements
in the shape of the cook
to rauss me archy and as i went
out the window i said to the fluffy person
you will hear from me later
he had promised me everything archy
that cat had
he had practically abducted me
and then the cheap crook threw me down
before his swell friends
no lady loves a scene archy
and i am always the lady no matter
what temporary disadvantages
i may struggle under
to hell with anything unrefined
has always been my motto
violence archy always does something
to my nerves
but an aristocrat must revenge
an insult i owe it to my family
to protect my good name
so i laid for that slob
for two days and nights and finally

i caught the boob in the shrubbery
pretty thing i said
it hurts me worse than it does you
to remove that left eye of yours
but i did it with one sweep of my claws
you call yourself a gentleman do you
i said as i took a strip out of his nose
you will think twice after this before
you offer an insult
to an unprotected young tabby
where is the little love nest you spoke
of i asked him
you go and lie down there i said
and maybe you can incubate another ear
because i am going to take one of
yours right off now
and with those words i made ribbons
out of it you are the guy
i said to him that was going to give
me an easy life sheltered from all
the rough ways of the world
fluffy dear you don t know what the
rough ways of the world are
and i am going to show you
i have got you out here
in the great open spaces
where cats are cats
and i m gonna make you understand
the affections of a lady ain t to be
trifled with by any slicker like you
where is that red ribbon with the
silver bells you promised me

the next time you betray the trust
of an innocent female
reflect on whether she may
carry a wallop little fiddle strings
this is just a mild lesson i am giving
you tonight i said as i took
the fur off his back and you oughta
be glad you didn t make me really
angry my sense of dignity is all that
saves you a lady little sweetness
never loses her poise and i thank god
i am always a lady even if i do
live my own life and with that i
picked him up by what was left of
his neck like a kitten and laid him
on the door mat slumber gently and
sweet dreams fluffy dear i said and
when you get well make it a rule of
your life never to trifle with another
girlish confidence i have been
abducted again and again by a dam
sight better cats than he ever was
or will be
well archy the world is full of ups
and downs but toujours gai is my motto
cheerio my deario

                                    archy

the flattered lightning bug

a lightning bug got
in here the other night a
regular hick from
the real country he was
awful proud of himself you
city insects may think
you are some punkins
but i don t see any
of you flashing in the dark
like we do in
the country all right go
to it says i mehitabel the
cat and that green
spider who lives in your locker
and two or three cockroach
friends of mine and a
friendly rat all gathered
around him and urged him on
and he lightened and
lightened and lightened you
don t see anything like this
in town often he says go to it
we told him it s a
real treat to us and

we nicknamed him broadway
which pleased him
this is the life
he said all i

BROADWAY

need is a harbor
under me to be a
statue of liberty and
he got so vain of
himself i had to take
him down a peg you ve
made lightning for two hours
little bug i told him
but i don t hear

any claps of thunder
yet there are some men
like that when he wore
himself out mehitabel
the cat ate him

                              archy

the robin and the worm

a robin said to an
angleworm as he ate him
i am sorry but a bird
has to live somehow the
worm being slow witted could
not gather his
dissent into a wise crack
and retort he was
effectually swallowed
before he could turn
a phrase
by the time he had
reflected long enough
to say but why must a
bird live
he felt the beginnings
of a gradual change
invading him

some new and disintegrating
influence
was stealing along him
from his positive
to his negative pole
and he did not have
the mental stamina
of a jonah to resist the
insidious
process of assimilation
which comes like a thief
in the night
demons and fishhooks
he exclaimed
i am losing my personal
identity as a worm
my individuality
is melting away from me
odds craw i am becoming
part and parcel of
this bloody robin
so help me i am thinking
like a robin and not
like a worm any
longer yes yes i even
find myself agreeing
that a robin must live
i still do not
understand with my mentality
why a robin must live
and yet i swoon into a
condition of belief

yes yes by heck that is
my dogma and i shout it a
robin must live
amen said a beetle who had
preceded him into the
interior that is the way i
feel myself is it not
wonderful when one arrives
at the place
where he can give up his
ambitions and resignedly
nay even with gladness
recognize that it is a far
far better thing to be
merged harmoniously
in the cosmic all
and this comfortable situation
in his midst
so affected the marauding
robin that he perched
upon a blooming twig
and sang until the
blossoms shook with ecstasy
he sang
i have a good digestion
and there is a god after all
which i was wicked
enough to doubt
yesterday when it rained
breakfast breakfast
i am full of breakfast
and they are at breakfast

in heaven
they breakfast in heaven
all s well with the world
so intent was this pious and
murderous robin
on his own sweet song
that he did not notice
mehitabel the cat
sneaking toward him
she pounced just as he
had extended his larynx
in a melodious burst of
thanksgiving and
he went the way of all
flesh fish and good red herring
a ha purred mehitabel
licking the last
feather from her whiskers
was not that a beautiful
song he was singing
just before i took him to
my bosom
they breakfast in heaven
all s well with the world
how true that is
and even yet his song
echoes in the haunted
woodland of my midriff
peace and joy in the world
and over all the
provident skies
how beautiful is the universe

when something digestible meets
with an eager digestion
how sweet the embrace
when atom rushes to the arms
of waiting atom
and they dance together
skimming with fairy feet
along a tide of gastric juices
oh feline cosmos you were
made for cats
and in the spring
old cosmic thing
i dine and dance with you
i shall creep through
yonder tall grass
to see if peradventure
some silly fledgling thrushes
newly from the nest
be not floundering therein
i have a gusto this
morning i have a hunger
i have a yearning to hear
from my stomach
further music in accord with
the mystic chanting
of the spheres of the stars that
sang together in the dawn of
creation prophesying food
for me i have a faith
that providence has hidden for me
in yonder tall grass
still more

ornithological delicatessen
oh gayly let me strangle
what is gayly given
well well boss there is
something to be said
for the lyric and imperial
attitude
believe that everything is for
you until you discover
that you are for it
sing your faith in what you
get to eat right up to the
minute you are eaten
for you are going
to be eaten
will the orchestra please
strike up that old
tutankhamen jazz while i dance
a few steps i learnt from an
egyptian scarab and some day i
will narrate to you the most
merry light headed wheeze
that the skull of yorick put
across in answer to the
melancholy of the dane and also
what the ghost of
hamlet s father replied to the skull
not forgetting the worm that
wriggled across one of the picks
the grave diggers had left behind
for the worm listened and winked
at horatio while the skull and the

ghost and the prince talked
saying there are more things
twixt the vermiform appendix
and nirvana than are dreamt of
in thy philosophy horatio
fol de riddle fol de rol
must every parrot be a poll

       archy

mehitabel and her kittens

well boss
mehitabel the cat
has reappeared in her old
haunts with a
flock of kittens
three of them this time

archy she said to me
yesterday
the life of a female
artist is continually
hampered what in hell
have i done to deserve
all these kittens
i look back on my life
and it seems to me to be
just one damned kitten
after another
i am a dancer archy
and my only prayer
is to be allowed
to give my best to my art
but just as i feel
that i am succeeding
in my life work

WHAT HAVE I DONE TO
DESERVE ALL THESE KITTENS.

Herriman

along comes another batch
of these damned kittens
it is not archy
that i am shy on mother love
god knows i care for
the sweet little things
curse them
but am i never to be allowed
to live my own life
i have purposely avoided
matrimony in the interests
of the higher life
but i might just
as well have been a domestic
slave for all the freedom
i have gained
i hope none of them
gets run over by
an automobile
my heart would bleed
if anything happened
to them and i found it out
but it isn t fair archy
it isn t fair
these damned tom cats have all
the fun and freedom
if i was like some of these
green eyed feline vamps i know
i would simply walk out on the
bunch of them and
let them shift for themselves
but i am not that kind

archy i am full of mother love
my kindness has always
been my curse
a tender heart is the cross i bear
self sacrifice always and forever
is my motto damn them
i will make a home
for the sweet innocent
little things
unless of course providence
in his wisdom should remove
them they are living
just now in an abandoned
garbage can just behind
a made over stable in greenwich
village and if it rained
into the can before i could
get back and rescue them
i am afraid the little
dears might drown
it makes me shudder just
to think of it
of course if i were a family cat
they would probably
be drowned anyhow
sometimes i think
the kinder thing would be
for me to carry the
sweet little things
over to the river
and drop them in myself
but a mother s love archy

is so unreasonable
something always prevents me
these terrible
conflicts are always
presenting themselves
to the artist
the eternal struggle
between art and life archy
is something fierce
yes something fierce
my what a dramatic
life i have lived
one moment up the next
moment down again
but always gay archy always gay
and always the lady too
in spite of hell
well boss it will
be interesting to note
just how mehitabel
works out her present problem
a dark mystery still broods
over the manner
in which the former
family of three kittens
disappeared
one day she was talking to me
of the kittens
and the next day when i asked
her about them
she said innocently
what kittens

interrogation point
and that was all
i could ever get out
of her on the subject

WE HAD A HEAVY RAIN

we had a heavy rain
right after she spoke to me
but probably that garbage can
leaks and so the kittens

have not yet
been drowned
               archy

archy is shocked

speaking of shocking things
as so many people are these days
i noted an incident
in a subway train recently
that made my blood run cold
a dignified looking
gentleman with a long
brown beard
in an absent minded manner
suddenly reached up and
pulled his own left eye
from the socket and ate it

the consternation in the car
may be imagined
people drew away from him
on all sides women screamed and
fainted in a moment every one
but the guard and myself
were huddled in the end of the car
looking at the dignified

gentleman with terror
the guard was sweating
with excitement but he stood
his ground sir said the guard
you cannot intimidate me
nor can you mystify me
i am a wise boid
you sir are a glass eater
and that was a glass eye

to the devil with a country
where people can t mind their own
business said the dignified
gentleman i am not a glass eater
if you must know and that was not
a glass eye it was a pickled onion
can not a man eat pickled
onions in this community
without exciting remark
the curse of this nation
is the number of meddlesome
matties
who are forever attempting
to restrict the liberty
of the individual i suppose
the next thing will be a law
on the statute books prohibiting
the consumption of pickled onions
and with another curse
he passed from the train
which had just then drawn up
beside

a station and went out
of my life forever

archy

mehitabel sings a song

well boss mehitabel the cat
has been wooing
the muse no pun please
and i am privileged
to present her song just
as she sang it to
several of her dubious
feline friends in the alley
last night as follows

there s a dance or two
in the old dame yet
believe me you
there s a dance or two
before i m through
you get me pet
there s a dance or two
in the old dame yet

life s too dam funny
for me to explain
it s kicks or money

life s too dam funny
it s one day sunny
the next day rain
life s too dam funny
for me to explain

THERE'S A DANCE IN
THE OLD DAME YET.

but toujours gai
is my motto kid
the devil s to pay
but toujours gai
and once in a way
let s lift the lid
but toujours gai
is my motto kid

thank god i m a lady
and class will tell
you hear me sadie
thank god i m a lady
my past is shady
but wotthehell
thank god i m a lady
and class will tell

a gentleman friend
i met t other day
coaxed me to amend
a gentleman friend
you meet on a bend
is often that way
a gentleman friend
i met t other day

i says to him dearie
i live my own life
of marriage i m leery
i says to him dearie
if you wasn t beery
you wouldn t say wife
i says to him dearie
i live my own life

i says to him bertie
i ll end down the bay
the garbage scow s dirty
i says to him bertie
but me here and gertie
is both on our way

i says to him bertie
i ll end down the bay

i never sing blue
wotthehell bill
believe me you
i never sing blue
there s a dance or two
in the old dame still
i never sing blue
wotthehell bill

it appears to me boss
that mehitabel is still far
from being the quiet
domestic character you and i
had hoped she might become

                                        archy

aesop revised by archy

a wolf met a spring
lamb drinking
at a stream
and said to her
you are the lamb
that muddied this stream
all last year

so that i could not get
a clean fresh drink
i am resolved that
this outrage
shall not be enacted again
this season
i am going to kill you
just a moment
said the lamb
i was not born last
year so it could not
have been i
the wolf then pulled
a number of other
arguments as to why the lamb
should die
but in each case the lamb
pretty innocent that she was
easily proved
herself guiltless
well well said the wolf
enough of argument
you are right and i am wrong
but i am going to eat
you anyhow
because i am hungry
stop exclamation point
cried a human voice
and a man came over
the slope of the ravine
vile lupine marauder
you shall not kill that

beautiful and innocent
lamb for i shall save her
exit the wolf
left upper entrance
snarling
poor little lamb
continued our human hero
sweet tender little thing
it is well that i appeared
just when i did
it makes my blood boil
to think of the fright
to which you have been
subjected in another
moment i would have been
too late come home with me
and the lamb frolicked
about her new found friend
gamboling as to the sound
of a wordsworthian tabor
and leaping for joy
as if propelled by a stanza
from william blake
these vile and bloody wolves
went on our hero
in honest indignation
they must be cleared out
of the country
the meads must be made safe
for sheepocracy
and so jollying her along
with the usual human hokum

he led her to his home
and the son of a gun
did not even blush when
they passed the mint bed

AND PIOUSLY
HE SAID A
GRACE.

gently he cut her throat
all the while inveighing
against the inhuman wolf
and tenderly he cooked her
and lovingly he sauced her
and meltingly he ate her

63

and piously he said a grace
thanking his gods
for their bountiful gifts to him
and after dinner
he sat with his pipe
before the fire meditating
on the brutality of wolves
and the injustice of
the universe
which allows them to harry
poor innocent lambs
and wondering if he
had not better
write to the papers
for as he said
for god s sake can t
something be done about it
                                    archy

cheerio my deario

well boss i met
mehitabel the cat
trying to dig a
frozen lamb chop
out of a snow
drift the other day

64

a heluva comedown
that is for me archy
she says a few
brief centuries
ago one of old
king
tut
ankh
amen s favorite
queens and today
the village scavenger
but wotthehell
archy wotthehell
it s cheerio
my deario that
pulls a lady through

see here mehitabel
i said i thought
you told me that
it was cleopatra
you used to be
before you
transmigrated into
the carcase of a cat
where do you get
this tut
ankh
amen stuff
question mark

i was several
ladies my little

insect says she
being cleopatra was
only an incident
in my career
and i was always getting
the rough end of it
always being
misunderstood by some
strait laced
prune faced bunch
of prissy mouthed
sisters of uncharity
the things that
have been said
about me archy
exclamation point

and all simply
because i was a
live dame
the palaces i have
been kicked out of
in my time
exclamation point

but wotthehell
little archy wot
thehell
it s cheerio
my deario
that pulls a
lady through
exclamation point

framed archy always
framed that is the
story of all my lives
no chance for a dame
with the anvil chorus
if she shows a little
motion it seems to
me only yesterday
that the luxor local
number one of
the ladies axe
association got me in
dutch with king tut and
he slipped me the
sarcophagus always my
luck yesterday an empress
and today too
emaciated to interest
a vivisectionist but
toujours gai archy
toujours gai and always
a lady in spite of hell
and transmigration
once a queen
always a queen
archy
period

one of her
feet was frozen
but on the other three
she began to caper and

dance singing its
cheerio my deario
that pulls a lady
through her morals may
have been mislaid somewhere
in the centuries boss but
i admire her spirit

                    archy

the lesson of the moth

i was talking to a moth
the other evening
he was trying to break into
an electric light bulb
and fry himself on the wires

why do you fellows
pull this stunt i asked him
because it is the conventional
thing for moths or why
if that had been an uncovered
candle instead of an electric
light bulb you would
now be a small unsightly cinder
have you no sense

plenty of it he answered
but at times we get tired

of using it
we get bored with the routine
and crave beauty
and excitement
fire is beautiful
and we know that if we get
too close it will kill us
but what does that matter
it is better to be happy
for a moment
and be burned up with beauty
than to live a long time
and be bored all the while
so we wad all our life up
into one little roll
and then we shoot the roll
that is what life is for
it is better to be a part of beauty
for one instant and then cease to
exist than to exist forever
and never be a part of beauty
our attitude toward life
is come easy go easy
we are like human beings
used to be before they became
too civilized to enjoy themselves

and before i could argue him
out of his philosophy
he went and immolated himself
on a patent cigar lighter
i do not agree with him

myself i would rather have
half the happiness and twice
the longevity

but at the same time i wish
there was something i wanted
as badly as he wanted to fry himself

                                        archy

pete the parrot and shakespeare

i got acquainted with
a parrot named pete recently
who is an interesting bird
pete says he used
to belong to the fellow
that ran the mermaid tavern
in london then i said
you must have known
shakespeare know him said pete
poor mutt i knew him well
he called me pete and i called him
bill but why do you say poor mutt
well said pete bill was a
disappointed man and was always
boring his friends about what
he might have been and done
if he only had a fair break

two or three pints of sack
and sherris and the tears
would trickle down into his
beard and his beard would get
soppy and wilt his collar
i remember one night when
bill and ben jonson and
frankie beaumont
were sopping it up

here i am ben says bill
nothing but a lousy playwright
and with anything like luck
in the breaks i might have been
a fairly decent sonnet writer
i might have been a poet
if i had kept away from the theatre

yes says ben i ve often
thought of that bill
but one consolation is
you are making pretty good money
out of the theatre

money money says bill what the hell
is money what i want is to be
a poet not a business man
these damned cheap shows
i turn out to keep the
theatre running break my heart
slap stick comedies and
blood and thunder tragedies
and melodramas say i wonder

if that boy heard you order
another bottle frankie
the only compensation is that i get
a chance now and then
to stick in a little poetry
when nobody is looking
but hells bells that isn t
what i want to do
i want to write sonnets and
songs and spenserian stanzas
and i might have done it too
if i hadn t got
into this frightful show game
business business business
grind grind grind
what a life for a man
that might have been a poet

well says frankie beaumont
why don t you cut it bill
i can t says bill
i need the money i ve got
a family to support down in
the country well says frankie
anyhow you write pretty good
plays bill any mutt can write
plays for this london public
says bill if he puts enough
murder in them what they want
is kings talking like kings
never had sense enough to talk
and stabbings and stranglings

and fat men making love
and clowns basting each
other with clubs and cheap puns
and off color allusions to all
the smut of the day oh i know
what the low brows want
and i give it to them

well says ben jonson
don t blubber into the drink
brace up like a man
and quit the rotten business
i can t i can t says bill
i ve been at it too long i ve got to
the place now where i can t
write anything else
but this cheap stuff
i m ashamed to look an honest
young sonneteer in the face
i live a hell of a life i do
the manager hands me some mouldy old
manuscript and says
bill here s a plot for you
this is the third of the month
by the tenth i want a good
script out of this that we
can start rehearsals on
not too big a cast
and not too much of your
damned poetry either
you know your old
familiar line of hokum

they eat up that falstaff stuff
of yours ring him in again
and give them a good ghost
or two and remember we gotta
have something dick burbage can get
his teeth into and be sure
and stick in a speech
somewhere the queen will take
for a personal compliment and if
you get in a line or two somewhere
about the honest english yeoman
it s always good stuff
and it s a pretty good stunt
bill to have the heavy villain
a moor or a dago or a jew
or something like that and say
i want another
comic welshman in this
but i don t need to tell
you bill you know this game
just some of your ordinary
hokum and maybe you could
kill a little kid or two a prince
or something they like
a little pathos along with
the dirt now you better see burbage
tonight and see what he wants
in that part oh says bill
to think i am
debasing my talents with junk
like that oh god what i wanted
was to be a poet

and write sonnet serials
like a gentleman should

well says i pete
bill s plays are highly
esteemed to this day
is that so says pete
poor mutt little he would
care what poor bill wanted
was to be a poet

archy

archy confesses

coarse
jocosity
catches the crowd
shakespeare
and i
are often
low browed

the fish wife
curse
and the laugh
of the horse
shakespeare
and i

are frequently
coarse

aesthetic
excuses
in bill s behalf
are adduced
to refine
big bill s
coarse laugh

HORSE
SHAKESPEARE
&

but bill
he would chuckle
to hear such guff
he pulled
rough stuff
and he liked
rough stuff

hoping you
are the same
                    archy

the old trouper

i ran onto mehitabel again
last evening
she is inhabiting
a decayed trunk
which lies in an alley
in greenwich village
in company with the
most villainous tom cat
i have ever seen
but there is nothing
wrong about the association
archy she told me
it is merely a plutonic
attachment
and the thing can be

believed for the tom
looks like one of pluto s demons
it is a theatre trunk
archy mehitabel told me
and tom is an old theatre cat
he has given his life
to the theatre
he claims that richard
mansfield once
kicked him out of the way
and then cried because
he had done it and
petted him
and at another time
he says in a case
of emergency
he played a bloodhound
in a production of
uncle tom s cabin
the stage is not what it
used to be tom says
he puts his front paw
on his breast and says
they don t have it any more
they don t have it here
the old troupers are gone
there s nobody can troupe
any more
they are all amateurs nowadays
they haven t got it
here
there are only

five or six of us oldtime
troupers left
this generation does not know
what stage presence is
personality is what they lack
personality
where would they get
the training my old friends
got in the stock companies
i knew mr booth very well
says tom
and a law should be passed
preventing anybody else
from ever playing
in any play he ever
played in
there was a trouper for you
i used to sit on his knee
and purr when i was
a kitten he used to tell me
how much he valued my opinion
finish is what they lack
finish
and they haven t got it
here
and again he laid his paw
on his breast
i remember mr daly very
well too
i was with mr daly s company
for several years
there was art for you

there was team work
there was direction
they knew the theatre
and they all had it
here
for two years mr daly
would not ring up the curtain
unless i was in the
prompter s box
they are amateurs nowadays
rank amateurs all of them
for two seasons i played
the dog in joseph
jefferson s rip van winkle
it is true i never came
on the stage
but he knew i was just off
and it helped him
i would like to see
one of your modern
theatre cats
act a dog so well
that it would convince
a trouper like jo jefferson
but they haven t got it
nowadays
they haven t got it
here
jo jefferson had it he had it
here
i come of a long line
of theatre cats

my grandfather
was with forrest
he had it he was a real trouper
my grandfather said
he had a voice
that used to shake
the ferryboats
on the north river
once he lost his beard
and my grandfather
dropped from the
fly gallery and landed
under his chin
and played his beard
for the rest of the act
you don t see any theatre
cats that could do that
nowadays
they haven t got it they
haven t got it
here
once i played the owl
in modjeska a production
of macbeth
i sat above the castle gate
in the murder scene
and made my yellow
eyes shine through the dusk
like an owl s eyes
modjeska was a real
trouper she knew how to pick
her support i would like

MEHITABEL, HE SAYS —

to see any of these modern
theatre cats play the owl s eyes
to modjeska s lady macbeth
but they haven t got it nowadays
they haven t got it
here

mehitabel he says
both our professions
are being ruined
by amateurs

archy

archy hears from mars

at eleven o clock
p m on last saturday evening
i received the following
message on my
own private radio set
good evening little archibald
and how are you
this is mars speaking
i replied at once
whom or who
as the case may be
do i know on mars
every one here is familiar

with your work archy
was the answer
and we feel well repaid
for all the trouble we have had
in getting in touch
with your planet
thank you i replied
i would rather hear
mars say that
than any other planet
mars has always been
one of my favorite planets
it is sweet of you
to think that way about us
said mars
and so we continued to pay
each other interstellar
compliments
what is or are
thirty five million miles
between kindred souls
tell us all about
your planet said mars
well i said it is
round like an orange
or a ball
and it is all cluttered
up with automobiles
and politicians
it doesn t know where it is
going nor why
but it is in a hurry

it is in charge of a
two legged animal called
man who is genuinely
puzzled as to whether
his grandfather was a god
or a monkey
i should think said mars
that what he is himself
would make more difference
than what his grandfather was
not to this animal i replied
he is the great alibi ike of
the cosmos when he raises hell
just because he feels like
raising hell
he wants somebody to blame it on
can t anything be done about him
said mars
i am doing the best i can
i answered
but after all i am only one
and my influence is limited
you are too modest archy
said mars
we all but worship you
here on this planet
a prophet said i is not
without honor save on his own
planet wait a minute
said mars
i want to write that down
that is one of your best things

archy is it original
it was once i answered truthfully
and may be again
won t you tell us a little
something said mars
about yourself what you look like
and what you think
is the best thing you have written
and your favorite games
and that sort of thing
well i said i am brunette
and stand over six feet
without any shoes on
the best skits i have done
were some little plays
i dashed off
under the general title
of shakespeare s plays
and my favorite sport is theology
you must meet
a great many interesting people
said mars
oh yes i said one becomes
accustomed to that after a while
what is your favorite dish
said mars and do you believe
in the immortality of the soul
stew i said and yes
at least mine is immortal
but i could name several others
that i have my doubts about
is there anything else

of interest about your planet
which you wish to tell your
many admirers on mars
asked mars
there is very little else
of any real interest i said
and now will you tune out
and let me do some work
you people who say you admire
my work are always butting in
and taking up my time
how the hell can i get any
serious literary work done
if you keep bothering me
all the time now you get off
the ether and let me do some
deep thinking
you might add that i am shy
and loathe publicity

archy

mehitabel dances with boreas

well boss i saw mehitabel
last evening
she was out in the alley
dancing on the cold cobbles

while the wild december wind
blew through her frozen whiskers
and as she danced
she wailed and sang to herself
uttering the fragments
that rattled in her cold brain
in part as follows

whirl mehitabel whirl
spin mehitabel spin
thank god you re a lady still
if you have got a frozen skin

blow wind out of the north
to hell with being a pet
my left front foot is brittle
but there s life in the old dame yet

dance mehitable dance
caper and shake a leg
what little blood is left
will fizz like wine in a keg

wind come out of the north
and pierce to the guts within
but some day mehitabel s guts
will string a violin

moon you re as cold as a frozen
skin of yellow banan
that sticks in the frost and ice
on top of a garbage can

and you throw a shadow so chilly
that it can scarcely leap
dance shadow dance
you ve got no place to sleep

whistle a tune north wind
on my hollow marrow bones
i ll dance the time with three good feet
here on the alley stones

freeze you bloody december
i never could stay a pet
but i am a lady in spite of hell
and there s life in the old dame yet

whirl mehitabel whirl
flirt your tail and spin
dance to the tune your guts will cry
when they string a violin

eight of my lives are gone
it s years since my fur was slicked
but blow north wind blow
i m damned if i am licked

girls we was all of us ladies
we was o what the hell
and once a lady always game
by crikey blood will tell

i might be somebody s pet
asleep by the fire on a rug
but me i was always romantic
i had the adventurous bug

caper mehitabel caper
leap shadow leap
you gotta dance till the sun comes up
for you got no place to sleep

i might have been many a tom cat s wife
but i got no regret
i lived my life as i liked my life
and there s pep in the old dame yet

blow wind out of the north
you cut like a piece of tin
slice my guts into fiddle strings
and we ll have a violin

spin mehitabel spin
you had a romantic past
and you re gonna cash in dancing
when you are croaked at last

i will not eat tomorrow
and i did not eat today
but wotthehell i ask you
the word is toujours gai

whirl mehitabel whirl
i once was a maltese pet
till i went and got abducted
and cripes i m a lady yet

whirl mehitabel whirl
and show your shadow how
tonight it s dance with the bloody moon
tomorrow the garbage scow

whirl mehitabel whirl
spin shadow spin
the wind will pipe on your marrow bones
your slats are a mandolin

by cripes i have danced the shimmy
in rooms as warm as a dream
and gone to sleep on a cushion
with a bellyfull of cream

it s one day up and next day down
i led a romantic life
it was being abducted so many times
as spoiled me for a wife

dance mehitabel dance
till your old bones fly apart
i ain t got any regrets
for i gave my life to my art

whirl mehitabel whirl
caper my girl and grin
and pick at your guts with your frosty feet
they re the strings of a violin

girls we was all of us ladies
until we went and fell
an oncet a thoroughbred always game
i ask you wotthehell

it s last week up and this week down
and always the devil to pay
but cripes i was always the lady
and the word is toujours gai

be a tabby tame if you want
somebody s pussy and pet
the life i led was the life i liked
and there s pep in the old dame yet

whirl mehitabel whirl
leap shadow leap
you gotta dance till the sun comes up
for you got no place to sleep

archy

the dissipated hornet

well boss i had a
great example of the corrupting
influence of the great
city brought to my notice recently a
drunken hornet blew in here
the other day and sat down in the
corner and dozed and buzzed not a
real sleep you know one of those wakeful
liquor trances with the
fuzzy talk oozing out of it to hear
this guy mumble in his dreams he was right
wicked my name he says is crusty bill
i never been licked and i never will and
then he would go half way asleep
again nobody around here wanted to

fight him and after a while he got
sober enough to know how drunk he had
been and began to cry over it and get
sentimental about himself mine is a wasted
life he says but i had a good
start red liquor ruined me he says and
sobbed tell me your story i
said two years ago he said i was a country
hornet young and strong and handsome i
lived in a rusty rainspout with my
parents and brothers and sisters and all was
innocent and merry often in that happy
pastoral life would we swoop down
with joyous laughter and sting the school
children on the village green but on an evil
day alas i came to the city in a crate
of peaches i found myself in a market
near the water front alone and friendless in the
great city its ways were strange to
me food seemed inaccessible i thought
that i might starve to death as i was buzzing
down the street thinking these gloomy
thoughts i met another hornet
just outside a speak easy kid he says
you look down in the mouth forget
it kid i will show you how to live without
working how i says watch me he says just
then a drunken fly came crawling out
of the bar room in a leisurely way my new
found friend stung dissected and consumed that fly
that s the way he says smacking his lips
this is the life that was a beer fly

94

wait and i will get you a cock tail fly this
is the life i took up that life alas the
flies around a bar room get so drunk drinking
what is spilled that they are helpless all a
hornet has to do is wait calmly until
they come staggering out and there is his
living ready made for him at first being
young and innocent i ate only beer flies but
the curse of drink got me the mad life began
to tell upon me i got so i would not eat a
fly that was not full of some strong and heady
liquor the lights and life got me i would
not eat fruits and vegetables any more i scorned
flies from a soda fountain
they seemed flat and insipid to me
finally i got so wicked that i
went back to the country and got six innocent
young hornets and brought them back
to the city with me i started them in the
business i debauched them and
they caught my flies for me now i am in
an awful situation my six hornets from the
country have struck and set up on their own
hook i have to catch my flies myself
and my months of idleness and
dissipation have spoiled my technique i
can t catch a fly now unless he is dead drunk
what is to become of me alas the curse
of alcoholic beverages especially with each
meal well i said it is a sad story
bill and of a sort only too
common in this day of ours it is he says i

have the gout in my stinger so bad
that i scream with pain every time i spear
a fly i got into a safe place on the
inside of the typewriter and yelled out at him
my advice is suicide bill all the time
he had been pitying himself my sympathy had
been with the flies

                                        archy

clarence the ghost

the longer i live the more i
realize that everything is
relative even morality is
relative things you would not do
sometimes you would do other
times for instance i would not consider
it honorable in me as a
righteous cockroach to crawl into a
near sighted man s soup that
man would not have a sporting chance but
with a man with ordinarily good eye
sight i should say it was
up to him to watch his soup himself and
yet if i was very tired and hungry
i would crawl into even a near
sighted man s soup knowing all the
time it was wrong and my necessity would

keep me from reproaching myself too
bitterly afterwards you can
not make any hard and fast rule
concerning the morality of crawling into

ALL A SPOOK HAS TO DO
IS STICK AROUND.

soup nor anything else a certain
alloy of expediency improves the
gold of morality and makes
it wear all the longer consider a
ghost if i were a ghost i
would not haunt ordinary people but i
would have all the fun i wanted to with

spiritualists for spiritualists are
awful nuisances to ghosts i knew a
ghost by the name of clarence one
time who hated spiritualists with a
great hatred you see said clarence they
give me no rest they have got my
number once one of those psychics gets a
ghost s number so he has to come
when he is called they work him till
the astral sweat stands out in beads
on his spectral brow they seem to think
said clarence that all a spook has to do
is to stick around waiting to dash in
with a message as to whether mrs millionbucks
pet pom has pneumonia or only wheezes
because he has been eating too many
squabs clarence was quite
bitter about it but wait he says till
the fat medium with the red nose
that has my number
passes over and i can get my
clutches on him on equal terms there s
going to be some initiation beside
the styx several of the boys are
sore on him a plump chance i have
don t i to improve myself and pass on
to another star with that medium
yanking me into somebody s parlor to
blow through one of these little tin
trumpets any time of the day or night
honest archy he says i hate the sight of a
ouija board would it be moral he

says to give that goof a bum tip on the
stock market life ain t worth
dying he says if you ve got to fag
for some chinless chump of a psychic
nor death ain t worth living
through would it be moral in me to
queer that simp with his
little circle by saying he s got an
anonymous diamond brooch in his pocket
and that his trances are rapidly developing
his kleptomania no clarence i said it
wouldn t be moral but it
might be expedient there s a ghost
around here i have been trying to get
acquainted with but he is shy i think he is
probably afraid of cockroaches

                                        archy

some natural history

the patagonian
penguin
is a most
peculiar
bird
he lives on
pussy

willows
and his tongue
is always furred
the porcupine
of chile
sleeps his life away
and that is how
the needles
get into the hay
the argentinian
oyster
is a very
subtle gink
for when he s
being eaten
he pretends he is
a skink
when you see
a sea gull
sitting
on a bald man s dome
she likely thinks
she s nesting
on her rocky
island home
do not tease
the inmates
when strolling
through the zoo
for they have
their finer feelings
the same

as me and you
oh deride not
the camel
if grief should
make him die

SHE LIKELY THINKS
SHE'S NESTING
ON HER ROCKY
ISLAND HOME.

his ghost will come
to haunt you
with tears
in either eye
and the spirit of
a camel
in the midnight gloom

can be so very
cheerless
as it wanders
round the room

                    archy

mehitabel meets an affinity

paris france
mehitabel the cat
has been passing her
time in the dubious
company of
a ragged eared tom cat
with one mean
eye and the other
eye missing whom
she calls francy
he has been the hero
or the victim of
many desperate encounters
for part of his tail
has been removed
and his back has been chewed
to the spine
one can see at a glance
that he is a sneak thief
and an apache

a bandit with long
curved claws
you see his likes hanging
about the outdoor markets
here in paris waiting
their chance to sneak
a fish or a bit
of unregarded meat
or whimpering
among the chair legs at the
sidewalk cafes in the
evenings or slinking
down the gutters of
alleys in the old
quarters of the town
he has a raucous voice
much damaged by the night
air and yet there is a
sentimental wheedling
note in it as well
and yet withal he carries
his visible disgrace with
a jaunty air
when i asked mehitabel
where in the name of st denis
did you pick up that
romantic criminal
in the luxembourg gardens
she replied where
we had both gone to kill
birds he has been showing me
paris he does not

understand english but speak of
him with respect
he is like myself
an example of the truth
of the pythagorean idea
you know that in my body
which is that of a cat
there is reincarnated
the soul of cleopatra
well this cat here
was not always a cat either
he has seen better days
he tells me that once he was
a bard and lived here in paris
tell archy here
something about yourself francy
thus encouraged the
murderous looking animal spoke
and i append a
rough translation of
what he said

tame cats on a web of the persian woof
may lick their coats and purr for cream
but i am a tougher kind of goof
scheming a freer kind of scheme
daily i climb where the pigeons gleam
over the gargoyles of notre dame
robbing their nests to hear them scream
for i am a cat of the devil i am

i ll tell the world i m a hard boiled oeuf
i rend the clouds when i let off steam

to the orderly life i cry pouf pouf
it is worth far less than the bourgeois deem
my life is a dance on the edge de l abime
and i am the singer you d love to slam
who murders the midnight anonyme
for i am a cat of the devil i am

when the ribald moon leers over the roof
and the mist reeks up from the chuckling stream
i pad the quais on a silent hoof
dreaming the vagabond s ancient dream
where the piebald toms of the quartier teem
and fight for a fish or a mouldy clam
my rival i rip and his guts unseam
for i am a cat of the devil i am

roach i could rattle you rhymes by the ream
in proof of the fact that i m no spring lamb

maybe the headsman will finish the theme
for i am a cat of the devil i am

mehitabel i said
your friend is nobody else
than francois villon
and he looks it too

archy

mehitabel in the catacombs

paris france
i would
fear greatly for the morals
of mehitabel the cat if she had any
the kind of life she
is leading is too violent
and undisciplined for words
she and the disreputable
tom cat who claims to have
been francois villon
when he was on earth
before have taken up their
permanent abode in the catacombs
whence they sally
forth nightly on excursions
of the most undignified nature
sometimes they honor

with their presence the cafes
of montparnasse and the boul mich
and sometimes they
seek diversion in the cabarets
on top of the butte
of montmartre
in these localities
it has become the fashion
among the humans
to feed beer to these
peculiar cats and they dance
and caper when they have
become well alcoholized
with this beverage
swinging their tails and
indulging in raucous feline
cries which they evidently
mistake for a song
it was my dubious
privilege to see them
when they returned to their
abode early yesterday morning
flushed as you might say
with bocks and still
in a holiday mood
the catacombs of paris are
not lined with the bones
of saints and martyrs
as are those of rome
but nevertheless these cats
should have more respect
for the relics of mortality

you may not believe me
but they actually danced and
capered among
the skeletons while the cat
who calls himself
francois villon gave forth
a chant of which the following
is a free translation

outcast bones from a thousand biers
click us a measure giddy and gleg
and caper my children dance my dears
skeleton rattle your mouldy leg
this one was a gourmet round as a keg
and that had the brow of semiramis
o fleshless forehead bald is an egg
all men s lovers come to this

this eyeless head that laughs and leers
was a chass daf once or a touareg
with golden rings in his yellow ears
skeleton rattle your mouldy leg
marot was this one or wilde or a wegg
who dropped into verses and down the abyss
and those are the bones of my old love meg
all men s lovers come to this

these bones were a ballet girl s for years
parbleu but she shook a wicked peg
and those ribs there were a noble peer s
skeleton rattle your mouldy leg
and here is a duchess that loved a yegg
with her lipless mouth that once drank bliss

down to the dreg of its ultimate dreg
all men s lovers come to this

prince if you pipe and plead and beg
you may yet be crowned with a grisly kiss
skeleton rattle your mouldy leg
all men s lovers come to this

archy

archy experiences a seizure

"Where have you been so long? And what on earth do you mean by coming in here soused?" we asked Archy as he zigzagged from the door to the desk.

He climbed onto the typewriter keys and replied indignantly:

> soused yourself i haven t had a drink
> and yet i am elevated i admit it i have
> been down to a second hand book
> store eating a lot of kipling s earlier
> poetry it always excites me if i eat
> a dozen stanzas of it i get all lit up
> and i try to imitate it get out of my
> way now i feel a poem in the kipling
> manner taking me

And before we could stop him he began to butt on the keys:

> the cockroach stood by the mickle
> wood in the flush of the astral dawn

We interrupted. "Don't you mean Austral instead of astral?"

Archy became angered and wrote peevishly:

i wrote astral and i meant astral
you let me be now i want to get this
poem off my chest you are jealous if
you were any kind of a sport at all
you would fix this machine so it could
write it in capitals it is a poem about
a fight between a cockroach and a
lot of other things get out of my way
i m off

the cockroach stood by the mickle
    wood in the flush of the astral dawn
and he sniffed the air from the hidden
    lair where the khyber swordfish spawn
and the bilge and belch of the glutton
welsh as they smelted their warlock cheese
surged to and fro where the grinding
    floe wrenched at the headlands knees
half seas over under up again
and the barnacles white in the moon
the pole stars chasing its tail like a pup again
and the dish ran away with the spoon

the waterspout came bellowing out of
    the red horizons rim
and the grey typhoon and the black
    monsoon surged forth to the
    fight with him

111

with three fold might they surged to
   the fight for they hated the great
   bull roach
and they cried begod as they lashed
   the sod and here is an egg to
   poach
we will bash his mug with his own raw
   lug new stripped from off his
   dome
for there is no law but teeth and claw
   to the nor nor east of nome

the punjab gull shall have his skull
   ere he goes to the burning ghaut
for there is no time for aught but crime
   where the jungle lore is taught
across the dark the afghan shark is
   whining for his head
there shall be no rule but death and
   dule till the deep red maws are
   fed
half seas under up and down
   again
and her keel was blown off in a
   squall
girls we misdoubt that we ll ever
   see town again
haul boys haul boys haul.

"Archy," we interrupted, "that haul, boys, is all
right to the eye, but the ear will surely make it hall
boys. Better change it."

112

the cockroach spat and he tilted his
   hat and he grinned through the
   lowering mirk
the cockroach felt in his rangoon belt
   for his good bengali dirk
he reefed his mast against the blast
   and he bent his mizzen free
and he pointed the cleats of his bin
   nacle sheets at the teeth of the
   yesty sea
he opened his mouth and he sluiced
   his drouth with his last good
   can of swipes
begod he cried they come in pride but
   they shall go home with the
   gripes
begod he said if they want my head it
   is here on top of my chine
it shall never be said that i doffed my
   head for the boast of a heathen
   line
and he scorned to wait but he dared
   his fate and loosed his bridle rein
and leapt to close with his red fanged
   foes in the trough of the
   screaming main
from hell to nome the blow went home
   and split the firmament
from hell to nome the yellow foam
   blew wide to veil the rent

      and the roaring ships they came to
        grips in the gloom of a dripping
        mist

"Archy," we interrupted again, "is there very much more of it? It seems that you might tell in a very few words now who won the fight, and let it go at that. Who did win the fight, Archy?"

But Archy was peeved, and went sadly away, after writing:

of course you won t let me finish i never saw as jealous a person as you are

random thoughts by archy

        one thing that
        shows that
        insects are
        superior to men
        is the fact that
        insects run their
        affairs without
        political campaigns
        elections and so forth

             •

        a man thinks
        he amounts to a lot

but to a mosquito
a man is
merely
something to eat

●

i have noticed
that when
chickens quit
quarrelling over their
food they often
find that there is
enough for all of them
i wonder if
it might not
be the same way
with the
human race

●

germs are very
objectionable to men
but a germ
thinks of a man
as only the swamp
in which
he has to live

●

a louse i
used to know
told me that
millionaires and

bums tasted
about alike
to him

•

the trouble with
most people is
that they
lose their sense of
proportion
of what use is
it for a
queen bee to fall in
love with a bull

•

what is all this mystery
about the sphinx
that has troubled so many
illustrious men
no doubt the very same
thoughts she thinks
are thought every day
by some obscure hen
                    archy

archy visits washington

washington d c july
23 well boss here
i am in washington
watching my step for fear
some one will push me
into the food bill up
to date i am the only thing
in this country that
has not been added to it by
the time this is
published nothing that
i have said may be
true however which is a
thing that is constantly happening
to thousands of
great journalists now in
washington it is so hot here that
i get stuck in the asphalt
every day on my
way from the senate press
gallery back to
shoemakers where the
affairs of the nation
are habitually settled by

you can fry fish
on the
sidewalk.

HERRIMAN

the old settlers it
is so hot that you can
fry fish on the
sidewalk in any part of
town and many people
are here with fish to fry
including now
and then a german
carp i am lodging on
top of the washington
monument where i can
overlook things
you can t keep a good bug
from the top of
the column all the time i
am taking my meals with
the specimens in the
smithsonian institution when i
see any one coming i hold
my breath and look like another
specimen but in the
capitol building there
is no attention paid to me
because there are so
many other insects
around it gives you a
great idea of the
american people when you
see some of the
things they elect after july
27 address me care
st elizabeth hospital

for the insane i am going out
there for a visit with
some of your other
contributors

                              archy

ballade of the under side

        by archy
        the roach that scurries
        skips and runs
        may read far more than those
        that fly
        i know what family skeletons
        within your closets
        swing and dry
        not that i ever
        play the spy
        but as in corners
        dim i bide
        i can t dodge knowledge
        though i try
        i see things from
        the under side

        the lordly ones the
        haughty ones
        with supercilious

heads held high
the up stage stiff
pretentious guns
miss much that meets
my humbler eye
not that i meddle
perk or pry
but i m too small
to feel great pride
and as the pompous world
goes by
i see things from
the under side

above me wheel
the stars and suns
but humans shut
me from the sky
you see their eyes as pure
as nuns
i see their wayward
feet and sly
i own and own it with
a sigh
my point of view
is somewhat wried
i am a pessimistic
guy
i see things from the
under side

l envoi
prince ere you pull a bluff

and lie
before you fake
and play the snide
consider whether
archy s nigh
i see things from
the under side

conferences

diplomatists and ambassadors
are rushing hither and yon
from country to country around the world
by train steamer and airplane
by which i judge that there is more trouble
in store for the human species
for i have noticed that conferences
to establish international good will
always break up with another row
there is no hope for the world
unless politicians of all sorts
are completely abolished
you cannot get a millennium by
laying a whole lot of five year plans
end to end if governments would just let people
    alone
things would straighten out of themselves
in the course of time

                                        archy the cockroach

the big bad wolf

i went to a movie show
the other evening in the cuff
of a friend s turned up trousers
and saw the three little pigs
and was greatly edified by the moral lesson
how cruel i said to myself
was the big bad wolf
how superior to wolves are men
the wolf would have eaten those pigs raw
and even alive
whereas a man would have kindly
cut their throats
and lovingly made them into
country sausage spare ribs and pigs knuckles
he would tenderly have roasted them
fried them and boiled them
cooked them feelingly with charity
towards all and malice towards none
and piously eaten them served with sauerkraut
and other trimmings
it is no wonder that the edible animals
are afraid of wolves and love men so
when a pig is eaten by a wolf
he realizes that something is wrong with the world
but when he is eaten by a man

he must thank god fervently
that he is being useful to a superior being
it must be the same way
with a colored man who is being lynched
he must be grateful that he is being lynched
in a land of freedom and liberty
and not in any of the old world countries
of darkness and oppression
where men are still the victims
of kings iniquity and constipation
we ought all to be grateful in this country
that our wall street robber barons
and crooked international bankers
are such highly respectable citizens
and do so much for the churches
and for charity
and support such noble institutions and foundations
for the welfare of mankind
and are such spiritually minded philanthropists
it would be horrid to be robbed
by the wrong kind of people
if i were a man i would not let
a cannibal eat me unless he showed me
a letter certifying to his character
from the pastor of his church
even our industrial murderers
in this country are usually affiliated
with political parties devoted
to the uplift
the enlightenment and the progress
of humankind
every time i get discouraged

and contemplate suicide
by impersonating a raisin and getting devoured
as part of a piece of pie
i think of our national blessings
and cheer up again
it is indeed
as i have been reading lately
a great period in which to be alive
and it is a cheering thought to think
that god is on the side of the best digestion
your moral little friend

archy the cockroach

archy in washington

Archy, the Famous Cockroach, surveys Washington—and finds the experts running around in circles surveying each other. Here are his views on Money, Radicals, Crop Control, and Whatnot.

I sent Archy down to Washington recently to make a Survey. Everyone else is making Surveys, and they puzzle me a good deal because I can't understand them. But Archy always uses words which I can comprehend, and I am inclined to trust his judgment on financial, industrial and economic problems. For he has no ax to grind.

Archy returned a little puzzled himself, and his

report to me falls naturally into the form of Question and Answer.

QUESTION: Well, Archy, what did you learn?

ANSWER: the first thing i found was a lot of other experts making surveys   the government is spending a good deal of time in surveying itself and in surveying the people who are surveying it   out in lafayette park survey experts are running around in circles surveying each other

Q: What about national finances?

A: i discovered that there are two kinds of dollars being planned   dollar number one is to be worth so little that no one can buy anything with it   everybody will have it   dollar number two will be worth so much that nobody can get hold of one to buy anything with   nobody will have it

Q: How about the industrial and economic situation, generally speaking?

A: well if you mean how are you going to get rich i can tell you that in a nutshell

Q: In a what?

A: you know what i said and i don t want to hear any cheap wisecracks from you

here is how you may get rich

you borrow enough money from one of the government agencies to buy 100,000 acres of land

then you go and tell the government that you are going to plant 100,000 acres of wheat

then the government pays you not to plant it for if all that wheat were raised it would mean more overproduction then you take the profits from the wheat you did not raise and buy another 100,000 acres of land

this time you tell the government that you are going to plant 100,000 acres of cotton and the government pays you not to

and so on and on it is an endless chain and will result in making everybody wealthy

Q: But suppose the government will not pay you not to plant it?

A: then you plant it and that puts the government in an embarrassing position they have to pay you to destroy it after it has been planted.

Q: Where is the government going to get the money to pay everyone for not producing anything?

A: they are getting it from the dentists

Q: But where do the dentists get it?

A: out of the teeth of the public i saw hundreds of thousands of dentists in washington

lanes of them miles long were filing into the basement of the treasury department handing over to the government the gold they had dug out of the teeth of the people

Q: But are not people going to object to this after while?

A: not at all it hooks up with the policy of not producing foodstuffs if people are not going to get foodstuffs to eat they have no use for their teeth and the government might just as well have them

Q: In a general way, how is the recovery program working out?

A: swell   but it is about time we had a program for recovering from the recovery

Q: What do you think of the danger of a revolution?

A: so many people think we have already had one that there is little danger of them trying to start it

besides how are you going to revolt against a government when you can t find out what kind of a government it is

suppose you were a radical and started a revolution

you would feel pretty cheap wouldn t you if you found out later that what you had revolted against was just what you had been advocating

the thing that is going to save the country is the fact that no one knows what is the matter with it

after while there will be a general agreement that maybe there isn t anything much the matter with it

Q: Archy, are you a conservative or a radical?

A: here don t you ask me that

i got worried almost to the point of insanity asking myself that when i was down in washington

finally i decided to end it all   i climbed to the top of the washington monument and jumped off to commit suicide   but i don t weigh so much   i floated to the ground as gently as a snowflake

hell i said what s the use

fate is against me i can t even kill myself

but there are a lot of other experts who are heavier than i am in every sense of the word

and there is the washington monument

they might have better luck and it might prove

one of the most popular features of the recovery program

Q: Did you gain any inkling of the way to abolish industrial troubles?

A: oh yes that is easy

just abolish industry and there will be no further industrial troubles

Q: Did you survey Congress?

A: i didn t like to run any risk of waking it up

Q: What was your general feeling after your investigations?

A: optimistic   decidedly so   i think what human beings have agreed to call civilization is on its way out not only in this country but all over the world

whatever succeeds it can t be worse and may be better

as the spiders wrote it

dear boss i met a spider
the other day in a museum
who gave me a good deal to think
about concerning governmental problems
this spider came of a long line of spiders
who had for thousands of years
inhabited the egyptian pyramids

and the american branch of the family
came over in a sarcophagus
along with the mummy
of one of the pharaohs

the ancient world saw all sorts
of governmental experiments
he said including monarchies
republics communes despotisms
democracies and everything else
but in the end the spiders got them all
thousands and thousands of years of
reforms and recoveries and depressions
and new deals and old deals
and square deals and crooked deals
and ideals and idealists
are wound around with spider webs
all the history of human kind
is written in the clots and filaments
and quaint patterns and ideographs
of spiders
it has been my observation
and experience and that of my family
that nothing human works out well
if you could read the writing
in the spider webs
you could understand the history of
human civilizations and understand
that man always fails because he
is not honest enough to succeed
there are not enough men
continuously on the square with

themselves and with other men
the system of government does not matter
so much the thing that matters
is what men do with any kind of system
they happen to have
many a time a strand of cobweb
has seemed to choke a burly empire to death
but the fact is that it was strangling anyhow
it was hanging itself in its own
crookedness and incompetence
there is no hope for human beings
unless they learn to organize their
social order as efficiently as spiders do
to say nothing of ants and bees
and coral insects

       archy

archy hunts a job

well boss i went up
to the circus
the other day
and tried to hire
out what do you
want they asked me a
job as an animal
or a job as an artist
an artist said i

what can you do they
said i can
walk the wire i said
either tight or slack
and i can swing
head downward from the
flying trapeze we do not
doubt it they said
but who could see
you at a distance
every one said i if you
gave them telescopes
and opera glasses it
is too expensive said they
to furnish opera
glasses to every one
just to see a cockroach
perform not at all
i said you sell the
glasses and make an
additional profit
you go out and hire
yourself out to a
trained flea outfit
said they we cannot use
you i consider it
an insult i replied to
be classed with
fleas you should consider
it a compliment said they
another word from you
i said and i

will die in a barrel
of your lemonade and
queer your show
and with this threat
the interview closed

archy

takes talent

there are two
kinds of human
beings in the world
so my observation
has told me
namely and to wit
as follows
firstly
those who
even though they
were to reveal
the secret of the universe
to you would fail
to impress you
with any sense
of the importance
of the news
and secondly
those who could

SELL THE GLASSES —

AND MAKE AN ADDITIONAL PROFIT.

communicate to you
that they had
just purchased
ten cents worth
of paper napkins
and make you
thrill and vibrate
with the intelligence
                    archy

archy climbs everest

may fifteenth nineteen
thirty five started climbing
mount everest early this morning
met the maharajah of nepal one hundred feet up
greetings old feather duster said i
that is not a feather duster he said
that is
stop i cried don t you tell me
that is your wife
that is my beard he said
i accept the apology i said
quick as a flash

may sixteen at one thousand feet
i met an avalanche coming down

as i was going up
we compromised and this morning
i am starting all over again
dancing on the avalanche
as it skidded towards sea level
were two strange figures
prancing on their hind legs
whom i identified as the dalai lama
and mehitabel the cat
they were singing in part as follows
oh the lama here
is a son of a gun
and mehitabel once
was a hindu nun
skip skip my himalaya honey
the rarefied air
of the mountain side
has completely withered
the lama s pride
hike hike my himalaya honey
if the bottom of the hills
were placed at the top
when we wanted to go up
we d merely have to drop
drill drill my himalaya honey

may seventeen oh lord
the maharajah of nepal
is following me with a squirt gun
full of insect poison
here comes another avalanche
                                    archy

archy on everest

may eighteenth fifteen
thousand feet up on mount
everest today i caught a ride
on an airplane going my way
everyone i meet is all hopped up
with the altitude
caught up with the maharajah of nepal
gaily hopping over the snow and ice
bare legged i said to him
hello spinach face are you starting
a nudist colony up here
and he replied
an avalanche
tore off my panche
and left me feeling funny
but we never rest
on everest
my himalaya honey
yes i says but who was that lady
i seen you walking with
a mile or so below
that wasn t no lady he says quick as a flash
that was the taj mahal
skipping along ahead of us were

MEHITABLE   WAS ONCE -

A HINDU NUN.

the dalai lama and mehitabel the cat
mehitabel had written in the snow
send a message to my public
in america please archy give them
love and kittens from mehitabel
and the dalai lama
may nineteenth spent the day
riding up in airplanes
and coasting down on avalanches
if you don t know anything about asia
it would surprise you how much traffic
there is in the himalayas
may twentieth twenty thousand feet up
overtook a bum who says he is
nicholas romanoff formerly czar
of all the russias and when i say all
i mean all archy he said
the sun never set on my dominions
why not i asked him
because they were too cold
to hatch he replied ask me another
the reds missed me he said
and i have been in siberia ever since
i figure if i can get to the top
and stay there i will be safe
have you got a can opener
what for i enquired
i have some canned heat he said
but i can t get into it
i have practically lived on canned heat
ever since i escaped from russia
may twenty first got carried down

four thousand feet by a snow slide
when i came to myself
i was on a ledge of rock
and sitting in a row with their feet
hanging over nothing were mehitabel the cat
the dalai lama and the taj mahal
nicholas romanoff and the maharajah of nepal
all drinking canned heat and singing
in part as follows
we have tried all sorts
of winter sports
and spent a mint of money
we have skied the alps
and cracked our scalps
and burrowed like a bunny
but everest is sure the best
my himalaya honey
listen now said the former czar
and i will tell you the story of my life
it was going off of gold that ruined me
you mean the gold standard asked the lama
no said the maharajah
he means the gold cure
nevertheless said nicholas romanoff
i will tell you now the
story of my life
with slides asked the taj mahal
can t you try and forget it
mister romanoff asked the maharajan
no said the former czar
sniffing the canned heat
not while i have this rosemary

it is for remembrance
and he hit his insides
a terrific wallop with the horrid stuff
yes and rue is for you
said the taj mahal
kicking him five thousand feet downhill
and larkspur is for cooties
the dalai lama shouted
after him as he whirled into space
i discovered a virgin gold mine
the next morning how do you know
it is virgin asked mehitabel
yes said the taj mahal explain
tush tush said the dalai lama
give it the benefit of the doubt
well it seems reasonable said i
there is a snow slide
over it every twenty minutes

archy

sociological

when the cold weather
comes i always
get a new interest in sociology
i am almost human that way
it worries me as to how
the other half

are going to get through
the winter
last evening i went
into a cheap eating house
and dropped into a beef stew
and had a warm bath
and a bite to eat
and listened afterwards
to a couple of bums
who had begged enough
during the day to get a supper
they were talking
about this new movement
on the part of the jobless
and homeless
to take possession of the churches
and live there during
the cold weather
said the first bum
i don t think i could do it
it would bring up
too many associations
you see i am a minister s son
you too exclaimed the second bum
why i also
am the son of a preacher
my father was a minister
in small towns all his life
he worked himself to death at it
he never got paid enough
to live on
and it was not until i left home

and became a hobo that i ever
got as much as i wanted to eat
at one meal
precisely my experience
said the other bum
have you ever had any temptation
said number one
to quit being a hobo
and take a regular job
yes said number two
very often
but i have always had
the strength of character
to resist temptation
it is my duty to my fellow men
to see that they have
material on which to wreak
their passion to be charitable
during the christmas holidays
it makes the well to do
more comfortable and gives
them a warm virtuous glow
when they give me a dime
and i should not feel justified
in taking from them
such a simple and inexpensive pleasure
yes said the other bum
the rich we have always with us
they are the great problem of the age
we must treat them as well
as we can and help them
to have a little fun by the way

so that they can forget
at least temporarily
the biblical assurance
that it is as hard for them to enter
the kingdom of heaven
as for a camel
to pass through a needle s eye
well said the other one
sometimes i think i would
be willing to change places
with a rich man
and run the risk
oh certainly said the other
i have never had any instinctive
hatred for riches
it is only work that i detest
riches are all very well
if you inherit them
but i doubt if they are worth
toiling for
think of all the millions
toiling miserably in order
to be damned
it is a pathetic sight
but if one inherits riches
he knows that the fates
have doomed him to be damned
before his birth
and it is of little use to struggle
that is far different from striving
desperately all one s life
to lay up enough wealth

to damn one
i perceive said his new found friend
that your early training
has stayed by you
you have a truly religious nature
yes replied the other
at the cost of great
personal sacrifice in many ways
i have kept myself
an object of charity
in order to foster
the spirituality of the well to do
the most passionate piety
could do but little more
but if you had inherited
great riches said the other bum
would you have given them to the poor
i doubt was the reply
that i would have felt justified
in doing that
i would more likely have said to myself
that providence
had by that token
marked me out as one destined
to hell fire
and i would have considered it
impious to struggle against
the manifest wishes of heaven
well sighed the other
life is full of terrible problems
indeed it is
rejoined his friend

but i am afraid that i shall
never solve even the least of them
when i am empty and cold
i am not in the mood for meditation
and when i am warm and replete
i go to sleep
the few guiding principles
i learned in father s church
have carried me thus far
and i shall go on to the end
never thinking beyond them
i merely apply them literally
and they work
they have made me what i am
he concluded complacently

archy

immorality

i was up to central
park yesterday watching some
kids build a snow man when
they were done and had
gone away i looked it
over they had used two
little chunks of wood for
the eyes i sat on one
of these and stared at

the bystanders along came a
prudish looking
lady from flatbush she
stopped and regarded the
snow man i stood
up on my hind legs in
the eye socket and
waved myself at her
horrors she cried even the
snow men in manhattan
are immoral officer arrest
that statue it winked
at me madam said the cop
accept the tribute
as a christmas present
and be happy my own
belief is that some
people have immorality
on the brain

                    archy

the suicide club

boss i ran onto a queer bunch
in the back room of a saloon on william street
the other night there were six of them
two cockroaches
a grass hopper

a flea
and two crickets
they have what they call a suicide club
not the sort our old
friend r l s made famous
the members of which intend to kill
themselves but each member of this
club has committed suicide already
they were once humans
as i was myself
at least i was a poet
after they killed themselves their souls
transmigrated into the bodies
of the insects mentioned
and so they have got together and
formed a club the other night the grass
hopper told why he had killed himself
it was a misunderstanding
with one i loved he said
which impelled me to the rash act
she and i were walking down a country
road and i got some gravel in one
of my shoes shortly afterward we
boarded a trolley car would you
mind i asked her if i took my shoe off
and shook out the gravel
help yourself she said
just as i got my shoe off we passed
a glue factory
i hastily put the shoe on again by the
time it was on again we were well past
the glue factory

the period during which the shoe was off
and the period during which we
were passing the glue factory exactly
synchronized
she did not see the glue factory
and refused to believe there had been
one in the neighborhood i could
never explain a month later
i killed myself tough luck
old top said the flea i will now
tell you why i took the fatal
plunge i will
tell you how it was i
committed suicide and transmigrated
into the body of an insect i was
the india rubber man in a circus side
show and fell in love with a
pair of beautiful siamese twins
public opinion was against
me marrying both of them
although both of them loved me as i
loved them both you
must choose between them said the
manager what god has joined together
let no man put asunder i said but
public opinion was too much for me
but the surgical operation which
severed them changed their
dispositions you can t fool with
a freak without running some such
risk when they were cut apart one of
them eloped with the surgeon

who had done the work and the other
married an interne in the
hospital they had a double
wedding and i slew myself that night
well said one of the crickets i will
now tell you how i shuffled off
this mortal coil and
transmigrated into the
body of a cricket and became a
member of this has been club my father
belonged to a religious sect which
forbids shaving and i was
brought up in that way no
razor ever touched my face when i was
forty years old i had a beard that hung
down to my knees it was red and
glossy i went around the country
posing as a doctor for a medicine
company hitting the tank towns in a
wagon and giving a spiel and
playing on the banjo i did well as
my beard attracted
crowds and was happy and
prosperous until one day a
malignant old man who
had just bought six bottles of tonic
for five dollars made of roots herbs
and nature s own remedies
containing no
mineral ingredients and brewed from
juniper leaves hazel roots choke
cherries and the bark of the

wild cohosh exactly
as the indians made it for a
thousand years
in the unpathed forests before the
pale face came said to me mister
can i ask you a question yes i
said i have nothing to conceal i am on
the level if one wine glass full before
meals does not give you an appetite
take two or three
mister he says the question is
personal go ahead i says i am the
seventh son
of a seventh son a soothsayer and a
seer i can tell by the way
you chew tobacco you have liver
trouble i will make a
special price to you fourteen
bottles for ten dollars cash no he said
it is about your beard it grew i told
him through using this medicine
my chin was bald at
birth it is a specific for erysipelas
botts neuralgia stomach trouble loss
of appetite heart s disease dandruff and
falling hair thirty bottles to you
for twenty dollars and i will throw
in an electric belt
mister he said i only want to ask
you if you sleep
with all your beard outside
of the covers or

under the covers when you go to
bed at night and he gave me an evil
grin and went on i
never thought of it
before i had just gone to bed and slept
as a rule but that night when i
climbed into bed i thought of the old
man s question i spread all my
beard outside of the covers and it
was immediately apparent to me
that i did not have the habit of
sleeping with it that way then i put it
under the covers and was
no less certain that i did not
sleep with it that way i worried
about it till morning and each way i
put it seemed at
once to be the wrong way
the next night it was the same
thing i could not keep from
thinking about it i got no sleep at all
and became the mere shadow of my
former self it so preyed upon me
that at last i saw i must either
shave off the beard or end it all but i
could not shave off the beard
without deserting the religious principles
instilled into me by my father and so i
took the fatal plunge hard lines said the
second cricket the way i happened to
commit suicide and undergo
transmigration and

thus qualify for a member of this club
was this when i was a
human i was wedded to a lady whose
mother had a very strong
and domineering character she
lived with us night after
night i would lie awake thinking
up schemes to get even
with her i thought up
some lovely schemes but when
morning came my nerve would
leave i never had the courage to
put them into execution finally
the thought came to me that if i was
a ghost i could haunt her and
she would have no come back i slew
myself but alas my soul transmigrated
into the body of a cricket and
if you had ever seen that strong and
bitter old woman slaying spiders and
crickets you could realize
the despair that has settled down on me
since too bad said one
of the cockroaches i will now narrate the
events which led up to my
determination to
take the leap into the
darkness
i can t say that i
had any good reason for
slaying myself i had done everything
else at least once i was a

young man possessed of a
considerable fortune which it was my only
occupation to dissipate when
everything else palled i
took up theology i made a bet
with another student that the soul
was not immortal the only way to
settle it was to die and find out we both
did well fellows we both lost mine
proved to be immortal for here i am but his
was not it completely disappeared and
has never been heard of again
which shows you never can tell and
yet i am still interested in
games of chance

archy

archy s statue

say boss but it s great to
be famous when i saw that pedestrian
statue of myself on your desk i reflected that not
every one is privileged to see his
monument erected before he dies nor
after either for that matter it
gave me the feeling that i was looking at my own
tombstone erected in memory of my good
deeds how noble i will have to be to live up

to all that i felt just as a person might
feel who was hearing his own funeral
sermon preached over him i
stared at the statue and the statue stared at
me and i resolved in the future to be
a better cockroach of course it doesn t flatter me
any my middle set of legs aren t really
that bowed but the intellectual look
on my face is all there

                                        archy

short course in natural history

you should be glad
you re not a tomcat
for when all is said
and done
you know you d hate
to pay insurance
on nine lives instead of one
be glad you re not
a centipede
you might your whole
ambition lose
if you had to find
the cash
to keep a centipede
in shoes

be glad you re not
a devilfish
if you had four pairs
of feet
what a trail
you d leave behind you
when you staggered
with the heat

                        archy

mehitabel pulls a party

dear boss mehitabel shows
no evidences of reform
she flung a party in shinbone alley
last night and six of the toughest
tabbies i ever saw were her guests
all seven of them danced on the ash cans
flirting their tails in the moonlight
and chanting as follows

oh wotthell do we care
if we are down and out
there s a dance or two in the old janes yet
so caper and swing about
up and down the alley
through and over the fence

SHE FLUNG A PARTY.

IN SHINBONE ALLEY.

for still we are attractive
to various feline gents
meow meow meow

now then sadie don t talk shady
try and remember you and myrtie
that you was raised a lady
that goes for you too gertie
oh i was chased down broadway
by a tom with a ribbon and bell
i says to him my limber jim
you seem to know me well
says he to me oh can it be
you are mehitabel
oh wotthell girls wotthell
as long as the gents is for us
we still got a job in the chorus
we ain t no maltese flappers
we all seen better days
but we got as much it
as an ingenue kit
and it is the art that pays
meow meow meow

arch your back and caper
and kick at the golden moon
mebby some yeggs
who sell butter and eggs
will fling us a party soon
now then gertie don t get dirty
frankie frankie don t get cranky
and call any lowlife names
remember that you and your sister

were once society dames
and me and nance was debutants
before we was abducted
remember pearl that you was a girl
that a college went and instructed
don t chew the fat with no common cat
for you still got an honored place
oh climb the fence and caper
and kick the moon in the face

oh mebby we all are busted
oh mebby the winters are chill
but all of us girls seen better days
and we are ladies still
remember nell you was once a swell
you was raised a social pet
be careful sweet and act discreet
you may have come down in the world my dear
and you got a cauliflower
onto your ear
but you are a lady yet
meow meow meow

oh wotthell oh wotthell
as i came into the alley
i met a brindle swell
he says to me oh this can be
none but mehitabel
oh willie says i as i passed him by
you know me far too well
then cheerio my deario
prance and pirouette
as long as gents has such intents

there s life in the old world yet
meow meow meow

oh wotthell oh wotthell
i spy you brindle bill
come off the fence you feline gents
there s a dance in the old dame still
meow meow miaow
now then girls no shady jests
here come the gentlemen guests
you try and dance refined
remember you all was ladies born
and still are so inclined
now then sadie don t talk shady
or out you go on your nut
this ain t any lousy harlem brawl
this ain t any party in webster hall
we gotta recall we are nice girls all
and never was anything but
meow meow meow

archy

mehitabel joins the navy

expenses going up
and income going down
but wotthehell do i care
the sailors are in town

a tom cat off a cruiser
was seeing of the city
says he between his whiskers
hello my pretty kitty

oh i am pure and careful
in manner well instructed
i ve seldom spoke to strangers
and seldom been abducted

so i replied discreetly
ain t you the nervy guy
how dare you brace a lady
so innocent and shy

oh look he said our warships
have all their flags unfurled
oh come and join the navy
and we will see the world

but the first place that he took me
was not a ship at all
it was a dive in harlem
where they hailed him admiral

a loud shebeen in harlem
which flowed with song and cheer
and we danced upon the tables
for oysters stewed in beer

the second place he took me
he had been there before
we danced for smelt and fishballs
and they called him commodore

twas down in coney island
they named me puss cafe
as we danced among the bottles
for cream and gin frappe

my room rent keeps a mounting
and credit going down
but wotthehell do i care
the sailors are in town

the next place that we landed
he done a noble deed
he sliced the eye from a fresh wharf cat
who tried to make my speed

avast you swabs and lubbers
when a sailor says ahoy
tis a patriotic duty
to give the navy joy

oh i always am the lady
discreet as well as gay
but the next place that he took me
the devil was to pay

for we seen the icebox open
and tried to raid the loot
and the next we knew we was out in the street
ahead of the barkeep s boot

but wotthehell do i care
i neither whine nor fret
what though my spine is out of line
there s a dance in the old dame yet

i would not desert the navy
nor leave it in the lurch
though each place that he took me
was less and less like a church

and now the fleet is sailing
with all its flags unfurled
and five little kittens with anchor marks
are tagging me round through the alleys and parks
but i have seen the world

oh my maternal instinct
has proved to be my curse
it started when i was an ingenue
and went from bad to worse

but wotthehell do i care
whether it s tom or bill
for any sailor off of the fleet
there s a dance in the old dame still

                                mehitabel the cat

not any proof

mehitabel the cat
tells me the feline
tribe were worshipped
in ancient egypt
and for that reason i

THE FELINE TRIBE

WAS WORSHIPED IN ANCIENT EGYPT.

should hold her in more
respect
well says i
minerva burst from
the head of jove
with a heluva yell
but that does not prove
that we should
stand in awe
of every case of
mastoiditis

                         archy

statesmanship

i was talking
with an insect the
other day about the
hard times that
cockroaches have to
get a living every
man s hand is against them
and occasionally his
foot meals
are few and far between
why in the world
says this

insect do you not
go to the country and become
grasshoppers if
living in town and being
cockroaches is getting
too difficult for you
i was astonished
at the simplicity of the
solution but as i
thought it over it occurred
to me that
perhaps it sounded more
statesmanlike than it
really was
how i asked him are
cockroaches to become
grasshoppers
that is a mere
detail he said which i
leave to you for
solution i have outlined
the general scheme for your
salvation so do not ask
me to settle the mere
details i trust to you for
that you must do
something for yourself
we philosophers cannot do it all
for you unaided you
must learn self help
but alas i fear that
your inherent stupidity will

balk all efforts
to improve your condition
boss i offer you
this little story
for what it is worth
if you are able to
find in it something
analogous to a number
of easy schemes
for the improvement of the
human race you
may do immense good by
printing it
yours for reform
                              archy

the author s desk

i climbed upon my boss his desk
to type a flaming ballad
and there i found a heap grotesque
of socks and songs and salad

some swedenborgian dope on hell
with modernistic hunches
remnants of plays that would not jell
and old forgotten lunches

a plate once flushed with pride and pie
now chill with pallid verses
a corkless jug of ink hard by
sobbed out its life with curses

six sad bedraggled things lay there
inertly as dead cats
three sexless rhymes that could not pair
and three discouraged spats

the feet of song be tender things
like to the feet of waiters
and need when winter bites and stings
sesquipedalian gaiters

peter the pup sprawled on the heap
disputing all approaches
or growled and grumbled in his sleep
or waked and snapped at roaches

i found a treatise on the soul
which bragged it undefeated
and a bill for thirteen tons of coal
by fate left unreceipted

books on the modern girl s advance
wrapped in a cutey sark
with honi soit qui mal y pense
worked for its laundry mark

mid broken glass the spider slinks
while memories stir and glow
of olden happy far off drinks
and bottles long ago

such is the litter at the root
of song and story rising
or noisome pipe or cast off boot
feeding and fertilizing

as lilies burgeon from the dirt
into the golden day
dud epic and lost undershirt
survive time s slow decay

still burrowing far and deep i found
a razor coldly soapy
and at the center of the mound
some most surprising opi

some modest pages chaste and shy
for pocket poke or sporran
written by archy published by
doubleday and doran

                    archy the cockroach

II The Old Soak

THE OLD SOAK

CHAPTER ONE

Introducing the Old Soak

Our friend, the Old Soak, came in from his home in Flatbush to see us not long ago, in anything but a jovial mood.

"I see that some persons think there is still hope for a liberal interpretation of the law so that beer and light wines may be sold," said we.

"Hope," said he, moodily, "is a fine thing, but it don't gurgle none when you pour it out of a bottle. Hope is all right, and so is Faith . . . but what I would like to see is a little Charity.

"As far as Hope is concerned, I'd rather have Despair combined with a case of Bourbon liquor than all the Hope in the world by itself.

"Hope is what these here fellows has got that is tryin' to make their own with a tea-kettle and a piece of hose. That's awful stuff, that is. There's a friend of mine made some of that stuff and he was scared of it, and he thinks before he drinks any he will try some of it onto a dumb beast.

"But there ain't no dumb beast anywheres handy,

181

so he feeds some of it to his wife's parrot. That there parrot was the only parrot I ever knowed of that wasn't named Polly. It was named Peter, and was supposed to be a gentleman parrot for the last eight or ten years. But whether it was or not, after it drank some of that there home-made hootch Peter went and laid an egg.

"That there home-made stuff ain't anything to trifle with.

"It's like amateur theatricals. Amateur theatricals is all right for an occupation for them that hasn't got anything to do nor nowhere to go, but they cause useless agony to an audience. Home-made booze may be all right to take the grease spots out of the rugs with, but it ain't for the human stomach to drink. Home-made booze is either a farce with no serious kick to it, or else a tragedy with an unhappy ending. No, sir, as soon as what is left has been drunk I will kiss good-bye to the shores of this land of holiness and suffering and go to some country where the vegetation just naturally works itself up into liquor in a professional manner, and end my days in contentment and iniquity.

"Unless," he continued, with a faint gleam of hope, "the smuggling business develops into what it ought to. And it may. There's some friends of mine already picked out a likely spot on the shores of Long Island and dug a hole in the sand that kegs might wash into if they was throwed from passing vessels. They've hoisted friendly signals, but so far nothing has been throwed overboard."

He had a little of the right sort on his hip, and after refreshing himself, he announced:

"I'm writing a diary. A diary of the past. A kind of gol-dinged autobiography of what me and Old King Booze done before he went into the grave and took one of my feet with him.

"In just a little while now there won't be any one in this here broad land of ours, speaking of it geographically, that knows what an old-fashioned barroom was like. They'll meet up with the word, future generations of posterity will, and wonder and wonder and wonder just what a saloon could have resembled, and they will cudgel their brains in vain, as the poet says.

"Often in my own perusal of reading matter I run onto institutions that I would like to know more of. But no one ever set down and described 'em because everyone knowed all about them in the time when the writing was done. Often I thought I would 'a' liked to knowed all about them Hanging Gardens of Babylon, for instance, and who was hanged in 'em and what for; but nobody ever described 'em, as fur as I know."

"Have you got any of it written?" we asked him.

"Here's the start of it," said he.

We present it just as the Old Soak penned it.

CHAPTER TWO

Beginning the Old Soak's History of the Rum Demon

I will hereinunder set down nothing but what is the truth, the whole truth and nothing but the truth, so help me God. Well, in the old days, before everybody got so gosh-amighty good, barrooms was so frequent that nobody thought of setting down their scenery and habits.

Usually you went into it by a pair of swinging doors that met in the middle and didn't go full length up, so you could see over the top of the door, and if any one was to come into one door you didn't want to have talk with or anything you could see him and have a chance to gravitate out the door at the other end of the barroom while he was getting in. But you couldn't see into the windows of them as a habitual custom, because who could tell whether a customer's family was going to pass by and glance in. Well, in your heart you knew you was doing nothing to be ashamed of, but all families even in the good old days contained some prohibition relations. The Good Book says that flies in the ointment send forth a smell to heaven. Well, you felt more private like with the windows fixed thataway. They was painted, soaped, and some stained glassed.

It had its good sides and it had its bad sides, but I will say I have been completely out of touch, just as much as if I was a native of some hot country, with all kinds of morality and religions of all sorts, ever since the barrooms was shut up. From childhood's earliest hours religion has been one of my favourite studies, and I never let a week pass without I get down on my knees some time or another and pray about something any more than I would let a week pass without I washed all over. It was early recollections of a good woman that kept me religious, and I hope I do not have to say anything further to this gang. Well, in spite of my religion I never went to church none. Because it ain't reasonable to suppose that a man could keep awake. He thinks, "What if I should nod," and he does. So that always throwed me back onto the barrooms for my religion.

Well, then, the first thing you know when you are up by the free lunch counter eating some of that delicatessen in comes a girl and says to contribute to the cause. Well, "What cause are you?" you ask her. Well, she says, Salvation Army or the Volunteers, or what not, and so forth, as the case may be, or maybe she was boosting for some of these new religions that gets out a paper and these girls go around and sell it for ten cents, which they always set a date for the world coming to an end. Well, then, you got a line on her religion, and you was ashamed not to give her a quarter, for you had spent a dollar for drinks already that morning. And then all through the day there was other religions come in, one after another, or maybe the same religion over and over again.

Well, then, you kept in touch with religions and it made a better man out of you, and along about evening time when you figured on going home you felt like it wouldn't be right to tell any prevarications to your wife about how you come to be so late, so you just said over the phone: "I am starting right away. I stopped into Ed's place to play a game of pool after work and met a fellow I used to know. I couldn't get away from him and I was too thoughtful of you to insist for him to come home to dinner so he insisted I ought to have a drink with him for old time's sake." And if it hadn't been for being in contact with different religions all day you would of lied outright to your wife and felt mean as a dog about it when she found you out.

Well, then, it needs no further proof that the abolishment of the saloon has taken away the common people's religions from them, but it is my message to tell just what the barrooms was like and not to criticize the laws of the land, even when they are dam-foolish as so many of them are. So I will confine myself to describing the barroom and the rum demon.

Well, I never saw much rum drunk in the places where I hung out. Sometimes some baccardy into a cocktail, but for my part cocktails always struck me as wicked. The good book says that the Lord started the people right but that men had made many adventures. Well, then, I took mine straight for the most part, except when I needed some special kind of a pick-up in the morning.

And the good book says not to tarry long over the wine cup, and I never done that, neither, except a little Rhine wine in the summer time, but mostly took mine straight.

Well, then, to come down to describing these phantom places over which the raven says nevermore but the posterity of the future may wish to have its own say so about. Well, there was a long counter always kept wiped off, not like these here sticky soda-water counters which the boys and girls back of them always look sticky, too, and their sleeves look sticky and the glasses is sticky, but in a decent barroom the counter was kept swiped off clean and self-respectable.

And there was a brass rail with cuspidors near to it, if you wanted to cuspidate it was handy right there, and there's no place to hawk and cuspidate in these here soda-water dives. Not that I ever been in them much. All that stuff rots the lining of your stomach. As far as I am concerned, being the posterity of a lot of Scotch ancestors, I never liked soft stuff in my insides.

I never drunk nothing but whiskey for comfort and pleasure, and I never took no medicine in my life except calomel, and I always held to the Presbyterian religion as my favourite religion because those three things has got some kick when took inside of you.

Well, then, to get down to telling just what these

places was like, it would surprise this generation of posterity how genteel some of them was. Which I will come down to in my next chapter. Well, I will close this chapter.

CHAPTER THREE

Liquor and Hennery Simms

"I never could see liquor drinking as a bad habit," said the Old Soak, "though I admit fair and free it will lead to bad habits if it ain't watched.

"In these here remarks of mine, I aim to tell the truth, and nothing but the truth, so help me Jehorsophat, as the good book says.

"One feller I knowed whose liquor drinking led to bad habits was my old friend Hennery Simms.

"Every time Hennery got anyways jingled he used to fall downstairs, and he fell down so often that it got to be a habit and you couldn't call it nothing else. He thought he had to.

"One time late at night I was going over to Brooklyn on the subway, and I seen one of these here escalators with Hennery onto it moving upwards, only Hennery wasn't riding on his feet, he was riding on the spine of his back.

"And when he got to the top of the thing and it

skated him out onto the level, what does Hennery do but pitch himself onto it again, head first, and again he was carried up.

"After I seen him do that three or four times I rode up to where Hennery was floundering at and I ast him what was he doing.

" 'I'm falling downstairs,' says Hennery.

" 'What you doing that fur?' I says.

" 'I'm drunk, ain't I?' says Hennery. 'You old fool, you knows I always falls downstairs when I'm drunk.'

" 'How many times you goin' to fall down these here stairs?' I ast him.

" 'I ain't fell down these here stairs once yet,' says Hennery, 'though I must of tried to a dozen times. I been tryin' to fall down these here stairs ever since dusk set in, but they's something wrong about 'em.

" 'If I didn't know I was drunk, I would swear these here stairs was movin'.'

" 'They be movin',' I tells him.

" 'You go about your business,' he says, 'and don't mock a man that's doing the best he can. In course they ain't movin'.

" 'They only looks like they was movin' to me because I'm drunk. You can't fool me.'

"And I left him still tryin' to fall down them stairs, and still bein' carried up again. Which, as I remarked at first, only goes to show that drink will lead to habits if it ain't watched, even when it ain't a habit itself."

"Do you have any more of your History of the Rum Demon written?" we asked him.

"Uh-huh," said he, and left us the second installment.

CHAPTER FOUR

The Old Soak's History—The Barroom as an Educative Influence

Well, as I said in my first installment, some of them barrooms was such genteel places they would surprise you if you had got the idea that they was all gems of iniquity and wickedness with the bartenders mostly in clean collars and their hair slicked, not like so many of these soda-water places, where the hair is stringy.

Well, this is for future generations of posterity that will have never saw a saloon, and the whole truth is to be set down, so help me God, and I will say that it took a good deal of sweeping sometimes to keep the floor clean and often the free lunch was approached with one fork for several people, especially the beans. Well, it has been three or four years even before that Eighteenth Commandment passed since free lunch was what it once was. And some barrooms was under par. But I am speaking of the average good class barroom, where you would take your own children or grandchildren, as the case may be.

They was some very kind-hearted places among them where if a man had spent all his money already for his own good they would refuse to let him have anything more to drink until maybe someone set them up for him.

But to get down to brass tacks and describe what they looked like more thoroughly I will say they was always attractive to me with those long expensive mirrors and brass fixtures like a scene of elegance and grandeur out of the Old Testament where it tells of Solomon in all his glory. And if a gent would forget to be genteel after he took too much and his money was all spent and imbue himself with loud talk or rough language and maybe want to hit somebody and there was none of his friends there to take charge of him often I have seen such throwed out on their ear, for the better class places always aimed to be decent and orderly and never to have an indecent reputation for loudness and roughhouseness.

Well, I will say I have not kept up with politics like I used to since the barrooms was vanished. My eyes ain't what they used to be and the newspapers are different from each other so who can tell what to believe, but in the old days you could keep in touch with politics in the barrooms. It made a better citizen out of you for every man ought to vote for what his consciousness tells him is right and to abide in politics by his consciousness.

Well, closing the barroom has shut off my chance

to be imbued with political dope and who to bet on in the next election and I am not so good a citizen as before the saloons was closed. I would not know who to bet on in any election but I used to get straight tips and in that way took an interest in politics which a man is scarcely to be called an American citizen unless he does.

Well I see everywhere where all the doctors and science sharks says to keep in touch with outdoor sports if you want to keep young. I used to know all about all those outdoor sports and who the Giants had bought and what they paid for him and who was the best pitcher and what the dope was on tomorrow's entries at Havana, but all that is taken away from me now the saloons is closed and I got no chance to get into touch with outdoor sports and I feel it in my health. Some of these days the Prohibition aliments will wake up and see they have ruined the country but then it will be too late. Taking the sports away from a nation is not going to do it any good when the next war comes along if one does.

Well, I promised I would describe more what they looked like. I will tackle that in the next chapter, so I will bring this installment to a close.

CHAPTER FIVE

Look Out for Crime Waves!

"They're going to take our tobacco next, are they?" said the Old Soak. "Well, me, I won't struggle none! I ain't fit to struggle. I'm licked; my heart's broke. They can come and take my blood if they want it, and all I'll do is ask 'em whether they'll have it a drop at a time, or the whole concerns in a bucket.

"All I say is: *Watch Out for Crime Waves!* I don't threaten nobody, I just predict. If you ever waked up about 1 o'clock in the morning, two or three miles from a store, and that store likely closed, and no neighbour near by, and the snow drifting the roads shut, and wanted a smoke, and there wasn't a single crumb of tobacco nowheres in the house, you know what I mean. You go and look for old cigar and cigarette butts to crumble into your pipe, and there ain't none. You go through all your clothes for little mites of tobacco that have maybe jolted into your pockets, and there ain't none. Your summer clothes is packed away into the bottom of a trunk somewheres, and you wake your wife to find the key to the trunk, and you get the clothes and there ain't no tobacco in them pockets, either.

"And then you and your wife has words. And you sit and suffer and cuss and chew the stem of your empty pipe. By 3 in the morning there ain't no customary crime known you wouldn't commit. By 4 o'clock you begin to think of new crimes, and how you'd like to commit them and then make up comic songs about 'em and go and sing them songs at the funerals of them you've slew.

"Hark to me: If tobacco goes next, there'll be a crime wave! Take away a man's booze, and he dies, or embraces dope or religion, or goes abroad, or makes it at home, or drinks varnish, or gets philosophical or something. But tobacco! No, sir! There ain't any substitute. Why, the only way they're getting away with this booze thing now is because millions and millions of shattered nerves is solacing and soothing theirselves with tobacco.

"I'm mild, myself. I won't explode. I'm getting my booze. I know where there's plenty of it. My heart's broke to see the saloons closed, and I'm licked by the overwhelming righteous . . . but I won't suffer any personal for a long time yet. But there's them that will. And on top of everything else, tobacco is to go! All right, take it—but I say solemn and warningly: *Look Out for Crime Waves!*

"The godly and the righteous can push us wicked persons just so far, but worms will turn. Look at the Garden of Eden! The mammal of iniquity ain't never yet been completely abolished. Look at the history of the world—every once in a while it has always looked as if the pious and the uplifter was going to bring in the millennium, with bells on it —but something has always happened just in time and the mammal of unrighteousness has come into his own again. I ain't threatening; I just predict— *Look Out for Crime Waves!*

"As for me, I may never see Satan come back home. I'm old. I ain't long for this weary land of purity and this vale of tears and virtue. I'll soon be in a place where the godly cease from troubling and the wicked are at rest. But I got children and grandchildren that'll fight against the millennium to the last gasp, if I know the breed, and I'm going to pass on full of hope and trust and calm belief.

"Here," concluded the Old Soak, unscrewing the top of his pocket flask, "here is to the mammal of unrighteousness!"

He deposited on our desk the next installment of his History.

CHAPTER SIX

Continuing the Old Soak's History—The Barroom and the Arts

Well, I promised to describe what the saloon that has been banished was like so that future generations of posterity will know what it was like they never having seen one. And maybe being curious, which I would give a good deal to know how they got all their animals into the ark only nobody that was on the spot thought to write it down and figure the room for the stalls and cages and when it comes to that how did they train animals to talk in those days like Balaam and his ass, and Moses knocking the water out of the rocks always interested me.

Which I will tell the truth, so help me. It used to be this way: some had tables and some did not. But I never was much of a one for tables, for if you set down your legs don't tell you anything about how you are standing it till you get up and find you have went further than you intended, but if you stand up your legs gives you a warning from time to time you better not have but one more.

Well, I will tell the truth. And one thing is the treating habit was a great evil. They would come too fast, and you would take a light drink like Rhine wine whilst they was coming too fast, and that way use up considerable room that you could of had more advantage from if you had saved it for something important.

Well, the good book says to beware of wine and evil communications corrupts a good many. Well, what I always wanted was that warm feeling that started about the equator and spread gentle all over you till you loved your neighbour as the good book says and wine never had the efficiency for me.

Well, I will say even if the treating habit was a great evil it is an ill wind that blows nobody any good. Well, I promised to come down to brass tacks and describe what the old-time barroom looked like. Some of the old timers had sawdust on the floor, which I never cared much for that as it never looked genteel to me and almost anything might be mixed into it.

I will tell the whole truth, so help me. And another kick I got is about business advantages. Which you used to be lined up by the bar five or six of you and suppose you was in the real estate business or something a fellow would say he had an idea that such and such a section would be going to have a boom and that started you figuring on it. Well, I missed a lot of business opportunities like that since the barroom has been vanished. What can a country expect if it destroys all chances a man has got to get ahead in business? The next time they ask us for business as usual to win a war with this country will find out something about closing up all chances a man has to get tips on their business chances.

Well, the good book says to laugh and grow fat and since the barroom has been taken away, what chance you got to hear any new stories I would like to know. Well, so help me, I said I would tell the truth, and the truth is some of them stories was not fit to offer up along with your prayers, but at the same time you got acquainted with some right up-to-date fellows. Well, what I want to know is how could you blame a country for turning into Bolshevisitors if all chance for sociability is shut off by the government from the plain people?

Well, the better class of them had pictures on the

walls, and since they been taken away what chance has a busy man like me got to go to a museum and see all them works of art hand painted by artists and looking as slick and shiny as one of these here circus lithographs. Well, a country wants to look out what it is doing when it shuts off from the plain people all the chance to educate itself in the high arts and hand painting. Some of the frames by themselves must of been worth a good deal of money.

The Good Book says you shalt not live by bread alone and if you ain't got a chance to educate yourself in the high arts or nothing after a while this country will get to the place where all the foreign countries will laugh at us for we won't know good hand painting when we see it. Well, they was a story to all them hand paintings, and often when business was slack I used to talk with Ed the bartender about them paintings and what did he suppose they was about.

What chance have I got to go and buy a box to set in every night at the Metropolitan Opera House I would like to know and hear singing. Well, the good book says not to have anything to do with a man that ain't got any music in his soul and the right kind of a crowd in the right kind of a barroom could all get to singing together and furnish me with music.

A government that takes away all its music like that from the plain people had better watch out. Some of these days there will be another big war and what will they do without music. I always been fond of music and there ain't anywhere I can go that it sounds the same sort of warmed up and friendly and careless. Let alone taking away my chance to meet up with different religions taking away my music has been a big blow to me.

Well, I will tell the truth so help me, it was a nice place to drop into on a rainy day; you don't want to be setting down at home on a rainy day, reading your Bible all the time. But since they been closed I had to do a lot of reading to get through the day somehow and the wife is too busy to talk to me and the rest of the family is at work or somewheres.

Well, another evil is I been doing too much reading and that will rot out your brains unless of course it is the good book and you get kind of mixed up with all them revelations and things. And you get tired figuring out almanacs and the book with 1,000 drummer's jokes in it don't sound so good in print as when a fellow tells them to you and I never was much of a one for novels. What I like is books about something you could maybe know about yourself and maybe some of them old-time wonders of the world with explanations of how they was made. But nobody that was on the spot took the trouble to explain a lot of them things which is why I am setting down what the barroom was like so help me.

Well, in the next chapter I will describe it some more or future generations will have no notion of them without the Constitution of the United States changes its mind and comes to its census again.

CHAPTER SEVEN

An Argument with the Old Woman

"The Old Woman and me had quite an argument last Sunday," said the Old Soak. "It ended up with her turning a saucepan full of hot peas onto my bald spot, which ain't no way to treat garden truck, with the cost of things what they be.

"But I won one of these here moral victories, even if she did get the best of me and chase me out of the house.

"It all come about over some pie we had for dinner on Sunday. It looked like mince pie to me when she set it on the table, and I says to her why don't she make some rhubarb pie or apple pie or something, for this is a hell of a time of year to be having mince pie. And mince pie ain't no good anyhow unless you put a shot of brandy or hard cider into it. She knows I orter be careful what I put into my stomach, which is all to the bad since I can't get the right kind of drink any more, and I told her so.

" 'Well, then,' says she, 'this ain't mince pie. This is raisin pie.'

" 'Raisin pie!' I says, and I was shocked and scandalized. 'Raisin pie! Good lord, woman, are you crazy? You don't mean to say you've went and took hundreds and hundreds of good raisins and went and wasted them thataway by puttin' 'em in a *pie!* It's the most extravagant thing I ever hearn tell on! Ain't you got sense enough to know that in these days raisins ain't something you eat?'

" 'Well, what are they, then?' she says.

" 'Raisins,' I told her, 'is something you make hootch out of, and you know I'm reduced to makin' my own stuff these days. And yet here you be, puttin' at least a quart of good raisins into a gosh-darned pie!'

"Well, one word led to another, and, as I said, she hit me with the peas. But I got away with that pie. I won the moral victory. I got that pie fermentin' now, in the bottom of a cask full of grape and berry juice and other truck I picked up here and there. No, sir, there ain't goin' to be no raisins wasted around my house by eatin' of 'em in this here time of need!"

The Old Soak was silent a moment, and then he said: "This here installment of my diary of booze takes up that very point of quarrellin' with the Old Woman."

CHAPTER EIGHT

The Old Soak's History—More Evils of Prohibition

Well, another kick I got on the abvolition of the barroom is the fact that you got to stay around home so much and that naturally leads to having a row with your wife.

When there was barrooms my wife used to jaw me every time I come home anyways lit up and I just let her jaw me and there wasn't any row for I figured better let her get away with it who knows maybe she thinks she is right about it.

But now I stick around home a good deal of the time and it leads to words.

Well, she says to me, why don't you go and get a job of work of some kind.

Well, I tell her, mind your own business I always been a good pervider ain't I. You have got five or six children working for you ain't you and a man that pervides his wife with five or six children to work for her is not going to listen to no back talk.

Well, she says, you ought to be ashamed to loaf around home all the time.

Well, I says, I'm thinking up a big business deal but that's the way with women they never understand they got to keep their mouth shut and give a man peace and quiet to do his thinking in so he can make them a good living all they think about is new-fangled ways to spend the money after he has slaved himself half to death making it.

Well, she says, I ain't seen you slaving any lately.

Well, I tells her, I done all my hard slaving when I was young and I got a little money coming in right along from them two houses I own, and I ain't going to work myself into the grave for no extravagant woman, and me with a heart pappitation you can hear half a mile on a clear day.

Well, she says, what rent money them two houses brings in don't any more than pay for the booze you drink.

Well, I says, you Prohibitionists done that to me. You went and made it plumb impossible to get good liquor for any reasonable price. That there rent money used to pay for three times the booze I drink.

Well, she says, you oughta get a job.

If I was to tie myself down to a job, I tells her, what chance would I have to trade and dicker around and make little turnovers, let alone thinking up this big business deal I am working on.

You are a liar, she said, and if I knowed where your whiskey was hid I'd bust every bottle and what kind of a business deal are you thinking up.

It is an invention I says to her and you mind your own business just because I have stood for you in-trupting me for forty years is no sign I am going to stand for it forty years more.

You can quit any time she says and good riddance

the children will keep me and there will be one less to cook for besides being ashamed of you before all my own friends and the nice people the children know.

Well, I said, here I set turning over the leaves of the Bible and you attack me that way and me trying to think up a business deal to buy you an automobile and the pappitation in my heart that bad it shakes the chair I am setting in and if a man with one foot in the grave can't get any peace and quiet to read his Bible in his own home against the time he is going to cash in then I will say that Prohibition has brought this country to a pretty pass.

Well, she says, what is that pappitation from but all the liquor you drunk.

It is from my constitution, I says, as the doctor will tell you if it hadn't been for a little mite of stimulant now and then I would of cashed in long ago and you would now have the life insurance money.

Well, she says, what kind of an invention is this you claim you are thinking up all the time?

Yes, I says, I would see myself telling you, wouldn't I and you blabbing it the next time a lot of them church women meets at our house and some old church deacon getting hold of it and getting rich off of it and me wandering the streets in destitution with the rain running down often my beard and the end of my nose because you and the children cast me into the street.

Well, she says, where is that thousand dollars that my uncle Lemuel willed to me and I give it to you for one of them inventions nearly thirty years ago and never seen hide nor hair on it since then.

Well, I says, that thousand dollars is gone and it went the same way as that money I loaned to your cousin Dan when he failed in business and would of starved to death him and his family if I hadn't come across with the cash that is where that thousand dollars is.

Well, that's the way it goes, until I get tired of trying to make her see any sense and sneak out to where my stuff is hid and fill me a pint bottle for my hip pocket and go and find a friend somewheres.

And in just that way Prohibition is breaking up millions and millions of homes every day.

CHAPTER TWELVE

More of the History—As It Used to Be of a Morning

Well, I promised I would tell just what those vanished barrooms was like, and I will tell the truth, so help me.

One thing that I can't get used to going without is that long brass railing where you would rest your feet, and I have got one of them fixed up in my own bedroom now so when I get tired setting down I can go and stand up and rest my feet one at a time.

Well, you would come in in the morning and you would say, Ed, I ain't feeling so good this morning.

I wonder what could the matter be, Ed says, though he has got a pretty good idea of what it could be all the time. But he's too kind hearted to let on.

I don't know, you says to Ed, I guess I am smoking too much lately. When you left here last night, Ed says, you seemed to be feeling all right, maybe what you got is a little touch of this here influenza.

It ain't influenza, Ed, you says to him, it is them heavy cigars we was all smoking in here last night. I swallered too much of that smoke, Ed, and I got a headache this morning and my stomach feels kind o' like it was a democratic stomach all surrounded by republican voters, and a lot of that tobacco must of got into my eyes and I feel so rotten this morning that when my wife said are you going downtown without your breakfast I just said to her Hell and walked out to dodge a row because I could see she was bad tempered this morning.

What would you say to a little absinthe, says Ed, sympathetic and helpful, a cocktail or frappy.

No, says you, if you was to say what I used to say, I leave that there stuff to these here young cigarette-smoking squirts, which it always tasted like paregoric to me.

Yes, sir, Ed says, it is one of them foreign things, and how about a milk punch, it is sometimes soothing when a person has smoked too much.

No, Ed, you says, a milk punch is too much like vittles and I can't stand the idea of vittles.

Yes, sir, Ed used to say, you are right, sir, how

about a gin fizz. A gin fizz will bring back your stomach to life right gradual, sir, and not with a shock like being raised from the dead.

Ed, you says to him, or leastways I always used to say, a silver fizz is too gentle, and one of them golden fizzes, with the yellow of an egg in it, has got the same objections as a milk punch, it is too much like vittles.

Yes, sir, Ed says, I think you are right about vittles. I can understand how you feel about not wanting vittles in the early part of the day. And that makes you love Ed, for you meet a lot of people who can't understand that. There ain't no sympathy and understanding left in the world since bartenders was abolished.

How about an old-fashioned whiskey cocktail, says Ed.

You feel he is getting nearer to it, and you tell him so, but it don't seem just like the right thing yet.

And then Ed sees you ain't never going to be satisfied with nothing till after it is into you and he takes the matter into his own hands.

I know what is the matter with you, he says, and what you want, and he mixes you up a whiskey sour and you get a little cross and say it helped some but there was too much sugar in it and not to put so much sugar in the next one.

And by the time you drink the third one, somewhere away down deep inside of you there is a warm spot wakes up and kind of smiles.

And that is your soul has waked up.

And you sort of wish you hadn't been so mean

with your wife when you left home, and you look around and see a friend and have one with him and your soul says to you away down deep inside of you for all you know about them old Bible stories they may be true after all and maybe there is a God and kind of feel glad there may be one, and if your friend says let's go and have some breakfast you are surprised to find out you could eat an egg if it ain't too soft or ain't too done.

Well, I promised, so help me, I would tell the truth about them barrooms that has perished away, and the truth I will tell, and the truth with me used to be that more than likely it wasn't really cigars that used to get me feeling that way in the mornings, and I will take up a different part of the subject in my next chapter.

CHAPTER FOURTEEN

Continuing the History of the Rum Demon —Unfermented Grape Juice

Well, as I said in my last chapter, it is time for me to get down to brass tacks and describe just what those barrooms that has been vanished was like so that future generations of posterity will know what they missed, and to tell the truth in all particulars, so help me.

Some of them was that arted up with hand paintings that if you had all them paintings in your home you would feel proud of yourself, like Solomon in all his glory, and would feel like you was living in the midst of a high art museum, and the shining brass cuspidores to spit in and the brass rail and all them shiny glasses and bottles and mirrors made up a scene of grandeur and glory like the good book mentions and you would think you was King Faro of Egypt, if you lived in the midst of all that or Job in all his riches before the itch broke out on him.

Well, speaking of the Good Book, my wife has always been more or less of a prohibitionist in order to show me that she is independent of me, and one day one of these here church friends of hers tries to tell me all the liquor that was drinked in the Bible wasn't nothing but unfermented grape juice.

Yes, it was, I said, don't you believe it was, like hell it was. You go and get your testament and see where King Solomon talks about the stuff that makes the heart merry and then go and swill yourself with grape juice and see if you could get the way he was when he wrote eat, drink, and be merry for tomorrow ye die. And how about the time when two women came to him with that one child and both claimed that it was hern and he says to the officer on duty, let me see that there sword of yourn for a minute I'll darned soon see who this kid belongs to. And verily the officer drawed his sword and the King he heaved it up and was about to cut the kid in two when one of the women says to stop unhand him King and not do the rash act it is the other woman's yew lamb and let her have it, it being her own all the time and her one yew lamb and her preferring to see the other woman grab it off than have half of it.

Well, says the King, half a loaf is better than no bread, but with infants it is different, take the child, it is yours woman, and go and sin no more.

Well, now, I ask you, was King Solomon drinking the unfermented juice of the grape when he got that there hunch, or was he not? I will say he was not. Them radical and righteous ideas never come to a man when he is cold sober. He has got to have a shot of something moving around under his belt before he gets thataway.

And how about them Bible hangovers, I said to this here church person. Man and boy I been a student of the Bible from cover to cover for a good many years now and I never seen a book with more evidences of hangovers and katzenjammers into it. How about that there book that says vanity, vanity, all is vanity. Well, I ask you, did you ever get that way in the morning after you had spent the night before drinking the unfermented juice of the grape.

That there Book of Exclusiastics is just one lone howl from the next morning head. Things seem right, says old Exclusiastic, and they look right; but if you bite into them they don't taste right, or words to that effect. And you stick around awhile, says old man Exclusiastic, and you'll darned soon see they ain't nothing right nowhere and never will be again. Moreover, says he, I was wrong when I used to think things was right; there ain't never anything anywhere been all right and I was all wrong when I was a young feller and used to think things was right and the wrongest thing about the whole business is the darned fools like I used to be who go around saying things is all right, and the sum and substance of everything is vanity, says he, vanity, vanity, all is vanity.

You could tell some folks that that there old Exclusiastic was writing as the result of unfermented grape juice, but a man with any experience of his own knows a good deal better and what kind of a taste was in his mouth. You can't tell an old Bible reader like me anything about this unfermented stuff. The trouble with these here church people is that too many of them ain't never read the Bible, or if they did read it they read it with the idea that it was saying something else like they wanted it to say.

I always stuck to the Bible in spite of the church folks and I always will for it has got some kick into it. There is three things in the world I always stick to, the Bible and hard liquor and calomel, for they has got the kick to them. You can have all your light wines and unfermented stuff and all your pretty new-thought religions and all your new-fangled medicines you want to, but for me I will stick to the Old Testament and corn whiskey and calomel like my forefathers done before me. You can't pull any of that unfermented stuff on me and get away with it.

CHAPTER SEVENTEEN

The Old Soak Finds a Way

"Yes, sir; yes, sir!" said the Old Soak, with a happy smile on his face. "I've done found out the way to beat the game—! Ask me no questions, and I'll tell ye no lies as to how I done it.

"Ye see this here bottle, do ye? Kentucky Bourbon, and nothin' else. Bottled in bond, an' there's plenty more where that comes from.—Ask me no questions, and I'll enrich ye with no misinformations!—Ye see that there little car parked out there by the curbstone, do ye? Well, sir, that there car is *my* car, and under the back seat of it is twelve quarts of this here stuff!—And it ain't home brewed, neither; it's some of the best liquor you ever throwed your lips over!—How do I do it?—Don't ply me with no questions, and I won't bring you no false witnesses!

"Notice these here new clothes of mine? Well, sir, that there suit's a bargain.—It only cost me two cases of rye.—I got three new suits like that to home, an' I'm figgerin' on buying one of these here low neck an' short sleeve dress suits for to wear to banquets this winter.—They's a whole passel o' folks

would like to give me banquets this comin' season.—
How do I do it?—Ask me no questions, and I'll give
you no back talk!

"If you was to come out to the house, I'd interduce ye to quite a lot of good liquor.—Can't drink
no more, huh?—Ain't ye got a friend ye could bring?
—I'd like to have ye meet my son-in-law.

"Yes, sir; yes, sir! Daughter was married two
months ago. The youngest one. Her and her husband is makin' their home with us temporary.—I'm
tryin' to persuade of 'em to stop to our house permanent.—Yes, sir, my son-in-law, he is one of these
here revenooers.—Well, so long!—I gotto see an old
friend o' mine that lives up to the Bronx this afternoon.—He ain't had a real drink fer nigh onto three
months, he tells me.—I'm headin' a rescue party into
them there regions.

"Yes, sir; yes, sir! I figger my daughter married
well!—Bring up yer kids in the way they should go
like the Good Book says, and Providence will do the
rest.—Henry, that's my son-in-law, is figgerin' mebby
he can get my son Jim made a revenooer, too.—Ask
me no questions, an I'll give away no fambly se-
crets!"

CHAPTER TWENTY

Continuing the History of the Rum Demon —The Barroom and Manners

Another thing about those barrooms that has been vanished forever is the fact that most of them was right polite sort of places if a fellow edged up to the bar and knocked over your glass of whiskey or something like that he would say, O excuse me stranger and you would say sure, but look where in hell you are going to after this.

Sure he would say no offence meant. No offence taken you would say to him. Have one with me he would say.

No sooner said than done.

But nowadays all you see and hear is bad manners and impoliteness with people hustling and bumping into each other on the subways and stepping on each other and women and children amongst them and nobody ever begging anybody's pardon and hard feelings everywhere.

The trouble is everybody is sore and wanting a drink all the time and there is no place where the younger generation is going to learn good manners now that the barrooms is gone. What is the young fellows just growing up to manhood going to do for their manners now that the barrooms is closed, is what I want to know.

It used to be you would get onto a subway train and there would be two or three women standing up and you would be setting down and there would be three or four drinks under your belt and you would be feeling good and you would say to yourself am I a gentleman or ain't I a gentleman.

You're damned right I am a gentleman, you would say to yourself, here, lady, you set down, and don't let any of these here bums roust you out of that seat.

If any of these here bums tries to roust you out of that seat I will put a tin ear onto them.

That's the kind of a gentleman I am, lady, they would have a hell of a time, lady, getting your seat away from you with me here.

And she seen you was a gentleman and she smiled at you and you hung onto a strap and felt good.

But nowadays there ain't no manners, with no place to get a drink or anything.

You are setting in the subway and a lady comes in and has nowheres to set, and you say to yourself let some of these other guys get up and give her a seat.

And you think a while and you say to yourself, I'll bet she is a Prohibitionist anyhow. Let her stand up. She has got to learn you can't have any manners with the barrooms all closed and everything.

Well, that's another thing closing the barroom has done. It has took away all the manners this town ever had.

In my next chapter I will get down to brass tacks and tell just what those barrooms was like for the benefit of future posterity that has never seen one.

CHAPTER TWENTY-TWO

The History of the Rum Demon Concluded —Prohibition Is Making a Free Thinker of the Old Soak

Another thing that going without barrooms is doing for this country is it is destroying Home Life.

It is pretty hard to get along with your wife after you have been married to her for twenty or thirty years and kind of settle down and realize you are going to be married to her as long as she lives for better or for worse unless something happens which it seldom does.

Not that you don't kind of like her and you know she kind of likes you but the thing is that her and you is apt to treat each other mean now and then because you get to thinking what a good time you could have if you didn't have to turn in so much of your money to making a home run smooth and you know even if you do row with each other you will make up again and you get to kind of looking forward to the rows because anyhow that is a change.

216

But sometimes you carry them rows too far and then you don't know how to get your Home Life running right again because she is always too stubborn to give in and you won't be the first one to give in because you know she is wrong.

But when there was liquor to be had in plenty it was easier to make up after one of them rows and Home Life went along smoother.

You would get up in the morning and she would say to you, would you have a boiled egg for breakfast or a fried, and you would say hades what an idea. Can't you never think of anything but eggs for breakfast. And she would say yesterday I didn't have eggs and you was sore because you wanted eggs. You would say just because I wanted eggs yesterday is that any sign I want them every day of my life till death do us part. I was only asking what you wanted she would say.

I will go where I can get what I want, you would say. I will eat my breakfast at a restaurant this morning and maybe I can keep them from shoving eggs in front of me when I don't ask for eggs. The trouble with your stomach is not what you put into it in the morning, she would say, but what you put into it the night before. The trouble with my stomach, you would say, is that I am worried to death and worked to death all the time trying to keep this house running and it gives me the dispepsy. It is the liquor gives you dispepsy she would say.

If it wasn't for a little stimulant in my stomach, like the Good Book says, you tell her, my dispepsy wouldn't let me digest anything at all and I would starve to death and the mortgage on the house would be foreclosed and you would go to the old woman's home. Whose money pays the interest on that mortgage she would say. Whose? you would say. Mine, she would say. You wouldn't have any money you tell her, if you paid me back what your relations has borrowed of me.

Well, one word leads to another, and you go off without any breakfast, for you see her taking the Bible down to set and read it, and when she sets and reads the Bible you know she is reading it against you and it gets you madder and madder.

And in the old days when there was barrooms you would go into one still feeling mad and say Ed, mix me one of the old-fashioned whiskey cocktails and don't put too much orange and that kind of damned garbage into it, I want the kick.

No sooner said than done.

And after a couple of them you would say, well after all, the Old Woman means well, I wonder if I didn't treat her a little mean this morning I orter call her up on the telephone and give her a jolly.

And then you would think of her relations that you hate and get mad at her again on account of always sticking up for them, and say, Ed, that don't set so well, let's try a whiskey sour.

And you would meet a friend and have another with him, and pretty soon eat some breakfast and think how, after all, it was eggs you was eating for breakfast and they wasn't cooked no ways as good as the old woman would of poached them for you on toast if you hadn't been so darned mean to her.

And your friend would say his old woman blowed him up for coming home pickled.

And you would have another drink and say that was one thing your old woman never done to you. My old woman has got some sense, you would say to him, she knows how a man feels about taking a drink, and she never blows me up.

And you would set and brag about your old woman and you had never had a cross word between you in thirty years. And then he would begin to brag about his old woman, too.

And pretty soon you would say to yourself you better go to the phone and call her up. She has her mean streaks all right, but who knows, she may have been right this morning after all, and you take another drink and get her on the telephone, and give her a chance to say how sorry she was about the way she treated you that morning and maybe you go and pay an installment on a new carpet sweeper for her.

Well, it was that way in the old days. Liquor kept your Home Life running along o. k. You would get mad with your wife and then you would get sorry for her and give her an excuse to make up with you again.

But now, with no chance to get a drink when I am away from home if I treat the Old Woman mean in the morning I don't give her a chance to get on my good side again. And I can see sometimes that it is breaking her heart.

That's what prohibition is doing to this country. It is breaking the women's hearts and it is breaking up the Home Life on every hand.

What is going to become of a country where all the Home Life is broke up?

And what is going to become of the children if there ain't any Home Life running along smooth any more?

These Prohibitionists that is so darned smart never thought of that I guess when they put that Eighteenth Commandment across onto us.

Whenever I think of all them women's hearts that is breaking and all that Home Life that is going plumb to the dogs all on account of the barrooms being closed up it well-nigh makes a free thinker out of me.

I don't claim to be a church man, but I never was a free thinker before, neither. But all the sorrow that is going on in the world on account of them barrooms being closed is making a free thinker of me.

III The Old Soak's
History of the World

CHAPTER ONE

Men Are Not Dessended Off of Monkeys

Well, what people want to find out about the history of the world is mostly how people acted at different times and what they et and drunk and thought about, which it is my idea that from the garden of Eden down the present times it has all been about the same.

But the Eighteenth Commandment has come along and things have changed and from the garden of Eden down to to-day is one area, and from now on is another area, with a great gulf fixed, as the Good Book says.

Well, one of the most prominent men in the old days was Sampson he never liked to work none but use to loaf around with his hair long and show how stout he was and as far as taking a drink was concerned it never hurt him none but he would liquor up and slay more Phillippines drunk than one of these here Prohibitionists was ever man enough to do sober.

If you had said to him he was descended off of a

223

monkey he would of beaned you with anything that was handy. And in my histry of the World it will be proved that men is not descended off of monkeys for if so why did not all the monkeys turn into men. You can't get back of the Good Book in them things, and for my part I don't hanker to.

There use to hang around Jake Smith's place a smart alec couisin of his by the name of Hennery Withers and every time this here Hennery Withers got too much to drink he use to say, Well, then, you tell me now, "Where did Cain get his wife?"

I says to Jake more than oncet, Well you tell Hennery to leave the Good Book alone or I will bean him one of these days with a bottle he is a damn little athyiss, and if there is anything I hate it is a dam little athyiss.

Well, Jake says, you leave him alone Clem, I keep a respectible place and I don't want a word of religion or any other trouble in here or no fuss for they will take away my lisence.

This feller Hennery Withers was proud of being an athyiss. You go and be one I says to him and keep your mouth shut about it and nobody will give a dam but I never saw one of these athyisses yet he didn't want to blah blah it around so the whole town would know it. It made him feel like he was important. He knowed he wasn't worth nothing and he's got to feel important some faked up way or he wouldn't have no reason to keep on living.

One difference of the old days in the early times of world whose histry I am going to write is that they didn't have no glass bottles, they kept it in jugs and skins which they was bladders I guess like they keep oil and putty in nowadays and they drunk it right out of the jug. Well, I have drunk cider that a way, and oncet I run onto a gang of Scandinavians building a barn and them fellows was drinking equival parts of sweet cider and straight alkohawl mixed right out of a jug and Oh boy! what a head ache you can get out of that stuff.

In Sampson's time they didn't have no alcohawl and it come into the world in recent years, what they had in the old days was wine and liquors.

He says the little foxes spoils the grapes, you can read it in the Good Book, and that made him sore and he went out and caught a hunderd of them foxes and tied all their tales together and set fire to them and turned them loose against the Phillippines.

Well, they finally got him, he married a new wife and she says you gotto cut that hair and he says bob your own and she slipped some nock out drops into his hootch and when he come to he was bob haired and it disturbed his balance.

Afore he got his hair cut when he wanted to set his self for a good lick his hair balanced him like the tale onto a kite, but when his balance was disturbed he couldn't set his self for a good lick and finally the enimy got him because he couldn't set him self for a good lick.

They took him and conkered him they bored his eyes out and they says now you gotto go to work.

Work, hell, he says, I won't do it, I never done nothing but drink liquor and fight and run with the women and I won't work.

You can see work was quite a come down to a gent that has always lived free and easy like that, but when they bored his eyes out they hooked him to a kind of a dog churn thing and he had to keep stepping or he would get his heels barked and he had to turn that mill.

But one day he notis his hair is down to his neck again and he says to his self these coots is got a big surprise coming to them some day. If I could get a jug of the old stuff I would show them.

Well, them Phillippines was an unreligious set. On Sundays they would play baseball and go fishing and have big parties. They had some kind of a church, but it wasn't a reg'lar orthodox church, neither Baptis or Methodis nor none of the churches we know about in this country. It was an idle church full of them heathen idles all carved out of elephants tushes and things and on Sundays they would have like a street fair in front of the church so one Sunday they says let us bring out this Sampson to the street fair and make him do stunts and we will thrown orange peel and tomatoes at him and mebby eggs that aint so young as they use to be. Well he got some of that grubbage in his face and he fetched one roar like a bull and he pulled that church full of idles down on top of the whole kit and biling of them and they perished.

Offen Jake Smith an me have argued wether he could of licked John Sullivan, and Jake says John would of out boxed him but with the old london prise ring rules Sampson would of licked him.

Well I see John L. oncet in Boston I was into his place and shook the hand that knocked Charlie michell cold.

CHAPTER FOUR

Jonah, and Jed Hawkins's Wife

Well, this feller Jonah I'm a gonna tell you about was quite a feller and the big fish et him and spit him out again and my idear has always been you can take that story or leave it alone but in telling the history of the world I wouldn't feel free to leave it out.

Well, oncet myself right out in L. Ileland sound I ketched a tom cod and ripped him open and there was a minnie in him was still alive, well you either believe that stuff or you don't.

But oncet this feller Hennery Withers I was telling you about was in Jake Smith's place and the dam little athyiss begun to sneer and stick up his nose at that Jonah story and I was drinking some beer for a change and I beans him with the beer stine.

I says I will laugh at that story my self if I want

to I can afford to for I got a record as a believer in the good book and I can take it or leave it alone.

But I ain't gonna let no dam little athyiss laugh at that story only its friends got a right to laugh at that story if its enimys laugh at that story I will bean them. That's me.

And Jake Smith says now Clem you got Hennery all bloody all over his mapp he will go home and Maria, she is his wife, will hear he got a lick into my bar room and that will give this place a black eye. How many times I told you fellers not to argy no religions in here and no ruff stuff like that I aim to keep a decent place.

Well this was long afore prohibishin broke out and all them wives setting at home waiting for theyr husbands to come home bunged up is what give liquor a black eye.

What they doant figger on is theyr husbands is nacherally mean little varmints or they wouldn't of got bunged up liquor or no liquor.

Well you cant learn a woman no sense about liquor axcept the women as uses liquor their selves and I never had no use for a woman that drunk liquor.

You can call me narrer minded if you want to but looking back onto the history of the world the lesson to be learnt is that liquor is for men.

You look at Marry queen of scotch, she drinked liquor so much they named some of it after her and well, what was the results.

She finally layed her head onto the block that was the results.

You look at Romio and Julyet, both them girls drinked liquor and how did it end? They layed theyr heads onto the block, thats how it ended.

You look at Queen Elyzabeth and the queen of France, they both drinked liquor. And how did it end?

They layed their heads under the jilloteen thats how it ended.

When a man comes home feeling a little tired out for mebby he has smoked too much he doant want a woman thare all lit up and no meel ready what he wants is somebudy to fix him something tasty.

Thare was Lotts wife she looked back she says I wisht I brought along a bottle of that home brew and she turned into a piller of salt right then and thare. Well the good book says oncet you put your hand to the plow you orter not look back.

Theres no uset talking about it liquor is for men and one burning sham at the present day is the fackt more women is drinking than before prohibisin and they orter be onselfish and leef it for the men who knows how to handle it theyr aint any too much for the men. Women been getting selfisher and selfisher since they got the voting balut.

Thare was Jed Hawkins wife that kept the drug store she started in onto some kind of malt extrack when she was nursin her twins and the habit growed and growed onto her.

Jed uset to bring it home to her from the drug store and the first thing he knowed she had another pare of twins and that called for more malt extrack and she went on like that drinking more malt ex-

track and having twins every oncet in a wile for
twelve years and then Jed says to me one day Clem
dam it what do you think has happened up to our
house.

What for the sake of argyment I says.

Triplets says Jed.

Great guns Jed I says to what do you impugn
it to.

I impugn it to that there malt extrack he says.
If I never carried a bottle of that stuff home to
Emmy I would be a happy man to-day with a medium size fambly and not made the laffing stock of
the Baycliff Weakly Palladium every year when
they prints my picture with the motto *Still Doing
as Well as Could be Expected.*

Cant you git Emmy to sign the pledge I says.

I asked her to he says and she told me I was a
brute to even to sugest taking her malt extrack away
from a nursing mother.

Well cheer up I says kind of foolish the way
you will to a man's in trouble cheer up the worset
is yet to come.

Quadrupeds he says my gawd Clem do you
think it will go as fur as quadrupeds and fell into
a faint.

Well it all goes to show a woman hadnt orter
take up with liquor.

One of the main moral lessons I will take up in
my histry of the world is that no woman orter drink
liquor.

CHAPTER NINE

The Founding of Rome

Well going back to the early days of the world, Roam was the greatest umpire of them all, and the great moral lesson about Roam is that you orter be kind to animles for Roam was found by a dumb beest. Well you can read about that in Esaw's fables where it tells all about all the animles. Theyre were two babes in the woods and they straighed away from thare parents, thyre names was Caster and Pollus and they layed down in the woods and the birds come and covered them up with leevs.

Well says Caster these leevs is all o. k. but for the sake of argyment do we eat or do we not eat.

Well says Pollus I would love to throw my lip over a cup of milk.

One of these here wolves hearn them babes in the woods pleading for milk and she comes through the bushes and looks at them and she says to her self it would serve them humans right if I et them, but I dunno, what the hell, they are kind of cute, here am I with a bag full of milk and no pups and here are these brats wanting the milk, what the hell,

I will take a chance, mebby theyer better than the common run of humans.

Well one word led to another till she adopts them brats and they growed up thinking they was wolves and that was one of the seven wonders of the world and after they growed up they found Roam and become the first umpires.

Well they was good sons to that old she wolf, they never let nothing harm her, and the lesson is you orter be kind to animles, you never can tell when an animle will do you a good turn.

There was this feller Lazarius in the good book, he was down and out and the dogs come and licked his sores and he got well and theyer was this feller Balum, he was riding onto a jack-ass and he lost his way and even forgot his own name and the jack-ass turned his head around and told him and on down to the days of Abram Lincoln, he was always kind to animiles and look where it landed him. He was good to colored men too, if it hadn't been for him Uncle Tom would of never been free nor his kids of crost the river on the ice.

Well I seen a good many shows in my time, regular shows and medicine shows and these here movies they got now a days but I never see any shows any more got as much general satisfaction in them as Uncle Toms cabin, what you want in a show is things moving lively and a little shooting and a chancet to laugh and the satisfaction of knowing the angils is looking out for them that has done right. Well when Abram Lincoln started that show going he knowed what he was doing.

I says to Jake Smith one day, this is the hand that shook the hand of John L. Sulivan and layed my hand ker flump onto the bar.

Well says Jake what the hell and he banged his hand onto the bar and he says this is the hand that shook the hand of Abram Lincoln, now where do you get off at.

I doant beleave it says Hennery Withers, but that dam little athyiss doant beleave anything.

Well Jake says when I was three years old I was out in Illinoyes and my dad took me to a rally and Abram Lincoln was speaking and he helt me up and I shook the hand of Abram Lincoln, and besides being a grand speaker he could of tied one hand behind him and licked John L. Sulivan.

The question aint which one could of licked, says Hennery Withers, the question is wich one done the most good in the world, John L. Sulivan or Abram Lincoln.

Shut up, I says to Hennery, I doant want any dam little athyiss butting in when me and Jake is talking of great men.

Jake, I says, it doant stand to reason you could of noticed much about him when you was three yeers old or whether he could of licked John L. Sulivan or not.

Noticed, says Jake, I noticed every thing about him, I even recolleck what he said in his speech, my dad says to me, boy this is a great day for you, I want you to git inspired by Mr. Lincoln and always remember what he said and you can tell it when you are an old man it will help you live right. And

233

it always has helped me, says Jake, I all ways lived right, I made up my mind when I went into the liquor business I would keap a decent place and I all ways done it.

Well so did John L. Sullivan, I says.

What is that speech if you recolleck it so well, says Hennery Withers, sticking up his nose.

Mebby you think I doant says Jake getting red in the face, and he said the speach. It was something about when in the course of human events, we the peeple of these United States, and I wished I had wrote it down the way Jake pulled it.

Now then says Jake, do I recolleck it or doant I, Hennery Withers.

Well then says Hennery Withers slinging his hand down onto the bar, here is the hand that oncet wroate a letter to Bob Ingersawl and got an answer to it.

Jake I says if you gonna have men like Bob Ingersawl bragged up in youer bar room you and me gotta part company. I drinked my liquor in youre place for more than twenty yeers and never had no trouble with nobody, but if Hennery Withers here is a gonna butt in and brag up Bob Ingersawl like he was a great man like John L. Sullivan or Abram Lincoln I'm gonna quit you, Jake.

It sounded easy enough in them days to say you would quit a bar room, theyre was all ways another on the next corner. But to-day I doant mind saying that fur the liberty of putting my stummick against a real bar I would lissen to Hennery Withers bragging up Volteer his self.

CHAPTER SEVENTEEN

The Taking of the Basteel

Mr. Hawley, while he was engaged on his History of the World, in 1923, took a trip to Paris, sending installments of his Work back to America. The subsequent chapters are somewhat colored by the environment in which they were written. With Mr. Hawley went his friend Al, Bartender, and they were joined later by Jake Smith himself. —EDITOR'S NOTE.

Paris, France, August 30.—Well, I promised, no matter wherever I was, I would keep right on with my histry of the world, well looking round over Paris the first place nacherally I made for was where the battle of the Basteel was fought.

Well in the erly days that Basteel was one of the seven wonders of the world, the old time kings had it built to throw these here reformers into it, they uset to set up onto the top of it with a spy glass and look out over Paris and all theyer queens and courteesyans would be setting round about them on the roof, and the king would say to the port cullis take a peek through this spy glass, do you see any disturbance anywheres?

Yes, your majisty, the port cullis would say, I see quite a disturbance over there in the shong.

Yes, the king would say, theyer is sure a lot of dust being kicked up over theer in that shong. What do you reckon it is, port cullis?

It is probable it is some of them reformers kicking up a rumpus, yure majisty, says the port cullis.

Send the Jong Darms after them, says the king, and they would ketch the reformers and bring them up to the roof of the Basteel and drop them down threw holes in the roof into the cells below and all the queens and courteesyans would nod at the king and wink and every body would take a shot of the reel stuff and say, That's that.

Well for thousands and thousands of yeers that way all the kings was able to keep the reformers out of Paris and all hands was happy and contented, till one day theyer was a reformer come along by the name of Saint Barthollomew, he was all the time kicking up a rumpus, and king Looey says, what the name of a hell, am I a king or ain't I a king, you would think this here Barthollomew was a king, for the sake of argyment, now, you ketch him and drop him into the Basteel.

But this hear Barthollomew beat them to it, he and his gang of reformers sneaked into the Basteel, and they rushed up onto the roof and massikered king Looey, and to this day that is known as the massiker of Saint Barthollomew.

Well the reformers got the best of it that time, and a little later theyer was another rumpus and the battle of the Basteel was fought, and the re-

236

formers took the entire royyal fambly and dropped them down threw those holes in the roof of the Basteel and poured kerosene oil onto them and set fire to the whole sheebang and that was the end of the Basteel and the royyal fambly.

Well it is a darned shame it is gone, since it is gone reform will come creeping in more and more, and some day Paris will be just as bad off as the Younited Staits, though I can't say as I see much to worry about just now, they tried to take theyer abbsinthe from them, but you can get it, I never liked the darned stuff it always reminded me of parrgoric, what I am enjoying is the brandy, the vang ain't got the kick I am used to.

Well theyer orter be a Basteel like the old Paris Basteel setting in the center of every town in America with a king setting on top of it looking out against reformers.

I am in favor of them Basteels myself, if we had a lot of Basteels in America mebby we would get some reel liberty and enjoyment of life and foresooth of happiness like it says in the declaration of inndependense.

If I was running for President of the U. S. I would make that my platform, a Basteel for every town, and every Basteel full of reformers, mebby then we would get some freedom.

Al, he says he is learning a lot of new tricks, and I says to him what in the name of a hell will you do with them when you learn them, you got nothing to practice them on when you go home, all you got when you go home is boot leg likker.

Well, he says, theyer is a lot more to the soul than theyer is to the body, Clem. In my soul I am a bartender and a artist even when my boddy has got nothing to work on.

I will pick up all the bartending tricks I can here in Paris, Al says, and get them down fine, and mebby theyr will come a happy day in the U. S. when I can use them again, annyhow when the grate moment comes I will be prepaired for it, I will of done my part.

And if my opportunity never comes again on this here earth, he says, my duty is done, and I will be prepaired for what the hereafter has to show for itself.

That is all a man can do, live the kinder life he ought to live, and prepair his self for the best, and then the rest of it is with fate and provvidense.

Well that is the way Al feels about it, and he is right. He is a good man, Al is, he has got a soul into his boddy, and a pride in his perfeshin.

One of the morel lessins theyer is going to be in my histry of the world is you orter do the best you can and leave the rest to provverdense, what in the name of a hell more can you do?

CHAPTER EIGHTEEN

Marie Antoinette

Paris, Sept. 7.—Well, I promised I would keep
right on with my histry of the world after I got
here in Paris, and Al and me was talking it over to-
day and we both desided it was on all sides of us,
well theyer is so much of it you would scarcely
know where to start.

Well, the best way, Al says, is to get a taxxy cab
and crews around a little bit, so I wrote down onto
a piece of paper Maree Antonette, and showed it to
the taxi man, which he says he speaks a little English and Al claims he speaks a little French, and
between the two of them we found six differnt
places yessterday afternoon where Maree Antonette was massicured. You could say for that girl she
had a charmed life.

One of them was the Eyefull Tower, and you
could see why they named it that, it is sure some
eye full.

Al, I says, ask this bird in French whether Maree
Antonette jumped off of it, or was she pushed, I got
to get this histry of the world correct.

We was setting at one of them little sidewalk
places, and the shofer was setting with us having

one. I will say this for the French, if you was to suggest prohibishin to them they would more than likely leed you to the jillyteen.

Al asks him something or other, and he says something to the garsong, and the garsong brings three bottles of vang, and I says what has that got to do with Maree Antonette.

You got to be pashent, Clem, Al says, you gotto take histry a little bit at a time in this town. They kind of wash it down, here, you leeve it to me.

All this vang, I says, is taking up room I had planned to save for something else. I doant want to throw any doubts onto your French, but so far you aint had the language to get me a shot of real booze. Eviry time we have found a place where Maree was massicured all afternoon it has been vang, vang, vang, and nothing but vang.

I am a goanto try it myself from now on. I says. I want some red liquor.

Garsong, you bring me a shot of whisky rooze.

Weesky, says the garsong, wee.

You have intellects, I says to the garsong, have one with us.

Cat weesky? he asks me.

Cat whisky, I says, or dog whisky, or any kind of whisky. I doant care what kind of annimals I see, so long as I get something that has got a kick in it.

Cat weesky, says the shofer, is four weeskies.

Well, we studied a little histry there, and then we went along down by the river, and we seen a building considerable longer than sevril trains of cars, and we set down at another one of these little sidewalk places acrost the way from it and Al and me speculated some about it.

By that time I was getting onto the langwidge a little myself. I says to the shofer, order cat more weeskies, and then tell us what that place is, it looks like all the raleroad stations in Europe had come to town.

He says we doant need cat more weeskies, and it is the Loov.

Order cat more anyhow, I says, I will drink two of them, it is too late to shows signs of weekness on this cat stuff, I suppose Maree was killed at this Loov place, too.

Wee, he says, and then he talks French to Al, and Al says we orter go in and see her statue.

Well, we went in and seen her statue, and I got a better idea of what must have happened to that poor queen than I ever had before.

It seems probably she wasn't killed all to oncet. They must of killed her piece meal.

There stood her statue in that Loov place, and the statue was made at the time her arms was broke off, and it was so quiet and respectful in there you could of heard a cork drop. From her waste line up her cloathes was all off, poor girl they must of tried to kill her by axposure to the weather.

What she must have suffered at one time or another would of drawed tears from the heart of a stone.

Well, Al says, after talking some more of his French to the shofer, he says the worst is yet to be seen, they got another statue of her in here.

I got to have cat weeskies afore I feel strong enough to look at it, I says, poor girl, all because she was a queen that had spunk enough to speak up and say the Basteel shall not fall to-night.

So we went out and had cat weeskies for each one of us and we come back and the shofer showed us another statue of her on a stairway, and in this one not only is her arms gone, but her head is gone, and she has got wings on in this one.

Ask him about the wings, I says to Al.

Al asks him something, and then says to me the wings is to show she went to heaven in the end.

Clem, he says, it is like little Eva in Uncle Tom's Cabin; the wings is to show you can't keep a good girl down.

Well, we went out and had cat weeskies, and I got to feeling pretty bad about poor Maree. I went back and took another look at her standing on that stairway, with her head gone and her arms gone, and them wings stretching back, and I ain't ashamed to say I cried.

Come along to the hotel, Al, I says to him, if I see another place to-day where Maree was killed I would break down entirely, if this French histry keeps on being as sad as this I'm a goanto go to London and look at something chearful like that tower whare they used to smother theyr princes in.

So we had cat more weeskies and went on home.

CHAPTER NINETEEN

Henri Quatre and Haig Soixante

Paris, Sept. 11.—Well, just like I promised, I am a goanto keep my histry of the world going from Paris, and between Pierre, the shofer, speaking a little English and Al speaking a little French I am getting quite a lot of facts, which we carry this Pierre with us in his taxxy cab all over town.

Well theyer was a lot of them old-time kings, and the most of them was humdingers, we seen the Moniment of one of them on the Pong Nuff yesterday, it seems he was a regular hell cat and was responsible for a good many of them massicures they used to be all ways having over here.

Al, I says, you ask Pierre what this bird's name was.

Al has waited on table in some purty good places in his time, he learnt his French partly that way and partly, he says, he felt it breaking out on him like a rash when he landed in this country; he says, it is easy, Clem, if you fix your face right and then shove part of the words up your nose, you just watch the motions I make and you will ketch on.

He talked with Pierre and he says this old king

was known in his day as The Ornery Cat, he was some panther, he was, he could have licked Jack Dempsey.

Mebby, I says, mebby he could, but just for the sake of argyment I will throw this here Pierre into the river if he says he could of licked John L. Sulivan.

Well, Al says, him and another bird by the name of Saint Bartholomew started the French revolushin and the massicures lasted for months and months.

Well, I says, mebby he started them, but if John L. Sulivan had of been on deck he could of stopped them, telling me what else this Ornery Cat done.

Well, says Al, theyer is a little place over here by the end of the bridge, and I think we better have seece weeskies, that will be two a peece, I am getting tired of ordering only four and you all ways getting the extry one.

Well, no sooner said than done.

We rode around a little while and I says, you ask Pierre, Al, what that little dump over there is, it looks like it would of been a armory but it got discouraged, mebby theyr is some new kind of beverages sold in there.

That, says Al, after he talks with Pierre, uset to be the place where they made the breath killers, it is called the tower of clovis, it was closed up on account of the war, but theyer is a place over there on the corner. So we went over theyr and had seece more weeskies.

What I want to see, I says, is the place where Napollion was born.

It is right around the corner, Al says, after he talked some with Pierre, and more than likely it has got chairs and tables setting out in front of it, and when we got there it had.

Well, it was a very humble little place, and I thought to myself what a wonder of the world he was to be born in such a little dump like that and make such a succes of life he got his self buried in a tomb as big as a United Staits post office bldg., and he owed his success in life to all ways doing what he dam pleased and not taking any back talk off of anybody.

They were cooking in that little dump, and I thought of the times Napollion didn't have a square meal to his name nor nothing to drink, and now his old home place was full of food and vang, and it made me so sad I asked Al to ask Pierre to order seece more weeskies, but Pierre had passed out of the picture, and when Al ordered them himself they brought sixteen weeskies instead of six, and I managed to make them understand it wasn't right, and then three waiters and the landlady that run the place got together and they talked with Al, and they looked surprised, but he showed them some money, and they went in and talked it over amongst themselves, and they come out to our table again and brought us sixty weeskies.

Well, I says to Al, here we are a long way from home and the question is do we weaken or doant we weaken.

Clem, Al says, I never done nothing yet to disgrace the American flag in a furrin land.

Me neither, I says, and I had a lot of axperience in my time, but even for an axperienced hand it is quite a task that has been set before us.

Clem, he says, all we need is time.

Thank heaven, I got nothing to leeve my family, I says, for theyer ain't any chance of me making a will in the French language.

They axpect it of us, Clem, he says, and we gotto go through with it.

And sure enough the three waiters and the landlady was standing and waiting and looking at us in admitashin, and four or five of theyer frends was thare, and the news was spreading.

I really would hate to tell them it is too beaucoup, Al says, they would be so disappointed.

Don't tell them nothing more, I says, you are getting us in worse with every chunk of French language you pull on them, if you say anything more they will bring six hunderd of them, wake up Pierre a little and we will pour six or eight of them into him.

No sooner said than done.

Well, I wont say how far we got, but we done the best we could, and as if by magic we found ourselves in the midst of frends purty soon, and I woant say what become of Pierre and Al, but after while I found myself sitting on some stone steps crying and a fellow says to me in American what are you so sorrowful about?

Well, I said, this is the river that Maree Antonette was drowned in.

She must of been a grate friend of yours, he says,

246

the way you take on over her, and if I hadn't of pulled you back a minute ago you would of been in the Seine.

I doant care, I says, if I do roll in; the way they used that poor queen is enough to brake any man's heart that has got any right feelings in him, you leeve me alone with my grief.

Lerning histry on the spot is a good deal more touching on the elements and emotions than lerning it out of books, you get to thinking how hard a time them poor people had, and if you are any kind of a man a tall you got to cry a little, and I told this feller so.

Uh-huh, he says, but it is pretty late to weep over the Boorbons now.

They wasn't Boorbons, I told him, they was Skotches, all of them was Haig and Haig.

Well, theyer is a place near here called Verrsigh, and they say it is one of the seven wonders of the world, after me and Al and Pierre gets rested up a little we are going out and give it the oncet over.

CHAPTER TWENTY-ONE

Gargoyles

Paris, Sept. 18.—Well, theyer is lots of arkytexture in Paris, almost every other bldg. you see is all arkytextured up in one way or the other, I never seen so many churches in all my born days, not even in Brooklin, theyer uset to be as many breweries as theyer was churches in Brooklin but now the noes have it.

Neerly all these Paris churches is erected to the memry of Saint Somebody, or other, and for the sake of argyment this Saint was as a usual thing massicured way back in the erly days.

Theyer was Saint Denny, he must of been an Irishman by his name, they cut his head off and he picked it up and beat it away from thare and carried his head in his hands for miles and miles, Pierre the showfure told me about it, and finally he stubbed his toe on them cobblestones and fell down, but his head kept on a rolling and a rolling and whare it stopped they errected a church to his memry.

Well, Al says, he couldn't of been an Irishman, if he had of been an Irishman he would have swung on somebody with that head and beaned them, you never seen an Irishman that wouldn't of swung on somebody.

Then thare was Saint Notary Dom, his church has been all arkytextured up with gargle oils, they are sticking out over the roof of it, with theyer necks stretched and theyer mouths open, they are mean looking goofs.

Well, Al says, why do they call them gargle oils.

Doant be an iggnoramus, I told him, annybody ought to see they call them gargle oils because they are cleering theyer throats. They are carved that natural you can almost hear them hawk and spit.

I will tell the world them gargle oils are nothing to look at after a feller has had from cat to seece weeskies, you can't quit looking at them and you go and get seece more shots and look at them again and then they begin to get pursonal the way they wiggle theyer heads and wink at you.

Poor Al he gets a little bit lit up the other evening and he goes up on top of a place called Mongmart and he gets down on his hands and knees at the edge of the bluff and stretches his neck out over the city and begins to whine and bark and make noises like a trayned blood hound in a uncle Tom's cabin show.

What in the name of a hell are you doing that for Al, I asks him, you better snap out of it.

You leeve me be, Clem, he says, I am a gargle oil. I guess I got a right to be a gargle oil if I want to.

You ain't as young as you uset to be, you will have lumbague in the small of your back tomorrow morning, I tells him.

Lumbague or no lumbague, he says, I can lick any other gargle oil my size in Paris.

The only way I could get him started for home was to coax him onto the top of Pierre's taxi cab, he wouldn't get inside of it, and he stretched his self over the edge and played he was a gargle oil and I had to set on his legs to keep him from rolling off, and that way we went through all the prinssiple streets.

And Pierre would stop his cab every time we come to one of them side walk cafes, and Al would ask if any gent would like to feed the gargle oils, and purty soon some fellers we never seen afore got cabs and come along with us and played they was gargle oils too and that gargle oil parade crossed over the river and we picked up some stewdents over on the bool mish and they played they was gargle oils and it got to be quite a sport by midnight, with Al leeding the percession and evry time we come to another cafe he would say, I'm a gargle oil, I'm a gargle oil, come and throw hoops at the gargle oils, the gargle oil you ring is the gargle oil you get.

The way some Americans drink in Paris is enough to make you a frend of moderashin for life, it was 4 o'clock a m in the morning afore I got that Al to bed and I says I am ashamed of you. He says you leeve me be, my shoulders is itching like wings is starting. If it wasn't for his fool friends holding him down, he says, he would fly over the city.

Well, arkytexture is a gift, but hand painting is a tallent, you can see lots of A number 1 hand painting in Paris, the Loov is bigger than the Pennsilvania station and it is jammed full of hand paintings.

The only way I could explain how theyer come to be so much hand painting in the Loov is on account of prohibishin brakeing out in America. When they closed the bar rooms in America they must of took all the hand paintings you uset to see and shipped them right over here to the Loov, thare must be hand paintings from a thousand bar rooms in the Loov.

It makes you feel right sad to think of them miles and miles of pictures that have come down to this. Now peeple have to cross the ocean to see good hand paintings or get a drink of reel liquor, that is what prohibishin has done to us.

As for the statues, I must say most of them ain't any too modest, but what the hell, it is only stone, it doant make any difference. And you could im-magin it was Angels and that would make it all o. k. and morel.

CHAPTER TWENTY-EIGHT

Mona Lisa

Paris, Oct. 15.—Come over to the Loov, Al says to me and Jake, theyr is a picture over thare Clem otto put something about into his histry of the world, it is a trick picture, nobody can guess the answer to it.

Well, I says to Al, what do you know about the histry of the world or about hand painting, and just for the sake of argyment who told you about this picture.

What the hell, he says, am I an iggnorramus just because I soshiate with iggnorramuses like you and Jake, I read about her in a Sunday suppliment back home, she was stole and the thief didn't know what she was about and brought her back again, and Pierre told me she is on view.

As a matter of fact, I says, what is her name.

Mona is her name, he says, Mona Lizzy.

Mona Lizzy what, I asks him, Lizzy ain't a last name, and what is the trick in this hand painting.

It is a last name in her case, he says, and the trick is to guess what the little dame is thinking about, she is a swell looking little dame, but she packs a wicked eye; you can't get anywheres that eye doant follow you, they say, and for hundreds of yeers they been guessing what she meant by it, and she's got a smile that may mean yes and may mean no and may not mean a dam thing, it's a riddle and that's whare the entertainment comes in.

So we mosyed along over to take a look at this hand painting, she was a Wop lady and not French, and a girl was making a copy of her and Jake Smith, the old goof, sticks his finger onto that copy and tells the girl she isn't getting the color of the hair the same way.

Be careful, says the girl, that paint isn't dry yet.

Oh, that doant make no difference, Miss, says Jake, doant apologize, I doant mind a little paint on my fingers, my hands aint very clean anyhow.

But you've spoiled my copy, says the girl.

That's all right, says Jake, how much is it, I will buy it offen you. She named a price and no sooner said than done, Jake give her the name of his hotel and paid for it and told her to send it around and a couple more when the paint got dry.

Now that them girls of mine is a goanto drag me

into society, Jake says, I will have to pay a lot of attention to hand painting, I suppose, and go to the opery house and hear them caterwaul and stand for all them dam things like that.

Well, now, I says to Al, looking at Mona, what would you say she was thinking of.

All I will say is this, says Al, she looks to me just exactly like Herb Simpson's first wife, Nell, back in Baycliff, L. Ileland.

I know what she is thinking about, says Jake Smith, I could tell at a glance what she is thinking about, she is thinking she is got a new dress on, and she is going to have still another new dress next week, and none of the other girls she knows has got two new dresses in one week, and is kind of putting it over on the other girls, and she feels pretty good about it, I seen that very same look on both my girls faces time and again after I begun to make so much money Bootlegging and they found out it could be spent for duds, that is what she is thinking about.

She looks just exactly like Herb Simpson's first wife, Al says, again.

You fellows ain't got any finer feelings, I told them, or you would see that she is thinking of something a dam site more hifaluting and refined and holy and religious than just merely duds, I am ashamed of you.

I doant know just what it is, says I, but it ain't anything either of you galoots could understand.

Barring the difference in age and sex, I says, and in looks, I seen just that same kind of a look onto my own face in the mirror in Jake's bar room when the boys got a little bit soused and commenced to singing about Home and Mother.

She looks just exactly like Herb Simpson's first wife, Nell, Al says again.

It's duds she is thinking of, says Jake, they always look refined and holy and religious when they are thinking of the new outfit of duds they are going to put on and come sailing down the street to church in next Sunday.

I will leave it to this lady here, he says, pointing to the hand painting girl he had bought the copy offen, if it ain't more than likely duds she is thinking of. Let her be the judge.

But before the girl could answer Jake, Al butts in again and says, she looks just like Herb Simpson's first wife, Nell.

Who was this Nell Simpson you are speaking of, says the hand painting girl, and why do you keep insisting on bringing her in, was there some story connected with her.

Thare was, Miss, says Al, but I doant know what it is just axactly fitten for your ears, you being pretty middling young, and like as not middling inaxperienced, and me being almost a perfect stranger to you I doant know as I would care to go to full lengths in telling you the story of Herb Simpson's first wife, Nell.

Which the hand painting girl tells him that conversationally speaking, and for the sake of argyment, he can go as fur as he likes, as she has got interested in Herb Simpson's first wife, Nell.

Miss, says Al, turning red, I will not go as fur as I like, but to make a long story short, I seen her the day after she got converted at a revival meeting talking to both her husband and the preacher that converted her, and when she turned her head from her husband to the precher she looked just like Mona here, and that was just two days afore she eloped with that preacher and left her husband and two children, she had the same look in her eyes.

Well, says the hand painting girl, if I am the judge, the eyes have it.

IV Short Stories

The Revolt of the Oyster

"Our remote ancestor was probably arboreal."
—Eminent scientist.

From his hut in the tree-top Probably Arboreal looked lazily down a broad vista, still strewn with fallen timber as the result of a whirlwind that had once played havoc in that part of the forest, toward the sea. Beyond the beach of hard white sand the water lay blue and vast and scarcely ruffled by the light morning wind. All the world and his wife were out fishing this fine day. Probably Arboreal could see dozens of people from where he crouched, splashing in the water or moving about the beach, and even hear their cries borne faintly to him on the breeze. They fished, for the most part, with their hands; and when one caught a fish it was his custom to eat it where he caught it, standing in the sea.

In Probably Arboreal's circle, one often bathed and breakfasted simultaneously; if a shark or sau-

259

rian were too quick for one, one sometimes was breakfasted upon as one bathed.

In the hut next to Probably Arboreal, his neighbour, Slightly Simian, was having an argument with Mrs. Slightly, as usual. And, as usual, it concerned the proper manner of bringing up the children. Probably listened with the bored distaste of a bachelor.

"I *will* slap his feet every time he picks things up with them!" screamed Slightly Simian's wife, an accredited shrew, in her shrill falsetto.

"It's *natural* for a child to use his feet that way," insisted the good-natured Slightly, "and I don't intend to have the boy punished for what's natural." Probably Arboreal grinned; he could fancy the expression on Old Sim's face as his friend made this characteristically plebeian plea.

"You can understand once for all, Slightly," said that gentleman's wife in a tone of finality, "that I intend to supervise the bringing-up of these children. Just because your people had neither birth nor breeding nor manners——"

"Mrs. S.!" broke in Slightly, with a warning in his voice. "Don't you work around to anything caudal, now, Mrs. S.! Or there'll be trouble. You get me?"

On one occasion Mrs. Slightly had twitted her spouse with the fact that his grandfather had a tail five inches long; she had never done so again. Slightly Simian himself, in his moments of excitement, picked things up with his feet, but like many other men of humble origin who have become personages in their maturity, he did not relish having such faults commented upon.

"Poor old Sim," mused Probably Arboreal, as he slid down the tree and ambled toward the beach, to be out of range of the family quarrel. "She married him for his property, and now she's sore on him because there isn't more of it."

Nevertheless, in spite of the unpleasant effect of the quarrel, Probably found his mind dwelling upon matrimony that morning. A girl with bright red hair, into which she had tastefully braided a number of green parrot feathers, hit him coquettishly between the shoulder blades with a handful of wet sand and gravel as he went into the water. Ordinarily he would either have taken no notice at all of her, or else would have broken her wrist in a slow, dignified, manly sort of way. But this morning he grabbed her tenderly by the hair and sentimentally ducked her. When she was nearly drowned he released her. She came out of the water squealing with rage like a wild-cat and bit him on the shoulder.

"Parrot Feathers," he said to her, with an unwonted softness in his eyes, as he clutched her by the throat and squeezed, "beware how you trifle with a man's affections—some day I may take you seriously!"

He let the girl squirm loose, and she scrambled out upon the beach and threw shells and jagged pieces of flint at him, with an affectation of coyness. He chased her, caught her by the hair again, and scored the wet skin on her arms with a sharp stone, until she screamed with the pain, and as he did it he hummed an old love tune, for to-day there was an April gladness in his heart.

"Probably! Probably Arboreal!" He spun around to face the girl's father, Crooked Nose, who was contentedly munching a mullet.

"Probably," said Crooked Nose, "you are flirting with my daughter!"

"Father!" breathed the girl, ashamed of her parent's tactlessness. "How can you say that!"

"I want to know," said Crooked Nose, as sternly as a man can who is masticating mullet, "whether your intentions are serious and honourable."

"Oh, father!" said Parrot Feathers again. And putting her hands in front of her face to hide her blushes she ran off. Nevertheless, she paused when a dozen feet away and threw a piece of drift-wood at Probably Arboreal. It hit him on the shin, and as he rubbed the spot, watching her disappear into the forest, he murmured aloud, "Now, I wonder what she means by that!"

"Means," said Crooked Nose. "Don't be an ass, Probably! Don't pretend to *me* you don't know what the child means. You made her love you. You have exercised your arts of fascination on an innocent young girl, and now you have the nerve to wonder what she means. What'll you give me for her?"

"See here, Crooked Nose," said Probably, "don't bluster with me." His finer sensibilities were outraged. He did not intend to be *coerced* into matrimony by any father, even though he were pleased with that father's daughter. "I'm not buying any wives to-day, Crooked Nose."

"You have hurt her market value," said Crooked Nose, dropping his domineering air, and affecting a willingness to reason. "Those marks on her arms will not come off for weeks. And what man wants to marry a scarred-up woman unless he has made the scars himself?"

"Crooked Nose," said Probably Arboreal, angry at the whole world because what might have been a youthful romance had been given such a sordid turn by this disgusting father, "if you don't go away I will scar every daughter you've got in your part of the woods. Do you get me?"

"I wish you'd look them over," said Crooked Nose. "You might do worse than marry all of them."

"I'll marry none of them!" cried Probably, in a rage, and turned to go into the sea again.

A heavy boulder hurtled past his head. He whirled about and discovered Crooked Nose in the act of recovering his balance after having flung it. He caught the old man half way between the beach and the edge of the forest. The clan, including Crooked Nose's four daughters, gathered round in a ring to watch the fight.

It was not much of a combat. When it was over, and the girls took hold of what remained of their late parent to drag him into the woods, Probably Arboreal stepped up to Parrot Feathers and laid his hand upon her arm.

"Feathers," he said, "now that there can be no

question of coercion, will you and your sisters marry me?"

She turned toward him with a sobered face. Grief had turned her from a girl into a woman.

"Probably," she said, "you are only making this offer out of generosity. It is not love that prompts it. I cannot accept. As for my sisters, they must speak for themselves."

"You are angry with me, Feathers?"

The girl turned sadly away. Probably watched the funeral cortège winding into the woods, and then went moodily back to the ocean. Now that she had refused him, he desired her above all things. But how to win her? He saw clearly that it could be no question of brute force. It had gone beyond that. If he used force with her, it must infallibly remind her of the unfortunate affair with her father. Some heroic action might attract her to him again. Probably resolved to be a hero at the very earliest opportunity.

In the meantime he would breakfast. Breakfast had already been long delayed; and it was as true then, far back in the dim dawn of time, as it is now, that he who does not breakfast at some time during the day must go hungry to bed at night. Once more Probably Arboreal stepped into the ocean—stepped in without any premonition that he was to be a hero indeed; that he was chosen by Fate, by Destiny, by the Presiding Genius of this planet, by whatever force or intelligence you will, to champion the cause of all Mankind in a crucial struggle for human supremacy.

He waded into the water up to his waist, and bent forward with his arms beneath the surface, patiently waiting. It was thus that our remote ancestors fished. Fish ran larger in those days, as a rule. In the deeper waters they were monstrous. The smaller fish therefore sought the shallows where the big ones, greedy cannibals, could not follow them. A man seldom stood in the sea as Probably Arboreal was doing more than ten minutes without a fish brushing against him either accidentally or because the fish thought the man was something good to eat. As soon as a fish touched him, the man would grab for it. If he were clumsy and missed too many fish, he starved to death. Experts survived because they *were* expert; by a natural process of weeding out the awkward it had come about that men were marvellously adept. A bear who stands by the edge of a river watching for salmon at the time of the year when they run up stream to spawn, and scoops them from the water with a deft twitch of his paw, was not more quick or skillful than Probably Arboreal.

Suddenly he pitched forward, struggling; he gave a gurgling shout, and his head disappeared beneath the water.

When it came up again, he twisted toward the shore, with lashing arms and something like panic on his face, and shouted:

"Oh! Oh! Oh!" he cried. "Something has me by the foot!"

Twenty or thirty men and women who heard the

265

cry stopped fishing and straightened up to look at him.

"Help! Help!" he shouted again. "It is pulling me out to sea!"

A knock-kneed old veteran, with long intelligent-looking mobile toes, broke from the surf and scurried to the safety of the beach, raising the cry:

"A god! A god! A water-god has caught Probably Arboreal!"

"More likely a devil!" cried Slightly Simian, who had followed Probably to the water.

And all his neighbours plunged to land and left Probably Arboreal to his fate, whatever his fate was to be. But since spectacles are always interesting, they sat down comfortably on the beach to see how long it would be before Probably Arboreal disappeared. Gods and devils, sharks and octopi, were forever grabbing one of their number and making off to deep water with him to devour him at their leisure. If the thing that dragged the man were seen, if it showed itself to be a shark or an octopus, a shark or an octopus it was; if it were unseen, it got the credit of being a god or a devil.

"Help me!" begged Probably Arboreal, who was now holding his own, although he was not able to pull himself into shallower water. "It is not a god or a devil. It doesn't feel like one. And it isn't a shark, because it hasn't any teeth. It is an animal like a cleft stick, and my foot is in the cleft."

But they did not help him. Instead, Big Mouth, a seer and *vers libre* poet of the day, smitten suddenly with an idea, raised a chant, and presently all the others joined in. The chant went like this:

"Probably, he killed Crooked Nose,
He killed him with his fists.
And Crooked Nose, he sent his ghost to sea
To catch his slayer by the foot!
The ghost of Crooked Nose will drown his slayer,
Drown, drown, drown his slayer,
The ghost of Crooked Nose will drown his slayer,
Drown his slayer in the sea!"

"You are a liar, Big Mouth!" spluttered Probably Arboreal, hopping on one foot and thrashing the water with his arms. "It is not a ghost; it is an animal."

But the chant kept up, growing louder and louder:

"The ghost of Crooked Nose will drown his slayer!
Drown, drown, drown his slayer,
Drown his slayer in the sea!"

Out of the woods came running more and more people at the noise of the chant. And as they caught what was going on, they took up the burden of it, until hundreds and thousands of them were singing it.

But, with a mighty turn and struggle, Probably Arboreal went under again, as to his head and body; his feet for an instant swished into the air, and everyone but Probably Arboreal himself saw what was hanging on to one of them.

It was neither ghost, shark, god, nor devil. It was

a monstrous oyster; a bull oyster, evidently. All oysters were much larger in those days than they are now, but this oyster was a giant, a mastodon, a mammoth among oysters, even for those days.

"It is an oyster, an oyster, an oyster!" cried the crowd, as Probably Arboreal's head and shoulders came out of the water again.

Big Mouth, the poet, naturally chagrined, and hating to yield up his dramatic idea, tried to raise another chant:

"The ghost of Crooked Nose went into an oyster,
The oyster caught his slayer by the foot
To drown, drown, drown him in the sea!"

But it didn't work. The world had seen that oyster, and had recognized it for an oyster.

"Oyster! Oyster! Oyster!" cried the crowd sternly at Big Mouth.

The bard tried to persevere, but Slightly Simian, feeling the crowd with him, advanced menacingly and said:

"See here, Big Mouth, we know a ghost when we see one, and we know an oyster! Yon animal is an oyster! You *sing* that it is an oyster, or shut up!"

"Ghost, ghost, ghost," chanted Big Mouth, tentatively. But he got no farther. Slightly Simian killed him with a club, and the matter was settled. Literary criticism was direct, straightforward, and effective in those days.

"But, oh, ye gods of the water, *what* an oyster!" cried Mrs. Slightly Simian.

And as the thought took them all, a silence fell

over the multitude. They looked at the struggling man in a new community of idea. Oysters they had seen before, but never an oyster like this. Oysters they knew not as food; but they had always regarded them as rather ineffectual and harmless creatures. Yet this bold oyster was actually giving battle, and on equal terms, to a man! Were oysters henceforth to be added to the number of man's enemies? Were oysters about to attempt to conquer mankind? This oyster, was he the champion of the sea, sent up out of its depths, to grapple with a mankind for supremacy?

Dimly, vaguely, as they watched the man attempt to pull the oyster ashore, and the oyster attempt to pull the man out to sea, some sense of the importance of this struggle was felt by mankind. Over forest, beach, and ocean hung the sense of momentous things. A haze passed across the face of the bright morning sun; the breeze died down; it was as if all nature held her breath at this struggle. And if mankind upon the land was interested, the sea was no less concerned. For, of a sudden, and as if by preconcerted signal, a hundred thousand oysters poked their heads above the surface of the waters and turned their eyes—they had small fiery opalescent eyes in those days—upon the combat.

At this appearance, mankind drew back with a gasp, but no word was uttered. The visible universe, perturbed earth and bending heavens alike, was tense and dumb. On their part, the oysters made no attempt to go to the assistance of their champion. Nor did mankind leap to the rescue of Probably

Arboreal. Tacitly, each side, in a spirit of fair play, agreed not to interfere; agreed to leave the combat to the champions; agreed to abide by the issue.

But while they were stirred and held by the sense of tremendous things impending, neither men nor oysters could be expected to understand definitely what almost infinite things depended upon this battle. There were no Darwins then. Evolution had not yet evolved the individual able to catch her at it.

But she was on her way. This very struggle was one of the crucial moments in the history of evolution. There have always been these critical periods when the two highest species in the world were about equal in intelligence, and it was touch and go as to which would survive and carry on the torch, and which species would lose the lead and become subservient. There have always been exact instants when the spirit of progress hesitated as between the forms of life, doubtful as to which one to make its representative.

Briefly, if the oyster conquered the man, more and more oysters, emboldened by this success, would prey upon men. Man, in the course of a few hundred thousand years, would become the creature of the oyster; the oyster's slave and food. Then the highest type of life on the planet would dwell in the sea. The civilization which was not yet would be a marine growth when it did come; the intellectual and spiritual and physical supremacy held by the biped would pass over to the bivalve.

Thought could not frame this concept then; neither shellfish nor tree-dweller uttered it. But both the species felt it; they watched Probably Arboreal and the oyster with a strangling emotion, with a quivering intentness, that was none the less poignant because there was no Huxley or Spencer present to interpret it for them; they thrilled and sweat and shivered with the shaken universe, and the red sun through its haze peered down unwinking like the vast bloodshot eye of life.

An hour had passed by in silence except for the sound of the battle, more and more men and more and more oysters had gathered about the scene of the struggle; the strain was telling on both champions. Probably Arboreal had succeeded in dragging the beast some ten feet nearer the shore, but the exertion had told upon him; he was growing tired; he was breathing with difficulty; he had swallowed a great deal of salt water. He too was dimly conscious of the importance of this frightful combat; he felt himself the representative of the human race. He was desperate but cool; he saved his breath; he opposed to the brute force of the oyster the cunning of a man. But he was growing weaker; he felt it.

If only those for whom he was fighting would fling him some word of encouragement! He was too proud to ask it, but he felt bitterly that he was not supported, for he could not realize what emotion had smitten dumb his fellow men. He had got to the place where a word of spiritual comfort and encouragement would have meant as much as fifty pounds of weight in his favour.

He had, in fact, arrived at the Psychological Moment. There were no professing psychologists then;

but there was psychology; and it worked itself up into moments even as it does to-day.

Probably Arboreal's head went under the water, tears and salt ocean mingled nauseatingly in his mouth.

"I am lost," he gurgled.

But at that instant a shout went up—the shrill, high cry of a woman. Even in his agony he recognized that voice—the voice of Parrot Feathers! With a splendid rally he turned his face toward the shore.

She was struggling through the crowd, fighting her way to the front rank with the fury of a wildcat. She had just buried her father, and the earth was still dark and damp upon her hands, but the magnificent creature had only one thought now. She thought only of her lover, her heroic lover; in her nobility of soul she had been able to rise above the pettiness of spirit which another woman might have felt; she knew no pique or spite. Her lover was in trouble, and her place was nigh him; so she flung a false maidenly modesty to the winds and acknowledged him and cheered him on, careless of what the assembled world might think.

She arrived at the Psychological Moment.

"Probably! Probably!" she cried. "Don't give up! Don't give up! For my sake!"

For her sake! The words were like fire in the veins of the struggling hero. He made another bursting effort, and gained a yard. But the rally had weakened him; the next instant his head went under the water once more. Would it ever appear again? There was a long, long moment, while all mankind strangled and gasped in sympathetic unison, and then our hero's dripping head did emerge. It had hit a stone under water, and it was bleeding, but it emerged. One eye was nearly closed.

"Watch him! Watch him!" shouted Parrot Feathers. "Don't let him do that again! When he has you under water he whacks your eye with his tail. He's trying to blind you!"

And, indeed, these seemed to be the desperate oyster's tactics. If he could once destroy our hero's sight, the end would soon come.

"Probably—do you hear me?"

He nodded his head; he was beyond speech.

"Take a long breath and dive! Do you get me? Dive! Dive at your own feet! Grab your feet in your hands and roll under water in a bunch! Roll toward the beach!"

It was a desperate manoeuvre, especially for a man who had already been under water so much that morning. But the situation was critical and called for the taking of big chances. It would either succeed—or fail. And death was no surer if it failed than if he waited. Probably Arboreal ceased to think; he yielded up his reasoning powers to the noble and courageous woman on the sand; he dived and grabbed his feet and rolled.

"Again! Again!" she cried. "Another long breath and roll again!"

Her bosom heaved, as if she were actually breathing for him. To Probably Arboreal, now all but drowned, and almost impervious to feeling, it also seemed as if he were breathing with her lungs; and

273

yet he hardly dared to dive and roll again. He struggled in the water and stared at her stupidly.

She sent her unusual and electric personality thrilling into him across the intervening distance; she held him with her eyes, and filled him with her spirit.

"Roll!" she commanded. "Probably! Roll!"

And under the lash of her courage, he rolled again. Three more times he rolled . . . and then . . . unconscious, but still breathing, he was in her arms.

As he reached the land half a million oysters sank into the sea in the silence of defeat and despair, while from the beaches rose a mighty shout.

The sun, as if it gestured, flung the mists from its face, and beamed benignly.

"Back! Back! Give him air!" cried Parrot Feathers, as she addressed herself to the task of removing the oyster from his foot.

The giant beast was dying, and its jaws were locked in the rigour of its suffering. There was no way to remove it gently. Parrot Feathers laid her unconscious hero's foot upon one rock, and broke the oyster loose with another.

Incidentally she smashed Probably Arboreal's toe.

He sat up in pained surprise. Unthinkingly, as you or I would put a hurt finger into our mouths, he put his crushed toe into his mouth. At that period of man's history the trick was not difficult. And then——

A beatific smile spread over his face!

Man had tasted the oyster!

In half an hour, mankind was plunging into the waves searching for oysters. The oyster's doom was sealed. His monstrous pretension that he belonged in the van of evolutionary progress was killed forever. He had been tasted, and found food. He would never again battle for supremacy. Meekly he yielded to his fate. He is food to this day.

Parrot Feathers and Probably Arboreal were married after breakfast. On the toes of their first child were ten cunning, diminutive oyster shells. Mankind, up to that time, had had sharp toenails like the claws of birds. But the flat, shell-like toenails, the symbols of man's triumph over, and trampling down of, the oyster were inherited from the children of this happy couple.

They persist to this day.

How Hank Signed the Pledge

AUTHOR'S NOTE: *Another version of this story appeared in a book entitled* Danny's Own Story, *published in 1912 by Doubleday, Page & Co.*

I'm not so sure about Prohibition and pledges and such things holding back a man that has got the liquor idea in his head. If meanness is in a man, it usually stays in him, in spite of all the pledges he signs and the promises he makes.

About the meanest man I ever knew was Hank Walters, a blacksmith in a little town in Illinois, the meanest and the whiskey-drinkingest. And I had a chance to know him well, for he and his wife Elmira brought me up. Somebody left me on their doorstep in a basket when I was a baby, and they took me in and raised me. I reckon they took me in so they could quarrel about me. They'd lived together a good many years and quarrelled about everything else under the sun, and were running out of topics to row over. A new topic of dissension sort of briskened things up for a while.

Not having any kids of his own to lick, Hank lambasted me when he was drunk and whaled me when he was sober. It was a change from licking his wife, I suppose. A man like Hank has just naturally got to have something he can cuss around and boss, so as to keep himself from finding out he don't amount to anything . . . although he must have known he didn't, too, way down deep in his inmost gizzards.

So I was unhappy when I was a kid, but not knowing anything else I never found out exactly how unhappy I was. There were worse places to live in than that little town, and there was one thing in our house that I always admired when I was a kid. That was a big cistern. Most people had their cisterns outside their houses, but ours was right in under our kitchen floor, and there was a trap door with leather hinges opened into it right by the kitchen stove. But that wasn't why I was so proud of it. It was because the cistern was full of fish—bullheads and redhorse and sunfish and pickerel.

Hank's father built the cistern. And one time he brought home some live fish in a bucket and dumped them in there. And they grew. And multiplied and refurnished the earth, as the Good Book says. That cistern full of fish had got to be a family custom. It was a comfort to Hank, for all the Walterses were great fish eaters, though it never went to brains any. We fed 'em now and then, and threw the little ones back in until they were grown, and kept the dead ones picked out as soon as we smelled anything wrong, and it never hurt the water any; and when I was a kid I wouldn't have taken anything for living in a house like that.

One time when I was a kid about six years old Hank came home drunk from Bill Nolan's barroom, and got to chasing Elmira's cat, because he said it was making faces at him. The cistern door was open, and Hank fell in. Elmira wasn't at home, and I was scared. Elmira had always told me not to fool around that cistern door any when I was a kid, for if I fell in there, she said, I'd be a corpse, quicker'n scatt.

So when Hank fell in and I heard him splash, being such a little fellow and awful scared because Elmira had always made it so strong, I supposed that Hank was probably a corpse already. I slammed the door shut over the cistern without looking in, for I heard Hank flopping around down there. I hadn't ever heard a corpse flop before and didn't know but what it might be somehow injurious to me, and I wasn't going to take any chances.

I went out and played in the front yard and waited for Elmira. But I couldn't seem to get my mind settled on playing I was a horse, or anything. I kept thinking of Hank being a corpse down in that cistern. And maybe that corpse is going to come flopping out pretty soon, I thought to myself, and lick me in some new and unusual way. I hadn't ever been licked by a corpse. Being young and innocent, I didn't rightly know what a corpse is, except I had the idea there was something about a corpse that kept them from being popular.

So after a while I sneaked back into the house and set all the flatirons on top of the cistern lid. I heard some flopping and splashing and fluttering, as if that corpse was trying to jump up and was falling back into the water, and I heard Hank's voice, and got scareder and scareder. When Elmira came along down the road she saw me by the gate crying and blubbering, and she asked me why.

"Hank is a corpse!" says I.

"A corpse!" says Elmira, dropping the pound of coffee she was carrying home from the general store and post-office. "Danny, what do you mean?"

I saw then I was to blame somehow, and I wished I hadn't said anything about Hank being a corpse. And I made up my mind I wouldn't say anything more. So when she grabbed hold of me and asked me again what I meant I blubbered harder, as a kid will, and said nothing. I wished I hadn't set those flatirons on the cistern lid, for it came to me all at once that even if Hank had turned into a corpse I hadn't any right to keep him in the cistern.

Just then old Mis' Rogers, one of our neighbours, came by, while Elmira was shaking me and yelling at me and asking how it happened, and had I seen it, and where was Hank's corpse.

"What's Danny been doing now?" asked Mis' Rogers—me being always up to something.

Elmira turned and saw her and gave a whoop and hollered out: "Hank is dead!" And she threw her apron over her head and sat right down in the path and boo-hooed like a baby. And I bellered and howled all the louder.

Mis' Rogers, she never waited to ask anything more. She saw she had a piece of news, and she wanted to be the first to spread it. She ran right across the road to where the Alexanderses lived. Mis' Alexander, she saw her coming and unhooked the screen door and Mis' Rogers hollered out before she reached the porch: "Hank Walters is dead!"

And then she went footing it up the street. There was a black plume on her bonnet, nodding the same as on a hearse, and she was into and out of seven front yards in less than five minutes.

Mis' Alexander she ran across the road to where we were, and kneeled down and put her arm around Elmira, who was still rocking back and forth in the path, and she said:

"How do you know he's dead, Elmira? I saw him not more than an hour ago."

"Danny saw it all," says Elmira.

Mis' Alexander turned to me and wanted to know

what happened and how it happened and where it happened. But I didn't want to say anything about that cistern. So I busted out crying all over again and I said: "He was drunk and he came home drunk and he did it then, and that's how he did it."

"And you saw him?" she asked.

I nodded.

"Where is he?" says she and Elmira, both together.

But I was scared to say anything about that cistern, so I just bawled some more.

"Was it in the blacksmith shop?" asks Mis' Alexander.

I nodded my head again, and let it go at that.

"Is he in there now?" she wants to know.

I nodded again. I hadn't meant to give out any untrue stories. But a kid will always lie, not meaning particular to lie, if you sort of invite him with questions like that, and get him scared by the way you're acting. Besides, I says to myself, so long as Hank has turned into a corpse, and being a corpse makes him dead, what's the difference whether he's in the blacksmith shop or in the cistern? I hadn't had any plain idea before that being a corpse meant the same thing as being dead. And I wasn't any too sure what being dead was like, either. Except I knew they had funerals over you then. I knew being a corpse must be a disadvantage from the way that Elmira has always said to keep away from that cistern, or I'd be one. And I began to see the whole thing was more important even than I had figured it was at first. I wondered if there'd be a funeral at our house. If there was one, that would be fine. They didn't have them every day in our town, and we hadn't ever had one of our own.

Mis' Alexander, she led Elmira into the house, both a-crying, and Mis' Alexander trying to comfort her, and me a-tagging along behind holding on to Elmira's skirts and sniffling into them. And in a few minutes all those women that Mis' Rogers had told came filing into the house, one at a time, looking sad and mournful. Only old Mis' Primrose, she was a little late getting there, because she stopped to put on the dress she always wore to funerals, with the black Paris lace on to it that her cousin Arminty White had sent her from Chicago.

When they found out that Hank had come home with liquor in him and done it himself they were all excited and they all crowded around and asked me questions, except two that were holding Elmira's hands where she sat moaning in a chair. And those questions scared me and egged me on to lies I hadn't had any idea of telling.

Says one woman: "Danny, you saw him do it in the blacksmith shop?"

I nodded.

"But how did he get in?" says another one. "The door was locked on the outside with a padlock just now when I came by. He couldn't have killed himself in there and then locked the door on the outside."

I didn't see how he could have done that myself, so I began to bawl again and said nothing at all.

"He must have crawled into the shop through

281

that little side window," says Mis' Primrose. "That window was open when I came by, even if the door was locked. Did you see him crawl through the little side window, Danny?"

I nodded. There wasn't anything else I could think of to do.

"But you aren't tall enough to look through that window," sings out Mis' Rogers. "How could you see into the shop, Danny?"

I didn't know, so I didn't say anything at all; I just sniffled.

"There's a store box right in under the window," says another one. "Danny must have climbed on to that store box and looked in after he saw Hank crawl through the window. Did you scramble on to the store box and look in, Danny?"

I just nodded again.

"And what was it you saw him do? How did he kill himself?" they all asked together.

I didn't know. So I just bellered and boo-hooed some more. Things were getting past anything I could see the way out of.

"He might have hung himself to one of the iron rings in the joists above the forge," says another woman.

"He climbed on to the forge and tied the rope to one of those rings, and tied the other end around his neck, and then he stepped off the forge and swung. Was that how he did it, Danny?"

I nodded. And I bellered louder than ever. I knew that Hank was down in that cistern below the kitchen, a corpse and a mighty wet corpse, all this time; but those women kind of got me to thinking he was hanging out in the blacksmith shop by the forge, too.

Pretty soon one woman says, shivery: "I wouldn't want to have the job of opening the door of the blacksmith shop the first one!"

And they all shivered, and looked at Elmira, and says to let some of the men open that door. And Mis' Alexander says she'll run and get her husband and make him do it. And all the time Elmira sits moaning in that chair. One woman says Elmira ought to have a cup of tea, and she'll lay off her bonnet and go to the kitchen and make it for her. But Elmira says no, she can't a-bear to think of tea, with poor Hennery hanging out there in the shop. But she was kind of enjoying all that fuss being made over her, too. And all the other women said: "Poor thing!" But most of them were mad because she said she didn't want any tea, for they wanted some and didn't feel free to take it without she took some. They coaxed her and made her see that it was her duty, and she said she'd have some finally.

So they all went out to the kitchen, taking along some of the best room chairs, Elmira coming, too, and me tagging along. The first thing they noticed was those flatirons on top of the cistern lid. Mis' Primrose says that looks funny. But Mis' Rogers says Danny must have playing with them. "Were you playing they were horses, Danny?"

I was feeling considerable like a liar by this time,

but I nodded. I couldn't see any use hurrying things up. I was bound to get a licking pretty soon anyhow. I could always bet on that. So they picked up the flatirons, and as they picked them up there came a splashing noise in the cistern. I thought to myself that Hank's corpse would be out of there in a minute, and then I'd catch it. One woman says: "Sakes alive! What's that noise?"

Elmira says the cistern is full of fish and it must be some of the biggest ones flopping around. If they hadn't been worked up and excited and talking all together and thinking of Hank hanging out in the blacksmith shop they might have suspicioned something, for that flopping and splashing kept up steady. Maybe I should have mentioned sooner it had been a dry summer and there was only three or four feet of water in the cistern and Hank wasn't in scarcely up to his big hairy chest. When Elmira says the cistern is full of fish that woman opens the trap door and looks in. Hank thinks it's Elmira come to get him out, he says afterward. And he allows he'll keep quiet in there and make believe he is drowned and give her a good scare and make her feel sorry for him.

But when the cistern door was opened he heard a lot of clacking tongues like a hen convention, and he allowed she had told the neighbours, and he'd scare them, too. So he laid low. And the woman that looked in, she sees nothing, for it's as dark down there as the insides of the whale that swallowed Jonah. But she left the door open and went on making tea, and there wasn't scarcely a sound from that cistern, only little ripply noises like it might have been fish.

Pretty soon Mis' Rogers says:

"It has drawed, Elmira; won't you have a cup?"

Elmira kicked some more, but she took hers. And each woman took hers. And one woman, a-sipping of hers, she says:

"The departed had his good points, Elmira."

Which was the best thing had been said of Hank in that town for years and years.

Old Mis' Primrose, she always prided herself on being honest, no matter what come of it, and she ups and says:

"I don't believe in any hypocritics at a time like this, any more'n any other time. The departed wasn't any good, and the whole town knows it, and Elmira ought to feel like it's good riddance of bad rubbish, and such is my sentiments and the sentiments of truth and righteousness."

All the other women sings out: "W'y, Mis' Primrose, I never!" But down in underneath more of 'em agreed than let on to. Elmira she wiped her eyes and says:

"Hennery and me had our troubles, there ain't any use denying that, Mis' Primrose. It has often been give and take between us and betwixt us. And the whole town knows he has lifted his hand against me more'n once. But I always stood up to Hennery and I fit him back, free and fair and open. I give him as good as he sent on this earth and I ain't the one to carry a mad beyond the grave. I forgive Hennery all the orneriness he did to me, and

285

there was a lot of it, as is becoming to a church member, which he never was."

All the women but Mis' Primrose says: "Elmira, you *have* got a Christian sperrit!" Which did her a heap of good, and she cried considerable harder, leaking out tears as fast as she poured tea in. And each one present tried to think up something nice to say about Hank, only there wasn't much they could say. And Hank in that cistern, listening to every word of it.

Mis' Rogers, she says: "Before he took to drinking like a fish, Hank Walters was as likely a lookin' young feller as ever I see."

Mis' White, she says: "Well, Hank he never was a stingy man, anyhow. Often and often White has told me about seeing Hank treating the crowd down in Nolan's saloon just as come-easy, go-easy as if it wasn't money he'd ought to have paid his honest debts with."

They sat there that way telling of what good points they could think of for ten minutes, and Hank hearing it and getting madder and madder all the time. By and by Tom Alexander came busting into the house.

"What's the matter with all you women?" he says. "There's nobody hanging in that blacksmith shop. I broke the door down and went in, and it's empty."

There was a pretty howdy-do, then, and they all sing out:

"Where's the corpse?"

Some thinks maybe someone has cut it down and

taken it away, and all gabbled at once. But for a minute or two no one thought that maybe little Danny had been egged on to tell lies. And little Danny ain't saying a word. But Elmira grabbed me and shook me and said:

"You little liar, what do you mean by that story of yours?"

I thought that licking was about due then. But whilst all eyes were turned on me and Elmira, there came a voice from the cistern. It was Hank's voice, but it sounded queer and hollow, and it said:

"Tom Alexander, is that you?"

Some of the women screamed, for they thought it was Hank's ghost. But Mis' Primrose says: "What would a ghost be doing in a cistern?"

Tom Alexander laughed and yelled down into the cistern: "What in blazes you want to jump in there for, Hank?"

"You darned ijut!" said Hank. "You quit mocking me and get a ladder, and when I get out'n here I'll learn you to ask me what I wanted to jump in here for!"

"You never saw the day you could do it," says Tom Alexander, meaning the day Hank could lick him. "And if you feel that way about it you can stay down there, for all of me. I guess a little water won't hurt you any, for a change." And he left the house.

"Elmira," sings out Hank, mad and bossy, "you go get me a ladder!"

But Elmira, her temper rose up, too, all of a sudden.

"Don't you dare order me around like I was the dirt under your feet, Hennery Walters," she says.

Hank fairly roared, he was so mad. "When I get out'n here," he shouted, "I'll give you what you won't forget in a hurry! I heard you a-forgivin' me and a-weepin' over me! And I won't be forgive nor weeped over by no one! You go and get that ladder!"

But Elmira only answered: "You was drunk when you fell in there, Hank Walters. And you can stay in there till you get a better temper on to you." And all the women laughed and said: "That's right, Elmira! Spunk up to him!"

There was considerable splashing around in the water for a couple of minutes. And then, of a sudden, a live fish came a-whirling out of that hole in the floor, which he catched with his hands. It was a big bullhead, and its whiskers around its mouth was stiffened into spikes, and it landed ker-plump on to Mis' Rogers' lap, a-wiggling, and it horned her on the hands. She was that surprised she fainted. Mis' Primrose, she got up and licked the fish back into the cistern and said, right decided:

"Elmira Walters, if you let Hank out of that cistern before he's signed the pledge and promised to jine the church, you're a bigger fool than I take you for. A woman has got to make a stand!"

And all the women sing out: "Send for Brother Cartwright! Send for Brother Cartwright!"

And they sent me scooting down the street to get him quick. He was the preacher. I never stopped to tell but two or three people on the way to his house, but they must have spread the news quick, for when I got back with him it looked like the whole town was at our house.

It was along about dusk by this time, and it was a prayer meeting night at the church. Mr. Cartwright told his wife to tell the folks that came to the prayer meeting he'd be back before long, and to wait for him. But she really told them where he'd gone, and what for.

Mr. Cartwright marched right into our kitchen. All the chairs in the house was in there, and the women were talking and laughing, and they had sent to the Alexanderses for their chairs, and to the Rogerses for theirs. Every once in a while there would be an awful burst of language come rolling up from the hole where that unregenerate old sinner was cooped up.

I have travelled around considerable since those days, and I have mixed up along with many kinds of people in many different places, and some of them were cussers to admire. But I never heard such cussing before or since as old Hank did that night. He busted his own records and he rose higher than his own water marks for previous years. I wasn't anything but a little kid then, not fit to admire the full beauty of it. They were deep down cusses that came from the heart. Looking back at it after these years, I can well believe what Brother Cartwright said himself that night—that it wasn't *natural* cussing, and that some higher power, like a demon or an evil sperrit, must have entered into Hank's human carcase and given that terrible eloquence to his remarks. It busted out every few minutes, and the women would put their fingers into their ears until a spell was over. And it was personal, too. Hank would listen tlil he heard a woman's voice he knew, and then he would let loose on her family, going back to her grandfathers and working downward to her children's children.

Brother Cartwright steps up to the hole in the floor and says gentle and soothing like an undertaker when he tells you where to sit at a home funeral:

"Brother Walters! Oh, Brother Walters!"

"Brother!" yelled Hank. "Don't ye brother me, you snifflin', psalm-singin', yaller-faced, pigeon-toed hyppercrit, you! Get me a ladder, gol dern ye, and I'll mount out o' here and learn ye to brother me, I will!" Only that wasn't anything to what Hank really said; no more like than a little yellow fluffy canary is like a turkey buzzard.

"Brother Walters," said the preacher, calm but firm, "we have all decided that you aren't going to get out of that cistern until you sign the pledge."

Then Hank told him what he thought of him and pledges and church doings, and it wasn't pretty. He said if he was as deep in the eternal fire of hell as he was in rain water, and every fish that nibbled at his toes was a devil with a red-hot pitchfork sicked on by a preacher, they could jab at him until the whole hereafter turned into icicles before he'd sign anything that a man like Mr. Cartwright gave him to sign. Hank was stubborner than any mule he ever nailed shoes on to, and proud of being that stubborn. That town was a most awful religious town, and Hank knew he was called the most unreligious man in it, and he was proud of that, too; and if any one called him a heathen it just plumb tickled him all over.

"Brother Walters," says the preacher, "we are going to pray for you."

And they did it. They brought all the chairs close up around the cistern door, in a ring, and they all knelt down there with their heads on the chairs and prayed for Hank's salvation. They did it up in style, too, one at a time, and the others singing out, "Amen!" every now and then, and they shed tears down on to Hank.

The front yard was crowded with men, all laughing and talking and chawing and spitting tobacco, and betting how long Hank would hold out. Si Emery, that was the city marshal, and always wore a big nickel-plated star, was out there with them. Si was in a sweat, because Bill Nolan, who ran the saloon, and some more of Hank's friends were out by the front fence trying to get Si to arrest the preacher. For they said that Hank was being gradually murdered in that water and would die if he was held there too long, and it would be a crime. Only they didn't come into the house amongst us religious folks to say it. But Si, he says he don't dare to arrest anybody, because Hank's house is just outside the village corporation line; he's considerable worried about what his duty is, not liking to displease Bill Nolan.

Pretty soon the gang that Mrs. Cartwright had

rounded up at the prayer meeting came stringing along in. They had brought their hymn books with them, and they sung. The whole town was there then, and they all sung. They sung revival hymns over Hank. And Hank, he would just cuss and cuss. Every time he busted out into another cussing spell they would start another hymn. Finally the men out in the front yard began to warm up and sing, too, all but Nolan's crowd, and they gave Hank up for lost and went back to the barroom.

The first thing they knew they had a regular old-fashioned revival meeting going there, and that preacher was preaching a regular revival sermon. I've been to more than one camp meeting, but for just naturally taking hold of the whole human race by the slack of the pants and dangling of it over hell fire, I never heard that sermon equalled. Two or three old backsliders in the crowd came right up and repented all over again. The whole kit-and-biling of them got the power, good and hard, and sung and shouted till the joints of the house cracked and it shook and swayed on its foundations. But Hank, he only cussed. He was obstinate, Hank was, and his pride and dander had risen up.

"Darn your ornery religious hides," he says, "you're takin' a low-down advantage of me, you are! Let me out on to dry land, and I'll show you who'll stick it out the longest, I will!"

Most of the folks there hadn't had any suppers, so after all the sinners but Hank had either got converted or sneaked away, some of the women said why not make a kind of a love feast of it, and bring some victuals, like they do at church sociables. Because it seemed that Satan was going to wrestle there all night, like he did with the angel Jacob, and they ought to be prepared. So they did it. They went and they came back with things to eat and they made hot coffee and they feasted that preacher and themselves and Elmira and me, right in Hank's hearing.

And Hank was getting pretty hungry himself. And he was cold in that water. And the fish were nibbling at him. And he was getting cussed out and weak and soaked full of despair. There wasn't any way for him to sit down and rest. He was scared of getting cramps in his legs and sinking down with his head under water and being drowned.

He said afterward he would have done the last with pleasure if there had been any way of starting a lawsuit for murder against that gang. So along between ten and eleven o'clock that night he sings out:

"I give in, gosh dern ye, I give in! Let me out and I'll sign your pesky pledge!"

Brother Cartwright was for getting a ladder and letting him climb out right away. But Elmira said:

"You don't know him like I do! If he gets out before he's signed the pledge, he'll never do it."

So Brother Cartwright wrote out a pledge on the inside leaf of the Bible, and tied it on to a string, and a pencil on to another string, and let them down, and held a lantern down, too, and Hank made his mark, for he couldn't write. But just as

Hank was making his mark that preacher spoke some words over Hank, and then he said:

"Now, Henry Walters, I have baptized you, and you are a member of the church."

You might have thought that Hank would have broken out into profanity again at that, for he hadn't agreed to anything but signing the pledge. But he didn't cuss. When they got the ladder and he climbed up into the kitchen, shivering and dripping, he said serious and solemn to Mr. Cartwright:

"Did I hear you baptizing me in that water?"

Mr. Cartwright said he had.

"That was a low-down trick," said Hank. "You knowed I always made my brags that I'd never jined a church and never would. You knowed I was proud of that. You knowed it was my glory to tell it, and that I set a heap of store by it, in every way. And now you've gone and took that away from me! You've gone and jined me to the church! You never fought it out fair and square, man strivin' to outlast man, like we done with the pledge, but you sneaked it on to me when I wasn't lookin'!"

And Hank always thought he had been baptized binding and regular. And he sorrowed and grieved over it, and got grouchier and meaner and drunkener. No pledge nor no Prohibition could hold Hank. He was a worse man in every way after that night in the cistern, and took to licking me harder and harder.

The Rivercliff Golf Killings

OR WHY PROFESSOR WADDEMS
NEVER BROKE A HUNDRED

I am telling this story to the public just as I told it in the grand jury room; the district attorney having given me a carbon copy of my sworn testimony.

THE CASE OF DOC GREEN

QUESTION: Professor Waddems, when did you first notice that Dr. Green seemed to harbor animosity towards you?

ANSWER: It was when we got to the second hole.

QUESTION: Professor, you may go ahead and tell the jury about it in your own words.

ANSWER: Yes, sir. The situation was this: My third shot lay in the sand in the shallow bunker—an easy pitch with a niblick to within a foot or two of the pin, for anyone who understands the theory of niblick play as well as I do. I had the hole in five, practically.

"Professor," said Doc Green, with whom I was playing——

QUESTION: This was Dr. James T. Green, the eminent surgeon, was it not?

ANSWER: Yes, sir. Dr. Green, with whom I was playing, remarked, "You are all wrong about Freud. Psychoanalysis is the greatest discovery of the age."

"Nonsense! Nonsense! Nonsense!" I replied. "Don't be a fool, Doc! I'll show you where Freud is all wrong, in a minute."

And I lifted the ball with an explosion shot to a spot eighteen inches from the pin, and holed out with an easy putt.

"Five," I said and marked it on my card.

"You mean eight," said Doc Green.

"Three into the bunker, four onto the green, and one putt—five," I said.

"You took four strokes in the bunker, Professor," he said. "Every time you said 'Nonsense' you made a swipe at the ball with your niblick."

"Great Godfrey," I said, "you don't mean to say you are going to count those gestures I made to illustrate my argument as *golf strokes*? Just mere gestures! And you know very well I have never delivered a lecture in twenty-five years without gestures like that!"

"You moved your ball an inch or two with your club at every gesture," he said.

QUESTION: Had you really done so, Professor? Remember, you are on oath.

ANSWER: I do not remember. In any case, the point is immaterial. They were merely gestures.

QUESTION: Did you take an eight, or insist on a five?

ANSWER: I took an eight. I gave in. Gentlemen, I am a good-natured person. Too good-natured. Calm and philosophical; unruffled and patient. My philosophy never leaves me. I took an eight.

(*Sensation in the grand jury room.*)

QUESTION: Will you tell something of your past life, Professor Waddems—who you are and what your lifework has been, and how you acquired the calmness you speak of?

ANSWER: For nearly twenty-five years I lectured on philosophy and psychology in various universities. Since I retired and took up golf it has been my habit to look at all the events and tendencies in the world's news from the standpoint of the philosopher.

QUESTION: Has this helped you in your golf?

ANSWER: Yes, sir. My philosophical and logical training and my specialization in psychology, combined with my natural calmness and patience, have made me the great golfer that I really am.

QUESTION: Have you ever received a square deal, Professor, throughout any eighteen holes of golf?

ANSWER: No, sir. Not once! Not once during the five years since I took the game up at the Rivercliff Country Club.

QUESTION: Have you ever broken a hundred, Professor Waddems?

ANSWER: No, sir. I would have, again and again, except that my opponents, and other persons playing matches on the course, and the very forces of nature themselves are always against me at critical moments. Even the bullfrogs at the three water holes treat me impertinently.

QUESTION: Bullfrogs? You said the bullfrogs, Professor?

ANSWER: Yes, sir. They have been trained by the caddies to treat me impertinently.

QUESTION: What sort of treatment have you received in the locker room?

ANSWER: The worst possible. In the case under consideration, I may say that I took an eight on the second hole, instead of insisting on a five, because I knew the sort of thing Dr. Green would say in the locker room after the match—I knew the scene he would make, and what the comments of my so-called friends would be. Whenever I do get down to a hundred an attempt is made to discredit me in the locker room.

QUESTION: Well, you took an eight on the second hole. What happened at the third hole?

ANSWER: Well, sir, I teed up for my drive, and just as I did so, Doc Green made a slighting remark about the League of Nations. "I think it is a good thing we kept out of it," he said.

QUESTION: What were your reactions?

ANSWER: A person of intelligence could only have one kind of reaction, sir. The remark was silly, narrow-minded, provincial, boneheaded, crass and ignorant. It was all the more criminal because Dr. Green knew quite well what I think of the League of Nations. The League of Nations was my idea. I thought about it even before the late President Wilson did, and talked about it and wrote about it and lectured about it in the university.

QUESTION: So that you consider Dr. Green's motives in mentioning it when you were about to drive——

ANSWER: The worst possible, sir. They could only come from a black heart at such a time.

QUESTION: Did you lose your temper, Professor?

ANSWER: No, sir! No, sir! No, sir! I *never* lose my temper! Not on any provocation. I said to myself, Be calm! Be philosophical! He's trying to get me excited! Remember what he'll say in the locker room afterwards! Be calm! Show him, show him, show him! Show him he can't get my goat.

QUESTION: Then you drove?

ANSWER: I addressed the ball the second time, sir. And I was about to drive when he said, with a sneer, "You must excuse me, Professor. I forgot that you invented the League of Nations."

QUESTION: Did you become violent, then, Professor?

ANSWER: No, sir! No, sir! I never become violent! I never——

QUESTION: Can you moderate your voice somewhat, Professor?

ANSWER: Yes, sir. I was explaining that I never become violent. I had every right to become violent. Any person less calm and philosophical would have become violent. Doc Green to criticize the League of Nations! The ass! Absurd! Preposterous! Silly! Abhorrent! Criminal! What the world wants is peace! Philosophic calm! The fool! Couldn't he understand that!

QUESTION: Aren't you departing, Professor, from the events of the 29th of last September at the Rivercliff golf course? What did you do next?

ANSWER: I drove.

QUESTION: Successfully?

ANSWER: It was a good drive, but the wind caught it, and it went out of bounds.

QUESTION: What did Dr. Green do then?

ANSWER: He grinned. A crass bonehead capable of sneering at the progress of the human race would sneer at a time like that.

QUESTION: But you kept your temper?

ANSWER: All my years of training as a philosopher came to my aid.

QUESTION: Go on, Professor.

ANSWER: I took my midiron from my bag and looked at it.

QUESTION: Well, go on, Professor. What did you think when you looked at it?

ANSWER: I do not remember, sir.

QUESTION: Come, come, Professor! You are under oath, you know. Did you think what a dent it would make in his skull?

ANSWER: Yes, sir. I remember now. I remember wondering if it would not do his brain good to be shaken up a little.

QUESTION: Did you strike him, then?

ANSWER: No, sir. I knew what they'd say in the locker room. They'd say that I lost my temper over a mere game. They would not understand that

`I had been jarring up his brain for his own good, in the hope of making him understand about the League of Nations. They'd say I was irritated. I know the things people always say.

QUESTION: Was there no other motive for not hitting him?

ANSWER: I don't remember.

QUESTION: Professor Waddems, again I call your attention to the fact that you are under oath. What was your other motive?

ANSWER: Oh yes, now I recall it. I reflected that if I hit him they might make me add another stroke to my score. People are always getting up the flimsiest excuses to make me add another stroke. And then accusing me of impatience if I do not acquiesce in their unfairness. I am never impatient or irritable!

QUESTION: Did you ever break a club on the course, Professor?

ANSWER: I don't remember.

QUESTION: Did you not break a mashie on the Rivercliff course last week, Professor Waddems? Reflect before you answer.

ANSWER: I either gave it away or broke it, I don't remember which.

QUESTION: Come, come, don't you remember that you broke it against a tree?

ANSWER: Oh, I think I know what you mean. But it was not through temper or irritation.

QUESTION: Tell the jury about it.

ANSWER: Well, gentlemen, I had a mashie that had a loose head on it, and I don't know how it got into my bag. My ball lay behind a sapling, and I tried to play it out from behind the tree and missed it entirely. And then I noticed I had this old mashie, which should have been gotten rid of long ago. The club had never been any good. The blade was laid back at the wrong angle. I decided that the time had come to get rid of it once and for all. So I hit it a little tap against the tree, and the head fell off. I threw the pieces over into the bushes.

QUESTION: Did you swear, Professor?

ANSWER: I don't remember. But the injustice of this incident was that my opponent insisted on counting it as a stroke and adding it to my score— my judicial, deliberate destruction of this old mashie. I never get a square deal.

QUESTION: Return to Dr. James T. Green, Professor. You are now at the third hole, and the wind has just carried your ball out of bounds.

ANSWER: Well, I didn't hit him when he sneered. I carried the ball within bounds.

"Shooting three," I said calmly. I topped the ball. Gentlemen, I have seen Walter Hagen top the ball the same way.

"Too bad, Professor," said Doc Green. He said it hypocritically. I knew it was hypocrisy. He was secretly gratified that I had topped the ball. He knew I knew it.

QUESTION: What were your emotions at this further insult, Professor?

ANSWER: I pitied him. I thought how inferior he was to me intellectually, and I pitied him. I addressed the ball again. "I pity him," I murmured. "Pity, pity, pity, pity, pity!"

He overheard me. "Your pity has cost you five more strokes," he said.

"I was merely gesticulating," I said.

QUESTION: Did the ball move? Remember, you are under oath, and you have waived immunity.

ANSWER: If the ball moved, it was because a strong breeze had sprung up.

QUESTION: Go on.

ANSWER: I laid the ball upon the green and again holed out with one putt. "I'm taking a five," I said, marking it on my card.

"I'm giving you a ten," he said, marking it on his card. "Five gesticulations on account of your pity."

QUESTION: Describe your reactions to this terrible injustice, Professor. Was there a red mist before your eyes? Did you turn giddy and wake up to find him lying lifeless at your feet? Just what happened?

ANSWER: Nothing, sir.

(*Sensation in the grand jury room.*)

QUESTION: Think again, Professor. Nothing?

ANSWER: I merely reflected that, in spite of his standing scientifically, Dr. James T. Green was a moron and utterly devoid of morality and that I should take this into acount. I did not lose my temper.

QUESTION: Did you snatch the card from his hands?

ANSWER: I took it, sir. I did not snatch it.

QUESTION: And then did you cram it down his throat?

ANSWER: I suggested that he eat it, sir, as it contained a falsehood in black and white, and Dr. Green complied with my request.

QUESTION: Did you lay hands upon him, Professor? Remember, now, we are still talking about the third hole.

ANSWER: I think I did steady him a little by holding him about the neck and throat while he masticated and swallowed the card.

QUESTION: And then what?

ANSWER: Well, gentlemen, after that there is very little more to tell until we reached the sixteenth hole. Dr. Green for some time made no further attempt to treat me unjustly and played in silence, acquiescing in the scores I had marked on my card. We were even as to holes, and it was a certainty that I was about to break a hundred. But I knew what was beneath this silence on Doc Green's part, and I did not trust it.

QUESTION: What do you mean? That you knew what he was thinking, although he did not speak?

ANSWER: Yes, sir. I knew just what kind of remarks he would have made if he had made any remarks.

QUESTION: Were these remarks which he suppressed derogatory remarks?

ANSWER: Yes, sir. Almost unbelievably so. They were deliberately intended to destroy my poise.

QUESTION: Did they do so, Professor?

ANSWER: I don't think so.

QUESTION: Go on, Professor.

ANSWER: At the sixteenth tee, as I drove off, this form of insult reached its climax. He accentuated his silence with a peculiar look, just as my club head was about to meet the ball. I knew what he meant. He knew that I knew it, and that I knew. I sliced into a bunker. He stood and watched me, as I stepped into the sand with my niblick—watched me with that look upon his face. I made three strokes at the ball and, as will sometimes happen even to the best of players, did not move it a foot. The fourth stroke drove it out of sight into the sand. The sixth stroke brought it to light again. Gentlemen, I did not lose my temper. I never do. But I admit that I did increase my tempo. I struck rapidly three more times at the ball. And all the time Doc Green was regarding me with that look, to which he now added a smile. Still I kept my temper, and he might be alive today if he had not spoken.

QUESTION (*by the foreman of the jury*): What did the man say at this trying time?

ANSWER: I know that you will not believe it is within the human heart to make the black remark that he made. And I hesitate to repeat it. But I have sworn to tell everything. What he said was, "Well, Professor, the club puts these bunkers here, and I suppose they have got to be used."

QUESTION (*by the foreman of the jury*): Was there something especially trying in the way he said it?

ANSWER: There was. He said it with an affectation of joviality.

QUESTION: You mean as if he thought he were making a joke, Professor?

ANSWER: Yes, sir.

QUESTION: What were your emotions at this point?

ANSWER: Well, sir, it came to me suddenly that I owed a duty to society; and for the sake of civilization I struck him with the niblick. It was an effort to reform him, gentlemen.

QUESTION: Why did you cover him with sand afterwards?

ANSWER: Well, I knew that if the crowd around the locker room discovered that I had hit him, they would insist on counting it as another stroke. And that is exactly what happened when the body was discovered—once again I was prevented from breaking a hundred.

THE DISTRICT ATTORNEY: Gentlemen of the jury, you have heard Professor Waddems' frank and open testimony in the case of Dr. James T. Green. My own recommendation is that he be not only released, but complimented, as far as this count is returned. If ever a homicide was justifiable, this one was. And I suggest that you report no indictment against the Professor, without leaving your seats. Many of you will wish to get in at least nine holes before dinner. Tomorrow Professor Waddems will tell us what he knows about the case of Silas W. Amherst, the banker.

The district attorney has given me the following certified copy of my sworn testimony, and I am telling the story of this golf game to the public just as I told it in the grand jury room.

THE CASE OF SILAS W. AMHERST, BANKER

QUESTION: Professor Waddems, will you tell the jury just when it was that you first noted evidences of the criminal tendencies, amounting to total depravity, in the late Silas W. Amherst?

ANSWER: It was on the 30th of September, 1936, at 4:17 p.m.

QUESTION: Where were you when you first began to suspect that the man had such an evil nature?

ANSWER: On the Rivercliff golf course, sir, at the second hole.

QUESTION: A par-four hole, Professor?

ANSWER: It is called that, yes, sir; but it is unfairly trapped.

QUESTION: What is your usual score on this hole, Professor Waddems? Remember, you are on oath, and you have waived immunity in this inquiry.

ANSWER: I have never yet received fair treatment with regard to this hole. My normal score on this hole is five, with an occasional par four and sometimes a birdie three. But disgraceful tactics have always been employed against me on this hole to prevent me from playing my normal game.

QUESTION: Is it a water hole?

ANSWER: Yes, sir.

QUESTION: Is it the same water hole from which the body of Silas W. Amherst was removed on October 3, 1936, a few days after he was last seen alone with you?

ANSWER: No, sir. That was the fifteenth hole. The water at the fifteenth hole is much deeper than the water at the second hole or the seventh hole. In the water at the fifteenth hole there are now several other bod——

QUESTION: Be careful, Professor! This inquiry is devoted entirely to Silas W. Amherst, and you are not compelled to incriminate or degrade yourself. Professor, are you a nervous, irritable, testy, violent person?

ANSWER: No, sir! No, sir! No, sir! And the man that dares to call me that is . . . (*A portion of Prof. Waddems' reply is stricken from the record.*)

QUESTION: Quietly, Professor, quietly! Tell these gentlemen how you gained the unruffled patience and philosophic calm that have made you the great golfer that you are.

ANSWER: For twenty-five years I lectured on philosophy and psychology at various universities. And I apply these principles to my golf game.

QUESTION: In spite of your thorough scientific knowledge of the game, have you ever broken a hundred?

ANSWER: Yes, sir, many times.

QUESTION: Think, Professor!

ANSWER: Yes, sir; yes, sir; yes, sir!

QUESTION: Mildly, please, Professor! Quietly! I will put the question in a different way. Professor, has any opponent with whom you played ever *admitted* that you broke a hundred, or has any card that you turned in after playing around alone been credited, if it showed you *had* broken a hundred?

ANSWER: I don't remember, sir. My game has been misrepresented and persecuted for years at Rivercliff.

QUESTION: To return to Mr. Amherst. Tell the jury exactly what happened at the second hole which revealed the man's irreclaimable blackness of character.

ANSWER: Well, sir, I teed up for my drive and addressed the ball. And just as I brought my club back, and it was poised for the down stroke, he said to me:

"Professor, you're driving with a brassie, aren't you?"

I gave him a look of mild expostulation, checked the drive, and stood in front of the ball again.

"I don't think your stance is right, Professor," he said. "Let me show you the proper stance—you don't mind my showing you, do you, Professor?"

Then he proceeded to show me—and I may say in passing that his theories were entirely faulty.

"I noticed on the first tee," he went on, "that you didn't understand how to pivot. You want to get your body into it, Professor. Like this," and he made a swing in demonstration.

"Your instruction, Mr. Amherst," I said politely, "is entirely gratuitous and all wrong."

"I thought you'd be glad to have me show you, Professor," he said. "And if I were you, I wouldn't play that new ball on this water hole. Here, I'll lend you a floater."

309

And the man actually took from his bag a floater, removed my ball, and teed up the one he had lent me.

"Now, Professor," he said, "a little more freedom in your swing. Keep your eye on the ball and don't let your hands come through ahead of the club. I noticed you had a tendency that way. I think your grip is wrong, Professor. Oh yes, certainly wrong! Here, let me show you the correct grip. And keep your head down, keep your head down!"

QUESTION: Was it then, Professor, that the tragedy occurred?

ANSWER: No, sir! No, sir! No, sir!

QUESTION: Quietly, Professor, quietly! You remained calm?

ANSWER: I am always calm! I never lose my temper! I am always patient! Self-contained! Restrained! Philosophical! Unperturbed! Nothing excites me! Nothing, I say, nothing! Nothing! Nothing! Nothing!

QUESTION: There, there, Professor, easily, easily now! What happened next?

ANSWER: I took a driving iron from my bag and addressed the ball again. I——

QUESTION: Just a moment, Professor. Why did you not continue with the brassie?

ANSWER: It was broken, sir.

QUESTION: Broken? How? I do not understand. How did it become broken?

ANSWER: I do not remember.

QUESTION: Between Mr. Amherst's instruction with the brassie and your taking the driving iron from the bag, as I understand it, the brassie was somehow broken. Please fill up this interval for the jury. What happened?

ANSWER: I can't recall, sir.

QUESTION: Come, come, Professor! How was the brassie broken?

ANSWER: It hit the sandbox, sir.

QUESTION: How could it hit the sandbox?

ANSWER: Well, it was an old brassie, and after I had made a few practice swings with it, I decided that it was poorly balanced and that I had better get rid of it once and for all. I did not wish to give it to a caddie, for I do not think it is fair to give poor clubs to these boys who are earnestly striving to educate themselves to be professionals; they are poor boys, for the most part, and we who are in better circumstances should see that they have a fair start in life. So I broke the brassie against the sandbox and took my driving iron, and——

QUESTION: Just a minute, Professor! These practice strokes that you made with the brassie, were there five or six of them?

ANSWER: I don't recollect, sir.

QUESTION: Did any one of them hit the ball?

ANSWER: No, sir! No, sir! No, sir! The brassie never touched the ball! The ball moved because there was a bent twig under it—this man Amherst had teed up his floater for me with a pat of sand upon a bent twig—and the twig straightened up and moved the sand, and the ball rolled off of it.

QUESTION (by the foreman of the jury): Professor Waddems, how far did the ball roll when the twig straightened up?

ANSWER: Well, sir, it had been teed up at the very edge of the driving green, and the ground is pretty high there, and the ball rolled down the slope, and it gained a great deal of momentum as it rolled down the slope, like an avalanche as it comes rolling down a mountainside, and at the bottom of the slope it struck a rut in the road the work-and-upkeep wagons use on the course, and that rut connects with the asphalt drive that leads in to the clubhouse, and when the ball struck the asphalt road it had already gained so much momentum that it rolled for some distance along the asphalt road, and then it crashed into the underbrush near the road and hit a sapling and bounded over onto the first fairway, all on account of the slope of the ground, for it had never been touched with the brassie at all.

QUESTION: Professor, did this happen to the ball five or six times before you discarded the brassie and took the driving iron?

ANSWER: No, sir. I only recall three times.

QUESTION: Go on, Professor. After these practice strokes, and your breaking of the brassie, you took the driving iron. What happened then?

ANSWER: Then Mr. Amherst stepped up and said to me, "Professor, let me give you a few tips about iron play. And you must keep your head down, keep your head down!"

QUESTION: Did you lose your temper then?

ANSWER: I never lose my temper! Never! Never! Never!

QUESTION: Quietly, now, Professor, quietly! Go on.

ANSWER: I made a magnificent drive, which cleared the water jump, and my second shot was on the green. I holed out with two putts. "A par four," I said, marking it on my card.

"You mean nine," said this man Amherst. Gentlemen, he had the effrontery to claim that the five practice swings I had made with the brassie, just simply to humor him in his demonstrations, were actual golf strokes!

(*Sensation in the grand jury room. Cries of "Outrageous!" "Impossible!" "The Dastard!" from various grand jurymen. The outburst quelled with difficulty by the district attorney.*)

QUESTION (*by the foreman of the jury*): Professor Waddems, did you end it all then?

ANSWER: No, sir. I kept my self-control. Gentlemen, I am always for peace! I am a meek person. I am mild. I will endure persecution to a point beyond anything that is possible to a man who has not had my years of training in philosophy and applied psychology. I merely got another caddie and proceeded with the game, yielding the point to Mr. Amherst for the sake of peace.

QUESTION: Got another caddie?

ANSWER: Yes, sir. The one I started out with was injured.

QUESTION: How, Professor?

ANSWER: I don't remember.

QUESTION: Think, Professor! Was it by a fall?

ANSWER: Oh yes, now I recollect! It *was* by a

313

fall. The caddie fell from a tree just beyond the second green and broke his shoulder.

QUESTION: What was he doing in the tree?

ANSWER: He had retired to the top of the tree under a peculiar misapprehension, sir. He had agreed with Mr. Amherst with regard to the question as to whether I should take nine strokes or a par four; and I think he misinterpreted some sudden motion of mine as a threat.

QUESTION: A motion with a golf club?

ANSWER: It may have been, sir. I had a club in my hand, and I remember that my mind at the moment was engrossed with a problem connected with the underlying psychology of the full swing with wooden clubs.

QUESTION: Well, Professor, the caddie is now at the top of the tree, laboring under a misapprehension. What caused his fall?

ANSWER: I think the wooden club must have slipped somehow from my hands, sir. It flew to the top of the tree and disturbed his balance, causing him to fall.

QUESTION: Was he a good caddie?

ANSWER: There are no good caddies, sir.

(*Ripple of acquiescent laughter goes round the grand jury room.*)

QUESTION: Then, Professor, you went on to the next driving green. Tell what happened from this point on to the fifteenth hole, where the body of Silas W. Amherst was found four days later.

ANSWER: Advice, sir, advice! That's what happened! Advice! One long, intolerable gehenna of gratuitous advice! Gentlemen, I don't know whether any of you ever had the misfortune to play golf with the late Silas W. Amherst, but if you had——

(*Cries from various grand jurors: "Yes, yes, I played with him!" "Ataboy, Professor!" "I knew him, Prof!" etc., etc. District attorney begs for order; witness continues.*)

ANSWER: Advice! Advice! Advice! And always the fiendish malignity of the man concealed under a cloak of helpful friendliness! Advice! Advice! Advice! And to me! I, who have studied the basic principles of the game more thoroughly than any other man in America today! Gentlemen, if I were not the most patient man in the world, Silas W. Amherst would have bit the dust twenty times between the second and the fifteenth holes that day! His explanations—to me! His continual babble and chatter! His demonstrations! Every club I took from my bag, he *explained* to me! Gentlemen, some of them were clubs that I had designed myself and had had manufactured to fit my own original theories with regard to golf! But I kept my temper! I never lose my temper! Never! Never! Never!

QUESTION: Does any particularly insulting phrase of advice stand out in your memory, Professor?

ANSWER: Yes, sir! A dozen times on every hole he would cry to me as I addressed the ball, "Keep your head down, Professor, keep your head down!"

THE DISTRICT ATTORNEY: Please sit down, Professor; and do not bang on the chairs with your walking stick as you talk. We cannot hear your testimony.

THE PROFESSOR: Yes, sir. Well, at the fifteenth hole, while he was standing on the edge of the water, looking for a ball——

QUESTION: Professor, is it true that the fifteenth hole at Rivercliff is really a pool, fed by subterranean springs, and so deep that no plummet has ever sounded its bottom?

ANSWER: Exactly sir. As Silas W. Amherst stood on the edge of it, it occurred to me that perhaps the man's conscience had awakened and that he was going to commit suicide for the good of the human race, gentlemen. And so I gave him a little pat of approval—on the back; and he fell in. Gentlemen, he judged himself and executed himself, and I still approve.

QUESTION: Would you mind telling the jurors, Professor, just what Mr. Amherst said immediately before you patted him approvingly on the back?

ANSWER: He said, "You just stick to me, Professor, and do as I show you, and I'll make some kind of golfer out of you yet."

QUESTION: Did he try to struggle to land, and did you hold his head under water?

ANSWER: Yes, sir, I generously assisted him in his purpose to that extent.

QUESTION: What did you say while you were assisting him?

ANSWER: I said, "Keep your head down, Mr. Amherst, keep your head down!"

THE FOREMAN OF THE JURY: Mr. District Attorney, speaking for the other members of this jury as well as for myself, it is ridiculous to consider the matter of finding any true bill or indictment of any sort against Professor Waddems in the case of the late Mr. Amherst. The pat of approval was more than justified, and we consider Professor Waddems a public benefactor.

THE DISTRICT ATTORNEY: Tomorrow we will take up the case of Willie, alias "Freckled," Briggs, the caddie who met his death on October 4, 1936, at the Rivercliff Country Club. I suggest that the slight rain we have had today, which is happily over with, should contribute greatly to what is known as a good brassie lie on the fairways. You are dismissed for the day.

When the Turtles Sing

"... *The time of the singing of birds is come, and
the voice of the turtle is heard in our land* ..."
—*The Song of Solomon*, 2:12.

"This world," said the Old Soak, "would be a
good deal better place if the days and ways of them
old-time peetryarchs the Good Book speaks of was
to come again."

And yet Mr. Hawley did not appear wholly displeased with this world; he spoke with the air of
one who has been thinking profoundly, but not
bitterly, of humankind. He was in his favourite
seat on the veranda of Jake Smith's Palace Hotel,
at the shady end. His feet were on the railing.
His corn-cob pipe was purring sweetly. Outside
him and round about him were the drowsy, pleasant life of the little town and the shimmer and
shadow of a perfect summer day. Inside him was
a golden warmth induced by a sample of one of
Jake Smith's more successful importations which

318.

had boasted on its label that it came from the land of Burns. Poetry was in the Old Soak's eye, poetry and benevolence and the promise of narration. I put my feet beside his on the railing and prepared to assimilate wisdom.

"If I was to wake up to-morrow morning with a crown onto my head and a skeptre in my hand and find myself the Umpire of the entire human universe," said Mr. Hawley, "my first commandment would be for everybody to go right back to the early days of the world. Them old peetryarchs was big and liberal in their elements and idears. They figgered that life was too short to waste it all in work. Just because Methusalem lived a thousand years was no sign that everybody else would. Eat, drink, and be merry, says they, for in five or six hundred years mebby we're gonna die. We're here to-day, they says, and gone in a few centuries; let's whoop her up while the whoopin's good!

"One of them peetryarchs would set up on his ivory throne with his flocks and herds around him, and his men-servants and maid-servants and oxen and asses and camels even to the third and fourth generation of posterity, and his wives and children and captives and conqueredbines, and all the in-laws and outlaws that went for to make up a tribe of them Bible beegats, and pass out judgments for an hour or so every Monday morning, just to get business out of the way for the week. And him and his soothsayers and interrupters of dreams and medicine-men would pull wise cracks on each other and proverbs and ketch-questions and riddles for another hour, mebby. And by noon on Monday he would be tired of it and say: 'Well, that's that! Is anybody gonna be five hundred years old this week? If there is we'll pull a feastivity that will last a month and crack every welkin 'twixt Dan and Burrsheba!' And usually there was somebody at least a hundred that week, but if nobody was he would ask: 'Can anybody think of some other good reason to have a barbecue?' Mostly they could, but if they couldn't he would say: 'Just for the sake of argument, can any of you think up any reason why we *shouldn't* have a barbecue?' And nobody ever could. And if a stranger was to wander along out of some poor ignorant heathen land and ask: 'Chief, you mean a reg'lar barbecue, or a prohibition barbecue?' he would take down the golden jug from his lips and wipe his foamin' beard onto his sleeves of purple and fine linen and say: 'What in blazes *is* a prohibition barbecue?' And if the stranger explained about unfermenticated drinks and soft stuff he would smite that heathen with the golden jug and say: 'Evil contaminations will spoil a whole barrel of good apples; we can't have a mammal of iniquity like that associatin' with this tribe! Leave him lay, poor heathen, and now all hands to the barbecue pits!'

"And the word would go forth from Dan to Burrsheba and from Alpha to Omega that Peetryarch Bill was fightin' dull care away from his lovin' people with a barbecue. And along about the third or fourth day the scouts and soothsayers would report there was a cloud of dust on the sky no bigger than a man's hand. And it would grow and grow and pretty soon Peetryarch Pete would come lopin' into sight acrost the hills and plains with all *his* posterity of in-laws and outlaws, and his cymbals and his drums and trumpets makin' a joyful noise. And from every direction, as the news spread, would come gallopin' a passel of prodigal sons, racin' home on ostriches and zebras from Babylon and Tyre, and ibexes out of the land of Egypt, with the smell of fatted calves and fried chicken and e-wee lambs tantalizin' their twitchin' nostrils.

"'Peace be with you,' the visitors would say, 'we smelled something cookin'.'

"'Alight, alight from off your jinglin' steeds,' Peetryarch Bill would say, 'and throw your lip over a wine-skin. Just stable your critters in the animal-tents, and spend the summer. Somebody in my outfit's havin' a birthday, or if they ain't they will afore this party breaks up. I was seven hundred years old myself last Ground Hog's Day, but there's a dance or two in the old boy yet. Light down, light down from your critters, and interduce your digestive ornaments to the fleshpots. You are now enterin' the incorporated town of Peetryarchville, and the speed limit is what you make it.'

"Yes, sir, they was large and liberal in their minds, them old peetryarchs was. And there ain't been any real wisdom in the world since. It was their wisdom made 'em live that long. Consider the lilies, they says to each other, they never done a day's work in their lives and yet they're all spangled up like a circus parade. Havin' sense

enough to whoop it up and oil their joints with joy
is what kept 'em wise and cheerful. There wasn't a
month passed by without a barbecue, with foot-
races and sack-races and wrasslin' matches and
climbin' the greased pole. And dancin' and fiddlin'
contests and balloon ascensions and striking ma-
chines. And leopards and hyenas racin' each other
hitched to these two-wheeled circus chariots. And
potato races and kissing games and turkey shoots
with bows and arrows and pitching horseshoes. And
wheelbarrow races and orators speaking pieces
about this fair land of ours. And merry-go-rounds
pulled by real animals on the gallop. And charades
and riddle contests and parades and these here uni-
corns and Egyptian spinxes fighting each other in
a bull ring. And steer-riding contests and soothsayers doing slight o' hand. And snake-charmers and
fellers summer-setting over elephants, and trained
dogs and cane-racks. And every now and then you
would hear another bung-starter go 'Whang!' and
there would be another outburst of trumpets then
and everybody would holler: 'Hoo-ray! Gran'pap's
openin' another barrel!' And it would keep up that
way for days and days, betting their critters and
their wives on the races, until one tribe was plumb
busted and had to jine the other one. And it was
always open house for everybody—for everybody
except them heathen Muslins. Them Muslins is
teetotallers because their prophet Mohammed had
the indigestion in his stomach and couldn't drink,
and didn't want anybody else to. Some of the puz-
zles and riddles and ketch-questions them old

peetryarchs and their soothsayers used to ask can't be answered in this age of posterity at all, because there ain't the wisdom left in the world to answer 'em with. If there was more dancin' and barbecues and whooping it up, and not so much store set by industriousness, mebby joy and wisdom would come back to the world again. Any darned ijut can work his fool head off, but it takes a wise man to keep his thoughts and elements a-jigging joyful."

The Old Soak paused, and squinted beneath his lowered lids as if lost in the ecstatic vision which his fancy had composed for him, and I forebore to shatter the dream. Presently he continued:

"The only man I ever knowed personal that was like them early peetryarchs was old Jason Tucker that used to live back there in the middle of the swamp. If he was livin' now Jason would be purty nigh onto a hundred, but lightnin' struck him on his ninety-second birthday whilst he was climbin' a tree to rob a crow's nest. He wanted a young crow to train up for a pet for one of his babies.

"You know what the swamp back there used to be years ago afore it was most of it dreened away. Twenty-five or thirty miles long it was, and a dozen miles wide in places, with heavy-wooded knolls and islands and hummocks stickin' up. In the wet season of the year it would be practically a lake, except for the high lands, with no roads anywheres. And ponds and sloughs and marches, and cricks connectin' 'em up, windin' every-whichways in the dryest times. Jason, he was born back there in the plumb middle of it, and he owned hundreds and hundreds of acres. If I said thousands and thousands I would be nearer right. His daddy had passed it onto him long years afore the Civil War. Even as late as when you was a kid that swamp land wasn't worth nothin' much. And when I was a boy it was worth even less. How Jason Tucker's dad ever come to get so much of it, or what he got it for, pretty near as far back as the Revolutionary War, nobody ever knowed; but his it was and it's certain it didn't cost him hardly anything.

"Along with the Tucker tribe was some other families that seemingly had always been there, and they mingled and multiplied and refurnished the earth. A lot of the younger ones was forever movin' out, so Jason's kingdom never got too crowded. And he was the law and the prophets in there, Jason was. He never let anybody put an axe into the woods on the high lands, except for firewood and to build their cabins, and up to the day of his death he never sold a single acre. I heard him myself turn down an offer of three hundred dollars an acre for five hundred acres of it just afore he died. 'What the blazes,' he says, 'I don't want money! What I want is a good time!' And he always kept open house for everybody that come along. He never dreened any of his own land; it was the dreenage all around him on every side, at the last, that made it worth all that money. For that's gotten to be the richest farmin' land in the world now.

"It was said when I was a kid that Jason Tucker's families was almost as mixed as Noah's in the Bible must 'a' been. Noah's son Shem was a He-

324

brew child, you remember, and his son Ham was a negro. And his son Japhet it don't say, but I always reckoned he was likely a United Brethren. But gosh! Jason's gang was joyous! How they all loved a good time. Jake Smith that runs this place, and me, and Judge Bill Wilson, that's in Congress now, used to go out into the swamp and visit with old Jason quite a good deal. We three was the closest friends he had in town, for the truth is the Tuckers didn't take so well with the villagers and farmin' people round about, for they didn't understand them and their joyousness. It was to Jake and Judge Bill Wilson and me that old Jase always come when he had something to talk over. Some of the meals and good times I have had out there! You couldn't get them vittles for love nor money anywheres now—duck and snipe and geese and turtles and pigeons and wild turkeys and rabbits and quails and squirrels! Say, that was the life!

"They raised some crops on the high land, to feed their cattle and horses, and fished and hunted and trapped, and when they wanted a barrel of liquor Jason would come to town with mink or muskrat skins or something; and every Sunday, from spring till winter, they pulled a joyous barbecue for all hands and any visitors that might be passin' through.

" 'What I got,' Jason used to say, 'belongs to my friends as long as I got it. And my friends is *everybody* that wants to have a good time!'

"He never set much store by up-to-date inventions. 'Steam-engines and patent churns is a-goin'

325

to be the ruination of this country yet,' he says to me once. 'And coal-mines and factories is bad for it too. If people would only stick to raisin' meat-critters and a little easy tillin' of the soil, and not go diggin' into the bowells of the earth or buildin' up into the air, there wouldn't be half the trouble in the world there is. They'd have time to dance and be joyful and go fishin' and huntin'. Them city folks that comes out my way to hunt ducks is always tired and troubled when they get there. Why, if they was gold-mines only six inches in under my land, and I knowed it, I wouldn't let none of my families dig for them. Every time you dig down into the earth you get that much nearer to hell. Not but what a little gold's all right for women folks to prettify themselves up with, I do admit that.'

"Jason always had quite an eye for women, and there was some good-lookers in his woods; most of his tribe was fine, up-standin', good-lookin' people. Not what you'd call stylish dressers, by no means, but clean enough and full of fun. And Jason, he was a moral man, too, like an old peetryarch orter be.

"One Sunday, about fifteen years ago it was, me and Jake and Judge Bill Wilson went out to see him, and we noticed he was kind of thoughtful about something, and Jake asked him what it was.

" 'Jake,' he says, 'my conscience ain't exactly right inside of me.'

" 'What's settin' onto it, Jase?' Jake asks him.

" 'I was just thinkin',' says Jason, 'there's always been a lot more families raised in amongst my woods here than there has been weddin's to match up with 'em, and it kind o' bothers me. Molly's been talkin' about it a good deal, too. Molly thinks as there ought to be at least one weddin' for every family raised.'

"Molly was the woman that would 'a' been Mrs. Jason Tucker at that time, if there had o' been a Mrs. Jason Tucker.

"'I always done what I dam' well please about raisin' families myself,' says Jase, 'and I know why I done it; and I got my answer all ready if any leadin' questions is to be asked about it on the Judgment Day. But at the same time I feel responsible for the morals of a lot of these here young folks. Molly says they all look up to me for guidance and I want to do my rightful duty by 'em.'

"'Well, then, Jase,' says Judge Wilson, 'you trot out the ones that have raised families without being married and I'll marry 'em for you this afternoon.'

"'Judge, it ain't so simple and easy as all that,' says Jason. 'You see, there's a lot of complifications and mix-ups amongst my families that you couldn't straighten out by just an ordinary person-to-person marriage thataway.'

"'How do you mean, Jase?' says the Judge.

"'Well,' says Jason, pointing to a right likely-looking girl in her twenties, 'there's Sadie there, for instance. Sadie's my granddaughter, or my great-granddaughter, or somethin', and she's a good girl, Sadie is. When she was about sixteen there was a young book-agent wandered through here, and he liked our way of livin' so well he stayed permanent. One day after he'd been here a few weeks Sadie come to me and says: "Gran'pap, I want you to splice Jim and me." I done it the same way I always been doin' it, though I knowed well enough it wasn't Bible-bindin' legal. I jumped 'em over a broomstick. And the usual offspring come along in the usual course of events. Two or three years later Sadie comes up and says: "Gran'pap, I want you to splice Tom and me." "I thought you was spliced to Jim," I says. "Me and Jim got kinda tired bein' married to each other," she says, "and Jim's figgerin' on hitchin' up with Arminty." Well, I knowed well enough how they might feel about that. I been fallin' into love all my life, over and over agin. I sympathize with young folks because I always kep' young myself, and I reckon I'll keep on gettin' married every oncet in a while as long as I live. So I jumped Sadie and Jim backwards over the broomstick, and divorced 'em, and she married Tom. And her and Tom has the usual offspring in the usual course of events. And then about a year ago Sadie goes and marries Jerd. Which Jerd had already been married for a while to Arminty afore Arminty wedded Jim. And that's just the way it is with a lot of my families, Judge. It ain't so easy to figger out.

" 'You can see for yourself a person-to-person weddin' wouldn't do much for Sadie. For instance, who would I tell Sadie to marry? Not Jim, because he's spliced again. Not Jerd, because he was married previous to Arminty. Not Tom, because first he was spliced to Elvira, and now he's spliced again. And they all get the usual offsprings in the usual course of events. What we need here, Judge, is a more *general* kind of a marriage than the common run, to make us all legal.'

"'Jason,' says the Judge, laughing at him, 'I tell you what we'll do. Line 'em all up, and I'll marry the whole swamp with one ceremony, and after that they can sort themselves into pairs.'

"So Jason blowed a horn and the whole tribe come runnin' up to the cleared space in front of his cabin where we was settin' havin' a few drinks.

"'Children,' he says, 'there's gonna be a great big weddin' this afternoon.'

"'Hooray, Gran'pap!' they all yells. 'Whose?'

"'All of us,' says Jason. 'Make a ring.'

"'Hooray for Gran'pap!' they yelled again. 'And afterwards can we have a barbecue?'

"'You can,' says he.

"And they all took hands and made a big ring. Jason and Jake Smith and me and Judge Wilson was in the middle of it. And also twenty or thirty kids too young to get married. And while they all danced and jumped and capered and laughed and sung and went round and round like kids playin' ring around a rosy, Judge Wilson pronounced some kind of ceremony.

"'Now, then,' says Jason, 'you're all spliced, criss-cross and in-and-out, double-stitched and whipped over, each to each and all to all, tight as a leather bottle, and the partickler pardners you pick out now you gotto stick to. Kill a critter and

329

get the pits ready, and roll out a barrel of liquor, and we'll have that barbecue.'

"'Hooray for Gran'pap!' they all yells again, and run off to start the celebration.

"Well, sir, them feastivities lasted for several days and nights, with dancin' and jubilations, and barbecues and bonfires and fiddles singin', and joy as unconfined as it used to be in the days of the old peetryarchs themselves. I come darned near jinin' Jason's outfit forevermore that time, and I would have too, if it hadn't been for my old woman.

"Along about the middle of the second or third night of the party, I woke up sudden on the pile of brush where I had been nappin' outside Jason's cabin, with the feelin' that the whole world had turned topsy-turvy. There was a moon and stars in the sky above me, and the first thing I seen was a gust of smoke whirl acrost the face of the moon, and then I thought it must be sunrise, for the sky was so light. And then my ears began to take in a most remarkable mixtry of strange noises, and I set up and looked around me.

"I jumped to my feet. The swamp was burnin'! It was late in August and there hadn't been any rain for a couple of weeks, and the tops of the grass and rushes, above the water in the sloughs and ponds, had caught from some bonfire.

"It was the darndest sight I ever seen. Around and between the islands there were strips and pools and ribbons of fire winding in and out and swinging back and forth, and long moving streaks that looked like winding rivers of flame. A belt of flame would run up to an island and jump and circle it like you had throwed a burning lasso around a stump.

"And there was the noise of cattle bellowing and snorting as they come running up the slopes to the high ground and crashing through the bushes. And horses whinnying and screaming, and dogs barking everywhere and roosters crowing. And clouds of ducks rising in the distance and wheeling through the sky, and frogs croaking, and away off somewheres I heard a wolf howling. And you could even see fish jumping in the cricks and bayous. And pigs was squealing as they made for the hummocks; and a big black snake hustling up the hill crawled right acrost my feet.

"'Gosh,' I says, out loud, 'I hope that fire don't get into the underbrush.'

"'The big timber never burns much, even if it does,' said Jason. I hadn't known he was standing in the cabin door looking out. 'It's burned off afore this,' he says, 'that sleazy top-stuff over the ponds.'

"He was standin', enjoying the sight. Tongues and loops and eddies of fire licked out in every direction for as much as four or five miles on every side of us. And pretty soon the whole tribe was awake, and it seemed to put new life into 'em. They begun to fiddle and to dance and sing, on top of the high land, with the ocean of fire below 'em and the sky full of sick-lookin' stars above 'em. And when the smoke full of sparks would whirl acrost the sky it looked as if the sparks and stars was dancin' with the tribe, whirlin' and swingin' and spinnin'. And what with all the noises and the swayin' lines of rushes too green to burn, and the jumpin' shadows of the dancers, and the runnin' fires that leapt and twisted and turned, it fair made a feller dizzy.

"Out from the cabin come runnin' Molly, and she was plumb hysterical.

"'Hell's reachin' for you, Jason Tucker!' she yelled. 'Hell's belchin' up through the mud to grab you!'

"'And for what reason should hell be after Jason?' says Judge Wilson, comin' out of the cabin with Jake.

"'For all the wickedness and drinkingness and carousings that's been goin' on in this here swamp the last sixty years,' says she.

"'You shut up, Molly,' says Jason, mildlike. 'Everybody's married now, ain't they? Well, then, what wickedness is there left in this here swamp?'

"'It's hell reachin' for you for the loose livin' you always done,' she says. 'One day won't wipe all that out.'

"'You go into your bed, and quit tryin' to spoil our party,' says Jason. She give him a mean look, but she went.

"'Molly,' says Jason, kind of apologizin'-like, 'used to be as full of fun as anybody, but last spring she went to a revival meetin' over to Springtown and got herself salvationed, and ever since then she's had notions about me bein' wicked. That's what comes of lettin' a woman go to town.'

"Well, mebby that fluffy top-stuff, grass and cat-

332

tails and reeds, would have burned itself to the water's edge everywheres without ketching the underbrush on the raised ground, but just the same I felt better when it clouded up sudden, the way it does in August, and a rain ended the thing.

"I didn't know at the time how serious Judge Bill Wilson took that general weddin', but Jason, he took it serious. He thought he was married to Molly, and it was the only time he ever thought he was married in his life, and it kind o' worried him.

"'Clem,' he said to me one day, 'I was worried when I thought I wasn't bein' moral, and I'm a dam' site more worried now I know I am. What's the answer? I keep right on fallin' in love just the same as ever, and I don't feel free, and a man orter always feel free.'

"'If I was you,' says I, 'I'd pull a barbecue and forget it.' Which he done, temporary.

"But it seems from what he told me Molly never could get over bein' salvationized. Some persons, when they get salvationized, get more joyous and happy, and easier to be friends with. But with other people it takes a different turn; it kind of seems to sour their elements, somehow.

"Jason, he used to tell me about it. He got to comin' to town oftener and droppin' in to gossip with Jake Smith and me.

"'That dam' Molly,' he says to me one time, 'is gettin' so I can't hardly stand her. If she wasn't married to me I'd chase her out'n the swamp for good. Why, she actually has got the notion now she wants me to wear a collar on Sundays!'

"And about a year later than that he come in and says she has got the notion now that she wanted him to dreen his swamp and sell the land and move into town. The dreenage round about had started by that time, and prices was going up, and Molly knowed there was oodles and oodles of money in it. But the idea of spoiling his kingdom and moving away from it was just plumb sacerlidge and blasphemiousness to Jason Tucker.

"'I never believed much in lambasting a woman,' says Jason, 'but when she sprung that onto me I went out and cut me a limb and showed it to her, and hung it over the door. And I says to her that if she ever utters such words agin I'll wear it out onto her.'

"It was a couple of years after that agin that old Jason was settin' inside there with Jake and me, and we was all havin' one, when Jason spoke up and says:

"'Boys, you ever hear a turtle make a noise?'

"'No,' says I, 'and just for the sake of argument, you never did neither.'

"'A catfish has got a voice, but a turtle ain't,' says Jake.

"'Well,' says Jason, 'I'd say you was right, if I didn't know you was wrong. I been eatin' turtles, man and boy, for nearly ninety years, and I never heard one sing yet. But how do you figger about the Bible sayin' that the voice of the turtle is heard in the land?'

"'That's a miracle,' says I, 'like Balaam's ass turnin' its head around and beginning a conversation with him. Leastways, I always figgered it so.'

" 'What difference does it make, anyhow?' says Jake. 'What you want to talk to turtles about?'

" 'Oh, nothin', nothin'! Exceptin', if a feller was to get so het-up, and young-feelin' and flustered-like that he heard the turtles singin', he could feel really *sure*. I often listen to the bull-frogs croakin' in the spring nights,' says Jason, kind o' dreamy-like, 'but I ain't heard the turtles yet, and I don't know if it's *true*.'

" 'If *what's* true?' I said.

" 'Bein' in love,' says Jason, still dreamy.

" 'You in love again? Hell!' says Jake. 'At your time of life?'

"Me, I'm always tactful and diplomatic about what my opinions is, so as not to hurt anybody's feelin's, so all I said was:

" 'Why, you dam' old fool, you ought to be ashamed of yourself.'

" 'I ain't, Clem,' he says, grinnin' all over himself. 'I ain't a mite ashamed. I'm proud. I'm plumb tickled to death.'

" 'If Molly finds it out she'll plumb tickle you to death,' says Jake, 'or jaw you to death, or somethin'.'

" 'I ain't told her yet,' says Jason. 'But I'm a goanto. I'm goanto have her get a divorce, I am. I'm a goanto get married agin. I feel it comin' on.'

" 'Well,' says I, 'Jason, who's the lucky woman?'

" 'It's Ruby Sparks,' says Jason, lookin' as shy as a twenty-year-old kid.

" 'Great Jehosaphats!' says Jake, risin' up in his

335

chair and slumpin' down heavy again, 'right under my very nose, and I never guessed it!'

"For Ruby was workin' right in this very place then, and had been for nearly a year, helpin' Jake and his wife run the hotel.

" 'Will she have you?' says I.

" 'If I can get free, she will,' says Jason. 'Why not? Women always does and always has.'

"Jake and me both stared at him, and it come to me mebby a woman might be willin' to marry him yet. He was straight as an arrow, and with his long thick white hair, and his long white beard, and his broad chest and Roman nose, Jase didn't really look a year over sixty.

" 'Turtles!' mutters Jake, lookin' at him meditative and thoughtful. 'Turtles been singin' to him! Hell!'

"And then he says: 'Jase, if Ruby Sparks makes up her mind to marry you, all Hades can't stop her, with Molly thrown in. Nothin' ever has stopped her yet, turtles or no turtles.'

"And just then who should walk through the room where we was sittin' but Ruby herself, on the way to the street.

" 'You heard the turtles singin', too, Ruby?' says Jake. She stopped at that, and looked puzzled; and then she seen from the looks of the three of us that Jason must have told us, and she looked at us steady for a minute as if sizin' up what we were thinkin', and then she threw back her head and laughed at us. And it come to me when she laughed that Ruby and her laugh just exactly fitted into Jason's tribe

336

in the swamp, and his notions of always bein' joyous; for it always was a laugh that made you want to laugh with it. She went over and run her hand through Jason's beard and hair like she was petting a big dog, and cocked her head on one side like she was admirin' him, and she says:

"'Say what you like, Jake, I'm going to take a chance!'

"With that she blew out. That was her word, always: 'I'm gonna take a chance!' I'd known her since she was born, and she was always takin' chances.

"Her dad wasn't ever any good, Lem Sparks wasn't. He run the printin' office here and got out the weekly paper, and Ruby set type for him in the office. Once, when Ruby was about seventeen, Lem needed a flat stone to make up his type on, and he sneaked down to the graveyard one night with a wagon and come back with a stone and put it onto a frame with the lettered side down. Lem must 'a' misjudged the location of the graves somewhat, or something, for it was his own first wife's stone he brought back, which *her* dad and not Lem had put up. And Ruby set type and made it up over that stone for months and never knew it was her own mother's. And then one day she felt letters on the other side, and felt along and found out. When her dad come in she picked up a bucket full of lye-water they used to clean type with, and poised it up to douse him in the face.

"'You sling that in my eyes,' says he, 'and I'll break your neck.'

" 'I'll take a chance on that,' says Ruby, and let him have it; and she marched out and married Elbert Perkins that everybody had warned her against. She said she'd take a chance on Elbert. But when he failed in business on account of not being able to carry his liquor like a man he told her she'd have to go back and set type in her dad's printing office again. Ruby hit him with the stick she was stirrin' the wash with at the time, and run away with a travellin' piano tuner. And it wasn't so long after that she took still another chance. I seen her myself on a trip I made to New York City; she was happy and doin' well, she said, and was then married to one of these human fly fellers that climbs up buildings for a living, Elbert having died.

" 'The thing I like about him is, he ain't afraid to take a chance, Uncle Clem,' she says to me; for she always used to call me Uncle Clem. And when he fell off a building and squashed himself she come back here and got a job in Jake's hotel. You couldn't help likin' Ruby, she was so cheerful and enterprisin'; and when she said she'd take a chance on old Jason's way of livin' I knowed she understood just the kind of fun he got out of it. There wasn't nothing but sixty years of age to separate 'em; and what's sixty years to a peetryarch that hears the turtles singin'?

"A week or so after old Jason first told us about the turtles Jake and me was sittin' in the corner of the dinin' room kind o' late one night, having a little drink, and the door from the street swings open sudden and in comes Molly Tucker.

"'Come on, you two,' says Molly, 'I want you two for witnesses.'

"'To what?' says Jake.

"'You come on over to Judge Bill Wilson's office,' she says.

"And we follered her there.

"Ruby Sparks and Judge Wilson and Jason himself was already there, and we could see somethin' serious had been goin' on.

"'Now, then,' Molly says to Jake and me, 'I want you to tell this woman here whether I'm married to Jason Tucker or not. Her and this lyin' Judge Bill Wilson are tryin' to fix it that I ain't.'

"It seems Ruby had inquired about that general weddin' in the swamp, and gone and asked Judge Bill Wilson if it was legal. The Judge had said it wasn't, and they'd all got together for this show-down.

"'Well,' says I to Molly. 'I can witness that I seen Judge Bill Wilson marry the whole swamp, that Sunday afternoon; but as to whether it was legal or not, I don't know. I often wondered.'

"'Me, too,' says Jake Smith.

"'This wicked old Jason Tucker,' says Molly to me, 'come and asked me to divorce him a week ago, and I got out of him what was in his wicked, crazy old head about this painted Jezebel here. And *now* they're sayin' he don't need a divorce because we weren't ever married. I'll swear him into the asylum for craziness,' says she, 'afore I'll see all that land go to that huzzy there with the red onto her lips!'

"'Don't call me names, please,' says Ruby. She spoke sweet and quiet-like, but anybody that knowed her could see that underneath she was mad. 'And I don't want Jason's land. You can have all of it, for all of me. But I do want to see him livin' on it, as long as he lives.'

"'I'm going to dreen it!' says Molly Tucker. 'It's been waste and wicked long enough! I'm goin' to clear out that lousy, low-lived tribe of wicked, carousin' good-for-nothings, every last one of them, and dreen that land and sell it, and my husband and me are goin' to move to town and live like white folks orter.'

"Jason hadn't said nothing, so fur, but now he kind o' shuddered, and he says in a low voice:

"'Dreen my swamp, Molly? You know I couldn't live without it!'

"'It don't stand to reason you could live forever, anyhow,' says Molly, 'the kind of life you've led! And you're comin' to town and pass your last days respectable and sober and try and make up a little for all the harm you done in the world. Either that, or I'll swear you into the asylum for craziness. A man of your age, tryin' to put his lawful wife aside and wed a painted Jezebel! I could get plenty of evidence you been crazy for years!'

"Jake and me looked at each other, and we both knowed mebby she could get away with that, and so did Judge Bill Wilson. For Jason wasn't understood generally, like a few of us understood him;

and always there had been some around town that called him 'Crazy Jase.'

"Ruby, she leaned over and patted Jason on the shoulder, like he was a pet bear or something, and she says:

"'Don't you worry, Old-Timer! You're not goin' to die so soon as all that. You got a lot of barbecues and dances comin' to you yet. And when you do kick in, it's goin' to be right there in your own woods, with me stickin' around, mebby.'

"'And the turtles singin',' says Jake Smith; but nobody but me and Jase knowed what he meant.

"'I always kind o' liked you, old Rough Neck,' says Ruby, laughin' at Jason.

"And you could see she really did. The whole idear of him and his woods and his tribe tickled Ruby. She was like that. I ain't sayin' she was altogether honest when she said she didn't want any of his land at all. But she did want to see him livin' on that land, wild and free, as long as there was life in him. And there was a lot of life in him yet, too.

"'Molly,' says Judge Bill Wilson, right serious, 'you keep saying what you're going to do, and what you're not going to do, with that land and with Jason, and the plain facts are that you can't do anything but what Jason wants to do. You're not the boss of that property. Jason is.'

"'I am,' says Molly. 'I'm his wife, and he's got to do what I tell him, or I'll lock him up for craziness!'

"'Molly,' says Jason, 'I offered to be fair with you. I'll give you a third of that land. You can have it willed to you now, so you'll get it when I die.'

" 'Yes, and have that woman there make you change your will, as soon as I've signed the quittance papers!' says Molly. 'I got a third comin' to me, as your lawful wife, and I'll have it deeded to me now, along with another third, afore I give you up to marry her.'

" 'If I deed it to you now, you'd cut it up and dreen it,' says Jason, 'and spoil my country.'

" 'That's what I'll do,' says Molly.

"Nobody said anything for a minute, and then Jason says, slow and thoughtful:

" 'More'n likely you'd 'a' had every acre of it, Molly, to do what you liked with when I'm gone, if you hadn't acted so mean the last four or five years. You used to be as full of fun as anybody. But you nearly pestered me to death lately. Every time I throwed my lip over a dipper of whiskey you told me I was bound to Hades. Every time we had a dance or a barbecue, you've flopped onto your knees and tried to pray the fun away. You pestered me to wear collars, and you pestered me to wear vests, and you pestered me to cut my hair, and you acted like hell had broke loose every time I cussed a little, and you jawed me and worried me and shot off your mouth about wickedness and sinfulness till you made my life a burden to me. And every time we bet on a wrasslin' match or a footrace or a turkey-shoot you got up and told us all we was goin' to be damned forever for the sin of gamblin'. It's been gettin' so I was nigh afraid to sneeze out there for fear I'd get told there was Satan's brimstone in my nose. I tell you free and fair, Molly, that there's been fifty times I would 'a' chased you from my cabin, if I hadn't been married to you.'

" 'You aren't married to her,' says Judge Bill Wilson.

" 'Why ain't he, then?' says Molly, her eyes blazin'. 'He told you to marry us legal, and we both thought you had. If we ain't married, it's your fault, Judge Bill Wilson. Was you bribed not to do it right, or something? That's a pretty story, comin' from you, Bill Wilson, that we ain't married! We are, too.'

" 'Yes,' says Jason, lookin' at Judge Bill Wilson, 'how come, Judge? Molly's right about that. We both thought we was wedded legal.'

"Judge Bill Wilson hawked and cleared his throat and acted right uncomfortable for a minute, and then he says:

" 'I know it's my fault. I was plumb foolish— we'd all had a couple of drinks that afternoon, and it seemed to me like it would be a good joke to marry the whole swamp together. I thought everybody took it more or less as a joke.' And he looked at me and Jake.

" 'I never knowed how to take it,' I says.

" 'I didn't hear any turtles singin' that afternoon,' says Jake, 'but the night of the fire everything else was.'

" 'Joke!' says Molly. 'It was a weddin'!'

" 'No,' says Judge Bill Wilson, 'you can't marry a whole community together that way, and make it stick. I've looked it up since then . . . here lately. You two are not married. You haven't even got a case against Jase as his common-law wife, Molly. He lived with five other women, and called each one his wife, before he took up with you. And a half dozen of the children, and two of the women are living yet. That's where you stand, Molly, and you'd have no case in a court.'

" 'See here, all of you,' said Jason. 'I'm gonna do the right thing by Molly. Mebby it wasn't legal, but I intended it should be, and I'm a gonna stick by my moral intentions, just the same. I'm a gonna will her one-third of my property, which she'll get after I've demised into my grave.'

" 'I'll have it deeded to me *now,* not one-third, but *two*-thirds,' says Molly, 'and he sha'n't marry that woman there until I get it!'

"And then she turned toward Judge Wilson and fairly screamed:

" 'What kind of a judge are you, Bill Wilson, goin' around the country makin' mock marriages! Fifty mock marriages of innocent people all in one afternoon! If you don't let my weddin' stand, I'll ruin you, Bill Wilson! Makin' weddin's, and sayin' they were legal, and lettin' people live together and raise families for years, and then tellin' 'em it was a joke, because you'd been drinkin' whiskey! I'll go into court with you any day on that, Bill Wilson! You suppose the people in this county would have you on the bench again? You can't run for the office of dog-ketcher in this county after I've got through with you, Bill Wilson! You're runnin' for the State Senate right now, on the Republican ticket, and I'll lick you with that story if you make a single move against my marriage! Women's got the ballot now! And there won't be a town or a crossroads or a farmhouse in this county where I don't tell that story of you makin' mock marriages when you're drunk, Bill Wilson, and you a judge on the bench, trusted by innocent people. Just *say* I ain't married! *Say* it! Say it private, or say it public, or say it in court, and I'll tell 'em why I ain't! I'll tell every man and woman in three counties why I ain't! I'll tell 'em! I got you licked, Bill Wilson!'

"Nobody said anything for quite a spell. Judge Bill Wilson was a good pal of Jake's and mine, and old Jase's, and we didn't like to see him licked. But it looked as if Molly had him. And he must 'a' thought so, too. For pretty soon he said:

" 'You've got me, Molly. As far as I'm concerned, personally, I'm out of it. You're right. I couldn't afford to be dragged into a court, on any kind of action, and testify that I'd made a mock marriage, with three drinks of whiskey in me, and let people think it was legal—all on account of a sense of humour. A court wouldn't understand it. And the voters wouldn't understand it. You've got me licked. What's next?'

" 'The next thing,' says Molly, 'is that I'm going to have two-thirds of that land deeded to me. And after that, he can have his divorce and marry that huzzy there, if he wants to. A third of it's enough for them—too much!'

" 'Thanks,' says Ruby, smiling.

" 'I'll have them deeds,' yells Molly, excited again, and her eyes glitterin', and her whole body shakin', 'and I'll oust that low-life gang, and dreen that land! It's mine, now! I'll cut it up, and have decent farms in there, and law-abidin' people, and a meetin'-house, and a preacher, to pray out of it all the hell and corruption of the last hundred years! I've waited for it and prayed for it and fought for it for years, and now I've *got* it! I'll have them deeds, or I'll ruin *you*, Bill Wilson, and send *you* to the crazy-farm, Jase Tucker!'

"And with that she went out. Nobody spoke for a while, and then Ruby says:

" 'Which of you sweet old kids has got a cigarette?'

"Judge Bill Wilson give her one, and she lit it, and took a couple of deep inhales, and then she laughed and blowed smoke through old Jason's whiskers, and says:

" 'Now, then, Davy Crockett, don't look so serious!'

" 'It is serious,' says Jason. 'She means it. I've a notion to foller after her, and twist her neck!'

" 'Nothing of the sort, Robinson Crusoe,' says Ruby, 'they *would* put you in the crazy-house then, for sure. And don't sign any papers, either. When she raves about those deeds, make promises, and put her off, and make more promises. Don't any of you sign anything, or say anything, or do anything—or buy, sell, plant, sow, make bargains, marry, or go on journeys—until you hear from me, and I tell you the moon's right for it. I'm going to bed.' And with that she went out.

"'All on account of turtles singin' in the moonlight,' says Jake Smith, as him and me left Judge Bill Wilson's office.

"It was six weeks after that was the election. I hadn't heard nothin' more of Jason and his affairs; neither Jake Smith nor me asked Ruby anything. And as for Jason, he kept away from town. I guess Judge Bill Wilson heaved a sigh of relief when Election Day come and Molly hadn't told her story. He wasn't so easy about the election, anyhow. The other two counties in the district went Republican oftener than they did Democrat, but here in our home county it was the teeteringest thing you ever seen—one time Democrat and the next time Republican.

"Election Day was fine, and the voting was early. The polls didn't close until six o'clock, but by four in the afternoon it looked as if almost everybody in the district had cast their ballots that was going to. Judge Bill Wilson and some of his friends, including Jake and me, was in the hotel parlour up there, and we had been getting reports all afternoon, by telephone and telegraph, and it was a darned close thing, at five in the afternoon, accordin' to the estimates from all over. A hundred or so votes one way or the other might swing it. It's the evenest district in the State, anyhow, and always was.

"At five o'clock, while we was sitting up there, in comes Ruby. And old Jason was follering her.

'Judge, we want to talk to you a minute,' she says.

"All the rest of us got up to go out.

" 'Jake, you and Uncle Clem stay here,' she says. 'I may need you.'

"And when the rest of 'em was gone she pulled a marriage license from her bag and said:

" 'Judge, Jason and me have come to get you to marry us.'

" 'Won't somebody else do as well as me, Ruby?' says Judge Wilson.

" 'No,' says Ruby, 'somebody else won't. Some day or other Molly *might* come into court, with some kind of a case, and tell about that joke weddin'. And it seems as if it's a case that could be made to stand or fall by the way *you* testified about it. But if you marry Jason and me here and now, I'll be pretty sure what your testimony would be.'

" 'She's got no case,' says the Judge. 'I told her so. There's only one way I could testify, and be honest, and that's against her.'

" 'Then marry us now,' says Ruby. 'Let's get it settled right now.'

" 'But if I marry you, then she *will* come into court,' says Judge Bill, 'and I'll have to confess publicly about performing that idiotic ceremony.'

" 'Some time or other that story's coming out on you, Judge,' says Ruby. 'The only question for you is, would you rather be *in* the State Senate when it comes out? Or would you rather be a man that had just been *licked* for the State Senate? Come to the window.'

"We follered her to the window and looked out.

In the square right in front there was the whole darned Tucker tribe—all but Molly. Ruby'd brought 'em in. The square was packed with 'em, men, women and children and dogs; the kids squalling in their mothers' arms and hanging onto their mothers' skirts. They'd never all been to town at one time before, and some of 'em hadn't never been to town in their lives. Out in the swamp they looked reasonable, but here in town, when they was all together, I must admit they was pretty wild and shaggy. But they were having a good time, laughing and singing and talking, and some of them were jigging and playing onto mouth-organs and Jew's-harps. The whole of the townspeople was gathered around the square, too, looking at them. When they seen Ruby and Jason at the window half a dozen of them yells to him: 'Which way, Gran'-pap, which way? What are we, Democrats or Republicans?'

" 'It ain't quite settled yet, which you be,' yells Jason. 'You just hold your horses a minute.'

" 'There's two hundred and eleven votes out there,' says Ruby, 'waiting to find out whether they're Democrats or Republicans.'

" 'Let me see that license, Ruby,' says Bill Wilson.

"And Jake and me was the witnesses.

"After the ceremony Jason steps to the window and yells out: 'You're Republicans!'

" 'Hooray! Hooray!' yells the Tucker tribe, laughin' and dancin' and jiggin' up and down and turnin' summersets and cartwheels, and the dogs jumpin' and barkin' in the street, as they moved toward the polling-place. 'Hooray for Gran'pap! Hooray for the Republican party! Get out of our way, here comes the Republicans! Hooray! Get out of the way! The Republicans is comin'!'

" 'Well,' says Judge Bill Wilson, looking out the window after them, 'it may be they'll fix *this* election for me. But Molly will kill me on the *next* one!'

" 'Don't worry about the next one,' says Ruby. 'You had to take a chance, and you took it.' And then she says: 'If it ever was to happen that I was the richest woman in this county, I'd maybe help you run for Congress some time, Judge.

" 'Come on now, old Teddy Bear,' she says to Jason, 'and be cheerful! Your swamp isn't going to be touched as long as you live. We'll get the tribe back home and pull a barbecue. You're all invited,' she says to us.

"It was two years after that old Jason was struck by lightnin' robbin' that crow's nest, for Ruby's kid and his. And when he died he left every acre to Ruby. She give every darned Tucker family forty acres, including Molly, and she sold the rest of it for enough to make herself a rich woman. As long as he lived she never let a ditch into that old peetryarch's swamp, nor an axe into his woods. She used to say to me: 'I'm kind o' crazy about old Santy Claus, Uncle Clem! He's like some old gazookus out of a story, Jason is.' "

"Where is she now?" I asked.

"In Paris," said Mr. Hawley. "And from what I've hearn from time to time she still hearkens to the turtles singin', and she's still a-takin' chances."

O'Meara, the Mayflower—
and Mrs. MacLirr

"It's a queer thing," said Terence O'Meara, with a wink at his brother Jack and a glance at the bald spot on the top of his father's head; "it's a queer thing that the Irish let the English and the French, the Spanish and the Dutch, all get ahead of them in exploring and settling America."

Mr. Timothy O'Meara, their father, had his face turned away from them, while he fumbled for a pipe-cleaner in the case of a great old clock that stood on the mantel. He grunted.

"I could never understand it myself," said Jack O'Meara, with an answering wink to his brother. "Why were none of the Irish great navigators?"

The senior O'Meara's bald spot suddenly flushed red, and the veins in it began to swell, and his sons, chuckling softly, knew just how his face would look when they saw it.

"Why were none of them discoverers?" continued Jack rhetorically. "Great sailors, or great whalers, or notable pioneers?"

Mr. Timothy O'Meara turned slowly and impressively toward them, where they sat at the table over their after-dinner pipes and coffee, and scorn made streaks and lines through the heat of his

351

countenance. But when he spoke it was with a measure of dignity.

"Shame to you both," said he, "and sorrow to me that has such sons! The greatest navigator of thim all, not aven barrin' Noah and his ark, was an Irishman! And the greatest whale-catcher of all times, not aven exceptin' Jonah, who used to proffer himself for bait, was an Irishman! Wan and the same Irishman they was, thim two, and his name was Timothy O'Meara, the same as me own, and my ancestor he was."

He suddenly tossed something hard upon the table, which he had taken out of the clock-case along with the pipe-cleaner, and the object rattled among the dishes.

"And what's that?" said Jack.

The young men were used to seeing their father take anything and everything out of that clock-case—valuable papers incidental to his contracting business, shirt-studs and shoe-strings, as well as bits of indeterminate junk of vast historical interest. Or, one might say, legendary interest, mythological interest, for the tales of Mr. O'Meara sometimes reeled and whirled and spun with an excess of imagination, as a muse might soar upon inebriate pinions. It was the delight of his sons to sting him to narration with insults; he usually retorted with an affectation of belief that his sons, who both had worthy records in the A.E.F., had really been dishonourably discharged from that organization.

"That," said Mr. O'Meara, "is a piece of Plymouth Rock. 'Twas chipped off by my ancestor,

Timothy O'Meara, the day he landed the *Mayflower* outfit there, and quit his many wanderin's, and sittled down to colonize New England and America. And it has been kept in the family ever since, as a memento of the occasion."

He had a way of excluding his sons from the illustrious family in his stories as if they were unworthy to bear the name of O'Meara. Terence looked at the bit of stone, and it seemed to him that it bore a certain resemblance to a piece of rock that had once come out of the clock-case as souvenir and evidence of the first gold discovery in California by a Timothy O'Meara. But he said nothing aloud. Internally he was asking himself:

"How the deuce is the old man going to get an Irish O'Meara aboard the *Mayflower?*"

There was a responsive wonder in Jack's countenance. Their father's visage was partially hidden again, as he bowed his head over his leisurely pipe-cleaning—if he was not wondering himself, he was at least arranging the details of his saga.

"Whales!" he murmured to himself, as he worked. "Whales!—not know whales? Of course he knew whales, did Tim O'Meara the navigator!"

Whales [said Mr. O'Meara, his pipe filled with plug-cut and drawing sweetly], whales are the most misunderstood of all God's craytures, by the common ginerality of mankind. The whale is the grandest and most intilligint and most ginerous of the bastes that roam the world, and it takes a large and noble nature to understand the whale—and a

353

large and noble nature was that of Timothy O'-
Meara, my ancestor, that I'm going to tell you about.
When the world was made, and the firmamint was
set up as siperates the hivens from the earth, the
whale was put into the seas and oceans, because
there is so much more wather than there is land;
and the nobility of the whale is fitted to a spacious
elemint. He floats in grandeur and magnificence
amidst the splendour of the icebergs at the pole,
and he leaps through the glory and power of the
hurricanes like a trout that is sportin' amongst the
ripples of a brook. He's a large baste with large
ideas, more intellictual than the iliphant, and with
a heart as tinder as wan of these little red-footed
pigeons on the roof.

For he isn't anny fish, the whale isn't, but he's
warm-blooded like a man or a dog, with more
gratitude than the wan and less suspicion than the
other—and I don't know why I'm sayin' "he" all the
time, for the faymale whales is equally mammalian
and ginteel.

'Twas this same Tim O'Meara I'm tellin' you of
that understood whales as no man has ever understood thim before or afther, for the solitude and
grandeur of the whale was in his own nature, and
the melancholy of the whale was in his wild and
tinder heart. And a roamer and a rover was this
Tim O'Meara, and the rims of his eyelids was red
with the salt of manny seas. 'Twas the woes of
Ireland that drove him from her shores, and set him
wanderin' here and there—the griefs of Ireland, and
the impossibility of doin' anything about thim, on

account of the Sassenach that was mainly causin' thim. I have no prejudices of anny kind in me heart against anny man nor anny man's country—unless a gineral feelin' that 'twould be a good deal betther if there wasn't anny British Empire annywheres could be called a prejudice. Which it could not, for 'tis merely good sinse and sound logic. And this Tim O'Meara, me ancestor, was the same as me in his feelin's.

"If I could but spake to the King of England, Ireland, and Scotland personal," says he to himself oftentimes, "we might patch somethin' up betwixt us. But I will not bandy words with anny man less than the king himsilf! 'Twould not be fittin' for thim to do so that was kings in Ireland in the ould days. If I had me rights, wan of the thrones that he's sittin' on this day would be mine!"

And 'twas at sea he lived mostly, for the shores of inhabited countries would always put him in mind he didn't have anny happy country of his own; and 'twas fishin' and whalin' that he made his most notable success at. Greenland and Iceland was known to him, and the coasts of Labrador, and manny a wild rock that was islanded lonesome in the wild seas. 'Twas often he would sit in his boat amongst the sparklin' icebergs, singin' to his Irish harp, and watchin' them Scandinavian fishers and whalers goin' back and forth 'twixt North America and Norway—for the bould men came and went and fished and came again for long years before anny man bothered with the notion of makin' anny sittlements over here.

And wan day whilst he was sittin' on wan of his lonely islands, singin' to the sea-gulls and the seals, he heard some great crayture bellowin' and moanin' and sighin' and whooshin' in the vicinity, and he clambered to an eminence of rock and gazed about him.

'Twas a big faymale whale, and she was rollin' her bulk about, and bangin' around and sprawlin' hersilf against a reef near by, which the ebbin' tide had lift uncovered.

"What's the baste doin'?" says Tim to himself. And then he realized she was moanin' with pain as she batthered herself and twisted against the crooked stones.

"She's scratchin' her back on the reef," says Tim. And it puzzled him, for he'd never heard these bastes had fleas. He got into his dory, and rowed out as near as he dared to the turmoil she was makin'. And then he saw that she was scratchin' her back indade.

Half a dozen broken harpoons was stickin' into it, and the intilligent animal was tryin' to get them caught and hooked amongst the crooked rocks of the reef and pull and scrape herself rid of thim.

"Poor crayture!" says Tim. For though he had hunted manny a wan of thim to its death, gradual he had come to sympathize with thim and pity thim, for it was gettin' to his mind that they're really tinder-hearted bastes, full of kindness and gintleness there ain't anny feasible way for them to expriss. "Poor crayture!" says Tim.

And just thin she cocked her eye in his direction,

the poor sufferin' mammalian, and looked at him as speculative and considerin' and pitiful as a stray pup with a thorn in his foot. And she lay quiet and moaned.

"Do ye want me to pull thim out, ma'am?" says Tim, his heart bleedin' for her.

There was somethin' so respictable-lookin' about her, like she might be the mother of ten childher, all bloated up with cares and nursin' and tay-drinkin' and housework, that he couldn't hilp callin' her ma'am.

She moaned again, and looked at him steady—a whale bein' the only wan of God's other craytures that can look a Christian steady in the eye and give him thought for thought. And that way they continued to gaze at aich other for some minutes, and the kindness that was in the heart of aich wan pinitrated to the bosom of the other—and there ain't anny matronly crayture annywheres that has an ampler bosom than a faymale whale.

"I'll do it, ma'am," says Timothy O'Meara, as she moaned again, and he stipped aboord of her and begun pullin' out harpoons.

"Roll over a bit, till I get that ugly divil out of your side," says Tim. And, as if she understood, she rolled a bit, standin' the pain of all this extraction with the gallantry and fortitude of a woman. He blushed when he saw 'twas one of his own old harpoons, with his initials in the shaft of it.

"And I'd axe your pardon, ma'am, if I thought ye remembered," says Tim; "I would that—Mrs. MacLirr!"

357

For it came to him with a rush and a shout what the name of the baste should be. The old and ancient Irish deity of the boundless seas, before Saint Patrick came and made us Christians (praise God!), was Mananan MacLirr, and this hugeous and intilligent baste, Timothy perceived, could be none other thin the wife of Mananan MacLirr, she herself. And 'twas always Mrs. MacLirr he called her ever afther that.

"Now, thin, Mrs. MacLirr," says Tim, "there's but one more, and I'll be as aisy as I can!"

But 'twas nearly Tim's destruction, for when Mrs. MacLirr felt the last barb lave her body she gave such a jump of joy and gratitude as took her twinty fathoms toward the smilin' sun, and down again she spanked her two thousand hundherdweight into the wather, while the bould Tim wint whirlin' through a flock of screamin' gulls.

Back he swum to land, and from the beach he saw her out at sea, leapin' and cavortin' in her joy, and blowin' great fountains into the air.

And then she came as near as she could to the shore where she saw him standin'. And she poked first one eye out of the wather and thin the other, and she rolled and capered—tryin' to thank him, she was.

"Don't mintion it, Mrs. MacLirr!" says Tim, smilin' at the poor crayture, and at the same time feelin' the pathos of her, too. For 'tis one of the most touchin' things about a whale that she has inside of her the sprightliness and coyness and good humour of a pup or a kitten, and wants to frolic and

358

fawn and cuddle in her friends' laps; and, coupled with that, she has the bulk of an ocean liner.

If I hadn't heard it from me own grandfather and he from his grandad before him, and so by word of mouth down a line of O'Mearas, I would find it hard mesilf to belave all the details of the fri'ndship that grew up between Mrs. MacLirr and Timothy O'Meara. On all his voyages hither and yon she accompanied him and 'twas for her sake he give up huntin' whales entirely. It was through her introduction and patronage that he became acquainted in a friendly way with manny another of thim splendid and poetic lords of the briny Atlantic.

Often he would sit in a cave on a rocky island playing the wild traditional music on his Irish harp, and singin' his Gaelic songs across the waves, with the aurora borealis hangin' over him like a halo, and Mrs. MacLirr leapin' in the moonlight. And sometimes as manny as twinty or thirty of her friends would join her for a social avenin'—over whole leagues of tameless wather the harp of the O'Meara would be flingin' its strains of music and the sea would be spoutin' and boilin' with the magnificent dances of the whales, and misty moonbeams driftin' over all!

He made a kind of a harness that fitted over Mrs. MacLirr's big head and fastened his boat to it with a rope, and he gave up sailin' entirely, for it was slow work and useless compared with the propulsion and the power that was now at his command. Or sometimes he would sit upon her back with the boat trailin' along behind and guide her by tappin' her on one side of the head or the other, like wan of thim Orientals does with an iliphant. And a fine sight it must have been to see Mrs. MacLirr and me ancestor, Timothy O'Meara, ridin' a storm—with Timothy singin' and playin' his wild minstrelsy out of his wild heart, and the forked tongues of lightnin' showing the gleeful eyes of Mrs. MacLirr and the floatin' red beard and hair of Timothy O'Meara as they bulged across the boilin' seas.

One time ('twas in the winter of 1620 anno domino is the word as it came down to me), Mrs. MacLirr and me bould ancestor were cruisin' quietly along about sunset, two or three hundherd miles due east of the prisint site of Boston, when what should they see limpin' up from the horizon like a draggled-wing duck but one of thim small ships.

Timothy could tell aven at that distance that she was some sort of a family ship with but little nautical knowledge aboord of her anywheres, from the way she was bein' handled, and he steered Mrs. MacLirr nearer to her.

It was very near indade he got before aither of thim was noticed by the people on board, for there was some kind of a row goin' on in the midst of this little windjammer that previnted anny of thim from takin' notice. Tim circled round her and came up behind and he noticed a sign-board on the stern with the word *Mayflower* painted onto it with big letters. And just about the time he noticed that, Mrs. MacLirr, bein' full of fayminine curiosity, cocked her starboard eye over the rail of the vissil to take a look at what was transpirin' on the deck.

And at the same time she opened her mouth to smile, bein' friendly by nature, and no longer frightened at the ways and works of humankind.

Anny wan that ain't used to havin' a whale ogle him in the eye and raise up and smile at him is apt to be narvous at the first expariance. And the people on boord the *Mayflower* are scarcely to be blamed for not realizin' the beneficince of Mrs. MacLirr's interest, for her lineamints was decaivin'.

There was one gineral shout from the scores of people gathered on the deck and they scurried in all directions. But they couldn't run far, for the ship was small. And all the time they was cryin' out.

"A witch! A witch!" Timothy heard a dozen of thim callin' at the same time.

"She is a witch and she has called up a fiend out of the deep to save her!" says wan man.

"'Tis the devil ridin' upon a dragon!" says another.

Tim, he leapt to the deck, and he walked right up to a solemn-lookin' man in black, who was standin' steady, with a hymn-book in wan hand and a soord in the other, apparently too proud to let himself be scairt, and he says to him very polite, says Tim:

"I'm the O'Meara, at your service, sir; and I am not plased with bein' mistook for the divil. I'll thank ye, sir, to ordher these people of yours to be more civil, or else there'll be trouble aboord the *Mayflower*. I take ye for the boss of this outfit, and I speak to ye as such."

"Mr. O'Meara," says this fella with the soord, "your appearance was the trifle unexpicted, as ye come red-bearded on that monster out of th' bloody wathers of the sunset. And I was shaken m'silf for a moment, albeit I have fought both man and fiend. And ye came on us dazzlin' like the flames of Tophet," says he, "at a time when we were considerin' most serious matters of a ghostly nature."

"Be that as it may," says Tim, "go aisy with the divil stuff, or ye'll have to lave my part of the ocean. I'm a sinsitive man, and I will not be miscalled out of me name. And what are these serious matters of yours?"

The man with the soord pointed to a lass that Tim now noticed for the first time.

Standin' by the mast she was, gold-haired and beautiful, with her chin in the air and a fire in her eyes. He seen manny of that ship's company was against her, and his heart wint out to her at wance, as was ever the case with Tim O'Meara whin he seen virtue and beauty in distress.

"She is on trial," says the man with the soord.

"She's innocint!" says Tim, prompt as a fist. "What's she charged with?"

"She whistled like a man," says he, "and that is an unseemly thing in a maiden. And she danced with her shadow as one possessed by demons might. And when one of the cocks crew, she crew again like a cock."

"What great matther is all this!" says Tim.

"Is this not the Sabbath day?" says he.

"Ye have the advantage of me there," says Tim. " 'Tis more than a year since I lost count. Come hither, colleen!"

The girl came forward, and she looked Tim straight between the eyes. And all the ship's company gathered as near as they dared, for their fright still clung to them.

"Are ye guilty of these terrible crimes, as charged, my dear?" says Tim, smilin' at the darlin' thing.

"The sunshine seemed good," says she, smilin' back at him, "and I cut a bit of a caper on the deck."

There was a groan wint up from manny on that ship, but Tim and this swate crayture was lookin' so intintly at wan another they never heeded it.

"They were plannin' to duck me over the side," said she, "and I cried out for help. And then you came, and they said I was a witch and had called up a fiend from the seas!"

Tim, his forehead turned as red as his hair with exasperation. "Fine doin's this is!" says he, turnin' on thim all. "Where do you come from?"

They tould him they was fleein' from England.

"'Tis more or less me own case," says Tim. "There's much in common between us—though I'll be damned if I can precisely put the name on it! At anny rate," says he, "we're both at outs with England—and that's somethin'! Drop this nonsinse about the colleen here, and I'll let ye sail the rest of the way acrost me ocean," he says. "But otherwise," says he, "Mrs. MacLirr and me will have siviral things to say to youse."

"Mrs. MacLirr?" says the man with the soord.

"Me pet whale there," says Tim.

They all turned toward her, where she was

loomin' over the port side of the vissil, waitin' on Tim's word—and Tim noticed a curious thing: Mrs. MacLirr's eye was fastened in a stare upon the lass that Tim was befri'ndin', and there was a glint like 'twas jealousy in her look. And the girl looked back at Mrs. MacLirr with no friendliness in her gaze.

When they seen Mrs. MacLirr lookin' like that, and the girl lookin' back at her, the anxiety of thim Mayflowers was aroused again.

"Burn her!" says wan ould woman, with the shriek of a banshee in her voice. "Burn Mary Mullins—she's a witch!" And manny of the rist of thim began to murmur and repate it.

"Mrs. MacLirr," says Tim, "will you kindly open your mouth a few fathoms?"

And whin she done so he pointed at it loomin' forninst the ship there, and he says: "If there is anny more talk about burnin' this young woman, or about witchcraft," says he, "into that mouth ye go, two at a time, as fast as I can throw ye from the deck here!"

And with Mrs. MacLirr dominatin' the situation in that way, Timothy had the trump hand for the minute. But at the same time he was worried, for his words and actions only seemed to make thim the surer that there must be witchcraft somewheres about, and that Mary Mullins had called him up by the power of witchcraft to save her.

He called her to one side, and he bade the others to stand back while he conferred with her—and as

364

he done so he realized that the circumstance looked bad in itself, in the eyes of the ship's company.

"Mary Mullins, my dear," says he, "I don't seem to be really helpin' you anny, with all the will in the world to do so. But there's wan thing certain, there's none shall burn ye, my child, while Timothy O'Meara is bossin' this part of the ocean!"

She laughed and she said: "Thank ye, Mr. O'Meara! And they wouldn't dare try to, annyhow, on the ship here. They couldn't do it without burnin' the ship. It's a function they will have to postpone until we land somewheres."

"By the Lord," says Tim, "thin they'll niver land! I'll take ye aboord Mrs. MacLirr with me, and we'll batther the ould tub to pieces!"

"Ye'll not do that," says she, "for there's manny good people on boord here."

"That's what's the matther with thim evidently," says Tim, "they're too good!"

She laughed at that again, and thin she said: "No, Mr. O'Meara, I mane manny fine men and women, that would have nothin' to do whatever with this witchcraft idea if they were not scared to death. There's me sister Priscilla," she says, "as swate a girl as iver lived; and there's a couple of young men as is tryin' to shine up to her—dacent people, all of thim. And they'll have to be landed," says she, "or we'll never get the United States of America started."

"Mary Mullins," says Tim, "how did ye come by that name? It sounds Irish to me."

365

"There must be Irish blood in us somewheres, Tim," says she, "or how could we have the name? And I think 'tis that Irish blood they're mistakin' for diviltry," says she. "They don't understand laughin' and dancin' and fancifulness."

And she smiled at me bould Tim, with the come-hither in her eyes—and there's no use postponin' the revelation anny longer; from that instant they was both madly in love with aich other.

"Moira," says Tim, just above a whisper, "by the hivens, I think 'tis a witch ye are, indade!"

"Tim," says she, in a low voice, laughin' and lookin' about her, "I belave ye have the rights of it! Sometimes I think I am!"

"'Tis somethin' to be carefully presarved, and not banished out of the world," says he.

He urged her once more to come with him at once. But she would not lave her sister behind her, nor anny other of the wans she liked.

"Tim," she says, "ye must be aisy with these people! For they'll niver get to land unless ye hilp thim. The rudder's gone from the ould tub now, and a bit of a gale would finish things."

"Come aboord Mrs. MacLirr with yer sister," says Tim, "and be damned to the rist of thim!"

"No," says she; "and while we're on the subject, I don't like this Mrs. MacLirr of yours anny too well. And by the looks of her, she doesn't like me!"

And Mrs. MacLirr was peerin' at Tim and Moira in a way to confirm that, her eyes red and jealous.

There wasn't but wan way that Tim could see— to stay aboord the ship with the colleen until it landed, to protect her, and thin to marry her and take her away. So he harnessed Mrs. MacLirr to the *Mayflower,* and he give her the signal full-speed-ahead, and whin the nixt morning came he drew up by the side of Plymouth Rock—the date he always remembered, 'twas the siventeenth of March, Patrick's Day. 'Tis written on that bit of rock somewheres, if it hasn't been rubbed off.

And Timothy and Moira climbed aboord Mrs. MacLirr and sailed off and was married and sittled South Boston, which was the first permanent sittlement in New England, and predominates with their kinsmen to this day. And if you don't belave that, go and look it up in the Boston tiliphone directory. And that's how the United States of America got its start, praise God!

And [said Jack] they lived happy in South Boston ever after!

I wish [said the old gentleman] as I could say the end was all happiness. But the truth is, it wasn't.

The most inordinate, unpleasant, and unraisonable jealousy sprung up betwixt Moira O'Meara and Mrs. MacLirr. For Tim, he went no more arovin', and Mrs. MacLirr used for to spout and caper in vain in the harbour below where the O'Mearas had built their house and was raisin' their childher. Tim, he paid but little attention to her; but Moira, she would call out to her now and thin: "Go away, you great ugly baste, you!" For well she knew that Mrs. MacLirr was trying to tempt her husband back to the wild, free life he'd lived before he married and sittled down, and that's a thing as no wife ever likes.

And wan spring Mrs. MacLirr disappeared, and ceased to haunt the harbour, and Moira believed she was rid of her, and of the menace of her, foriver. And as for Tim, with the fickleness of all men, he thought nothin' more about Mrs. MacLirr's tinder heart, wan way or the other, nor did he realize how bruised it was by his neglict. He should have known that the intilligent and sinsitive whale, bein' one of the most lovin' of all bastes, is therefore equally agitated whin 'tis insulted. For after Mrs. MacLirr had been gone six weeks, back she come one afthernoon, and a hundherd whales was with her!

'Twas in the afthernoon of a breezy day whin Tim and Moira seen thim comin' into the harbour, and 'twas a sight majestic and splendid to see these noble monsters of the spacious deep movin' forward in naval formation, jettin' great fountains into the air, which the wind whipped to spray and the sunlight wove into flauntin' rainbows.

"Tim," says his wife, turnin' pale, for she had recognized Mrs. MacLirr in the lead of thim, "they mane deviltry!"

"They do not," says Tim; "they're all my ould fri'nds! They've called on us for a bit of a frolic and some music!"

And he wint and got his harp, and sated himself upon a rock in front of his house, and out acrost the movin' wathers, he flung the wild music of his ancestors. And he sang the afthernoon away, and the rainbows ceased when the sun laid low and level in the sky, and all thim scores of great mammalians danced in the red sunset; they danced a dance that was like the sport of naked thunders in the caves above the firmamint where the ragin' storms is made.

"They intind no good," says Moira; "they're workin' thimselves up to do some mischief!"

"They're wild with joy," says Tim; "they've found the O'Meara and his music again!"

And he harped the sunset out, and with the twilight the wather changed from burnin' brass to silver, and he harped the twilight out, and with the gatherin' dusk the wather turned to fire again; a phosphorescent fire it was that spouted when they blew and rose and waved like plumes and fell again.

"'Tis hatred and revinge they are afther!" cried Moira.

"They come in love and fri'ndship!" says Tim, exalted with his ringin' harp.

And which it was, no wan iver knew. As the dark thickened they all turned in the sea as one whale, at a signal from Mrs. MacLirr, and came rushin' up the beach on the crest and reach of the risin' tide, as if they would fling themselves flamin' out of their fiery sea against the O'Meara house and the rocks on which it stood.

"The saints defend us!" screamed Moira, her knees turnin' wake and feeble.

Mrs. MacLirr was in the lead and comin' fast, but the wather receded from in under her far up the shore, and she hit her head against a point of rock, and groaned and died; and a dozen more was stranded and extinguished, perishin' like exploded rockets.

But Mrs. MacLirr, she give Tim just wan look before she died.

"I'm afraid," says Tim, lookin' melancholy at Mrs. MacLirr's remains, "that she's committed suicide out of a broken heart! Why couldn't ye have been nicer to her, Moira?"

"She tried to murther us all!" says Moira.

And nobody is quite sure to this day which the truth was. But it give Timothy and Moira somethin' to argue about for many years—which is always a handy thing in ivery marriage. But don't ayther wan of you iver tell me again that the Irish niver projuced anny great navigators, nor great sailors, nor great whalers, nor great pioneer settlers; or I'll take wan of youse over aich knee and larrup ye, as I have done often in the past and as I am still well able to do, praise God!

In the Bulrushes

"The thing I like about the Good Book," said Mr. Clem Hawley, otherwise known as the Old Soak, "is the way it keeps right on comin' true."

He was sitting, as he has sat a portion of each day for many years, weather permitting, in front of Smith's Palace Hotel, with his chair tilted back and his feet on the low veranda railing, observing and speculating upon a world with which, for the most part, he is at peace. Sometimes he reads the newspapers, but his favourite reading has always been the Good Book and the Almanacs which he picks up in the drug store.

"There ain't hardly a story in the Old Testament," he continues, "that I couldn't match up with a story that's happened right here in this village. And they keep right on a-happenin'. I'm sixty years old, and I been readin' the Good Book and lookin' round about me at this neighbourhood for most of them three score years; and when another three score years has come and gone and I been gathered into Abraham's bosom, the same kind o' stories will still be comin' true.—H'lo, Squire."

The salutation was for Squire Purdy, who nodded sourly and passed down the street and into the bank, of which he was president and cashier. Mr. Hawley looked after him with a distaste which matched the squire's own evident dislike.

"The Squire's idear about *me*," said Mr. Hawley, "is that I'm a Mammal of Iniquity; and he's more or less right about it, too. And my idear about the Squire is that *he's* a damned old Whited Sepulchre. We both always done more or less what we wanted to, but he's got away with it; and he's respectable and looked up to and a leadin' citizen, and all that. If you're *respectable* in this here town you can do what you please, and not get talked about. And if you *ain't* respectable it makes no difference how innocent your acts and motivations is—you'll get the worst of it, anything you do or say."

He paused and filled his corncob pipe, and got it to going. I knew there was a story somewhere in the back of his mind, but I also knew that it would be bad tactics to urge him to tell it. Either he would, or he wouldn't, as the notion took him; and if he saw that I was anxious he certainly wouldn't.

"One way to prove you're respectable in this town," he continued presently, "is not to associate too much with *me*. You seen the look Squire Purdy give me, mebby—like he'd been eatin' persimmons? If he was to look pleasant at me just once all the mammals of righteousness in town would think there was something wrong with his bank and go and take their money out."

He paused again, and his pipe began to bubble and chuckle, with that peculiar noise of the corncob pipe which has been allowed to fall into a condition of—unkemptness, shall I say? And the Old Soak chuckled himself, softly.

"Oncet I seen Squire Purdy in a situation, not to say a fix," he continued, "where if it had been anybody else he would 'a' been plumb ruined. But he repented his way out of it. And bein' respectable to start with, his repentance took the turn of makin' him more respectable. But for just a minute or two Squire Purdy and his respectability teetered onto the edge of destruction."

"Tell me about it," I ventured.

It was an error. I had displayed too much eagerness. The Old Soak looked at me with a blank gaze as if he didn't know what I was talking about. He is the only man I ever knew who chewed tobacco and smoked simultaneously, and now he took a chew from his plug and for ten minutes acted as if I were not in existence. Finally he said:

"Mebby you remember readin' in the Good Book about Moses bein' found in the bulrushes, and all the gossip around Egypt as to how it was he got there?"

I silently assented, thinking that now he would probably get back to Squire Purdy in his own roundabout way.

"It was Pharaoh's daughter that found him, and more'n likely she was a nice girl and everything;

but the gossips don't care. You can't tell those wise birds anything good about anybody. And the gossips in this here town are just like they was in Egypt thousands of years ago. Give 'em an inch and they'll take en ell.

"First and last, King Pharaoh of Egypt had a heap of trouble with Moses and the Children of Israel, which was descended direct off of the original Beegat tribes of the Bible.

"There was gay times in Egypt in the early days, and if it hadn't been for the Children of Israel King Pharaoh would 'a' been happy. The Children of Israel had been admitted into the land to build sepulchres and peerymids. If one king says he is goin' to have a peerymid the size of a barn, the next one says to watch his smoke, he will have one the size of two barns. And the next one would send for Uncle Hiram of Tyre and say, 'You seen what my ancestors has done? Well, expense is no object; you build me a sepulchre that will lay over all these past issues for size and style.' Well, this particular King Pharaoh says he is going to have the finest sepulchre yet, and at the least expense, and he tells the Children of Israel the straw they've been putting into the bricks runs up the expenses, and they gotta leave it out in the future.

"The head Child of Israel says to him, 'What shall we put in, instead of straw, boss?'

"King Pharaoh says, 'You can bite off your finger nails and put them in, for all I care; what I want is bricks. Or you can shave off your beards and put them in. I'm tired of seeing them Beegat beards of yours wavin' in the wind all over Egypt, anyhow.'

" 'That's rough talk, boss,' says the head Child of Israel, 'them beards is our glory from the times of Methoosalem on down through all the Beegats to Israel himself.'

"King Pharaoh got angered in his elements then, and he yelled out, 'You shave them beards and put 'em into the concrete mixer or just for the sake of argument I'll nick the necks of the entire Children of Israel and feed 'em to the royal ibexes!'

"One word led to another like that until the head Child of Israel says they are gonna beat it away from Egypt, and King Pharaoh turns onto his heel and walks back to the palace as mad as a fresh-caught bullhead and calls in his chief of police and says to him, 'How does it come you're letting those Children of Israel get so chesty? You been letting them eat fleshpots against my orders, instead of roots and yarbs and vegetation. How am I a-gonna get my peerymids and sepulchres built if that bunch walks out on me? What's the use of being a Pharaoh if you gotta take back talk from that whole Beegat tribe? Who's running Egypt, anyhow, them Beegat tribes, or me?'

" 'Well, Your Majesty,' says the chief of police, 'I'll tell you who comes pretty near runnin' Egypt. There's a young feller by the name of Moses comes pretty near runnin' Egypt.'

" 'Moses? Moses?' says King Pharaoh. 'Where have I heard that name before?'

" 'Around the palace, more'n likely,' says the chief of police.

"'You doan't mean that young feller my sister picked out of the bulrushes when Dad was Pharaoh and I was the Prince of Wales, do you?' says the King.

"'The same,' says the chief of police.

"'What do people say about that bird?' says King Pharaoh, cutting a look out of the corner of his eye at the chief of police.

"'Just for the sake of argument,' says the chief, 'I'd rather not say.'

"'Spill it,' says the King, 'or I'll nick your bean.'

"'Well, Your Majesty,' says the chief, 'Egypt is no exception to the rule that there's gossip everywhere. There has always been a good deal of talk about that bulrush story ever since the princess first pulled it. Nobody doubts she found him there, but the question is, *Who put him there?* Naturally, the gossip wouldn't be talked much around the royal palace here, nor where the Pharaoh family could hear it——'

"'That's enough,' says the Pharaoh, and he nicked his bean, and then sent the captain of the host to tell this young Moses to come into the judgment room.

"And the Pharaoh puts on his purple robes and fine linen and his crown onto his head, and climbs onto his throne, and when Moses comes in he looks a long time at him, like he is searchin' for family traits in his elements, and he says:

"'Just for the sake of argument, who runs this country?'

"'You do, Your Majesty,' says this Moses, who was a likely-lookin' young lad.

"'Humph!' says the King. 'I been hearin' that you and the other Children of Israel are gettin' so strong in Egypt there's some question about it.'

"'Well, Pharaoh,' says Moses, 'we ask nothing better than to leave.'

"'Don't answer me so uppity,' says the Pharaoh. 'Just for the sake of argyment, who the hell do you think you are?'

"'Your Majesty,' says Moses, 'I always left that more or less to the Pharaoh family to figure out for theirselves. The story around the palace is that my mother was one of the Children of Israel and put me into the bulrushes when the princess came down to the river to bathe, and then got herself picked for my nurse after I was adopted by the Pharaoh family.'

"'Well,' says King Pharaoh, 'if that's the story around the palace it must be the true story, ain't it?'

"'Of course,' says Moses. 'Of course, Uncle Pharaoh.'

"'Uncle?' roars Pharaoh, grabbing his sceptre like he is going to bean him.

"'Well,' says Moses, 'the princess always encouraged me to call you that, when nobody else was around.'

"The Pharaoh thought for a while, and then he says to Moses, 'You and me are gonna settle this question, once for all, right this afternoon. Egypt's been buzzin' with gossip for nearly twenty years, and I'm gonna find out the true facts.'

"So he sent for his sister, the princess, and for the nurse that had nursed Moses when he was a kid, and was said around the palace to be his mother. And he says to them:

"'One of you two has been gettin' away with somethin' for a long time. Which one is it? Which one of you is this uppity young Beegat's real mother?'

"'I am,' says the nurse, stepping forward.

"'There's been gossip,' says King Pharaoh, lookin' at his sister.

"'I hope you don't mean to insinuate that one of the Pharaoh family has been mixed up in it,' says the princess, very proud and haughty.

"'It's been insinuated,' says the King.

"'You insult me,' says the princess.

"'All right, then,' says the King. 'If he's no relation to the Pharaoh family let the execution proceed.' And he motioned to the captain of the guard, who pulled out his sword and stepped forward.

"'Execution!' cries both women, with one voice.

"'Uh-huh,' says King Pharaoh. 'This young feller has got the whole Children of Israel roused up to the point of walkin' out on me, and he's gonna be beheaded. Give me that weapon.'

"And while young Moses knelt down King Pharaoh heaved up the sword as if to smite off his head, and the princess screamed and throwed herself between him and the sword. King Pharaoh paused.

" 'Sister,' he says, 'I'm afraid you have given your-self away.'

" 'I just couldn't bear to see my old servant's son slaughtered,' says the princess.

" 'Of course,' says King Pharaoh. 'That's the story us Pharaohs always told, and that's the story we'll stick to. All I wanted was to find out the truth. You can all go now.' "

"Clem," I said to Mr. Hawley, "haven't you got two of the Bible stories mixed up together, some-how? That sounds to me a little like something that King Solomon did one time."

"Mebby Solomon did," said the Old Soak easily. "I wouldn't put it past Solomon. As a matter of fact, it probably was a regular stunt with all them old Bible kings and peetryarchs, when they wanted to find out who one of the young roosters around the palace really belonged to. There was some gay old birds in the early days; they done what they damned well pleased, and when they got fed up with it they went and repented.

"It all goes to show that sometimes gossip is right, and sometimes gossip is wrong. And you can't never tell which, unless some unusual circumstance comes along and brings the real truth to the surface.

"There was a case right here in this town seven or eight years ago that set all the gossips to rattlin' away just the same as they did in Egypt when the princess allowed she found that baby in the bul-rushes.

"Only this wasn't a princess. It was Elvira Semple, a girl that lived with her mother on the other side of the woods, right on the edge of the swamp, about a mile from the village.

"Elvira found a baby in a washtub one spring, so she and her mother said, floatin' in the water at the edge of the swamp, and took it home to raise. And, of course, all the gossips says to each other, 'Uh! Huh!' And on account of it bein' found in the swamp like that, among the rushes, of course everybody called it Moses.

"But Elvira stuck to her story so strong that them that wasn't dyed-in-the-wool gossips, wishin' ill luck to everybody, got to thinkin' probably she had told the truth, at that. For after all, it might be true. And nobody wished Elvira any particular harm. In fact, she was one of them kind of people you never thought much about unless you happened to see them. Her dad was dead, and she and her mother owned a little house and a few acres over on the edge of the swamp, and they raised pigs and chickens and vegetables, and they both hired out sometimes, as extry help at housework, and they done plain sewing, and got along somehow or other, and nobody paid much attention to 'em. Except on Sundays, when they was always both treated nice and polite when they went to church.

"Both of 'em was awful strong church women. Most of the women is, around here. My old woman is. She is always pesterin' me to jine, and as a matter of fact I *have* jined seven or eight times in the last thirty years, at revival meetin's. But I always backslide, for some reason or other. I enjoy a good hot revival meetin' as well as anybody else in the world, but I never go to church except when there is some excitement like that goin' on, in spite of the fact that I believe the Book from kiver to kiver. There's a kind of a sentiment, you might call it, against me among a good many of the church people here, on account of my takin' a drink when I feel like it. Time and again I have told 'em all, includin' Squire Purdy himself, that the old-time peetryarchs of the Good Book wasn't teetotallers, by no means, and that I'm willin' to model my life after theirs. But they ain't reasonable. Years ago they made up their minds in this town that I wasn't respectable, and nothin' I could do would change that verdict. I'm a mammal of iniquity, and everybody knows it.

"There's two churches here, of different denominations but everybody calls 'em simply the White Church and the Hill Church. If you belong regular and go regular to one of them you can do what you like here. My old woman, Matilda, belongs to the Hill Church, and so did Elvira Semple and her mother. A little while after young Moses was found into his tub a kind of a committee from the Hill Church went over to see Elvira and her mother. It was the Reverend Mr. Hoskins, the pastor of the church, and Squire Jonathan Purdy, that you seen lookin' at me a little while ago like I was the dirt under his feet, and Matilda, my old woman.

"Well, Matilda told me more or less of what happened on that visit. Mrs. Semple and Elvira just simply told a plain straight story of havin' found that baby in the bulrushes on a moonlight night, and hearin' of it cry, and takin' it home with 'em, and that's all there was to it. They told it so calm and so self-possessed, and so straightforward, that anybody would 'a' believed it, Matilda said, remindin' me that Squire Purdy wasn't never any too anxious to believe the best of anybody. He hadn't wanted to go as one of the church committee, Matilda said, in spite of bein' a deacon, and practically runnin' the church, bein' the richest and most prominent man in it. In fact, he just about runs the whole town.

"The next Sunday after that Mrs. Semple and Elvira was at church, and settin' down in one of the front pews, and the Reverend Mr. Hoskins preached a sermon on charity. It wasn't about *them*—and yet it *was*, too. He didn't mention them by name, but everybody knowed who he meant. He talked on what a deadly sin gossip and bearin' false witness was in a community, and said he hoped there would never be any innocent reputations destroyed in this town. And so on. And the upshot of it was that in a kind of semmy-official way, as the newspapers say, everybody got onto the fact that Mr. Hoskins and Squire Purdy and all the prominent members of the Hill Church was standin' by Elvira and was satisfied her story about young Moses was true.

"After that, for the most part, Elvira got away with it. Of course, some of the people in the White Church pretended they didn't believe it; for anything the Hill Church is for the White Church is usually against. You know how these churches work. If the White Church pulls a chicken supper, inside of two weeks the Hill Church pulls a sociable of some kind, or a raffle or a fair or something. And always when one of 'em starts a revival meetin', and starts to savin' the mammals of iniquity, includin' all us old backsliders, the other one follows suit. There ain't so many awful poor people in this town; that is to say, nearly everyone has enough to eat most of the time, and some sort of clothes to wear, and a roof of some kind or other over their heads. But a coupla families over by the swamp ain't doin' any too well, neither. Well, the Hill Church people is always givin' duds to 'em; and then the White Church people get het up and give 'em more duds; and them families has got so they don't have to work at all any more. They are what I call trained charioteers—educated up to live off'n charity. They have got so they consider themselves a slum, like in the big cities, and live contented and happy off'n the grub and duds that is shoved onto 'em, along with the reform.

"About five years ago, it was, the White Church had a most rippin' revival meetin'. It lasted more than a week, and quite a few was saved. They almost got me, for it had been six or eight years then since I had been converted. But no, I thinks to myself, I will wait and see what the Hill Church pulls. Because they're sure to follow up with something that lays over this. And I'm kinda loyal to Matilda, my old woman, too. She's fussed with me steady for over thirty years, about my drinkin', and gamblin', and evil ways generally; but whenever I do reform I always make it a point that I shall get

383

converted in her church. It never lasts long, and I guess I'm the only person in town that takes it serious when it hits me; but them is my sentiments about it, for a man owes somethin' to his wife. I always liked Matilda, in spite of the fact that there's a lot of things she's got no sense about. And a man ought to do something for his wife.

"Sure enough, the Hill Church went the White Church one better. They sent off and got a lady evangelist to help out. Miss Kit Carson, she called herself; and I'll say she was some blonde. Not only did she evangelize, but she played onto the cornet. She would start a revival hymn, and get 'em all to singin', and then she'd lead 'em with her cornet. The first meetin' I was into I could tell that Satan was goin' to get his come-uppance in our town before Miss Kit Carson got through with it.

"You know what them meetin's is like. The main aim is to get people to shouting and excited. And there's always half a dozen earnest workers belongin' to the church that goes up and down the aisles pleadin' with the sinners to come forward to the mercy seat, and urgin' 'em on, and startin' up prayers and testimonies, and gettin' the tumult and the hurly-burly to goin' good.

"This Miss Kit Carson could make a talk that would just naturally make you want to jine whether you believed in it or not; she could take the whole human race up by the slack of its pants and dangle it over hell fire, and the next minute you'd be cryin' over your mother's grave, whether your mother was dead or not. The first night I got a good deal of enjoyment out of watchin' Hennery Withers tryin' to hold onto himself. Hennery Withers and Newt Ackles was for years our two village atheists, and both of 'em proud as all get-out over it. Hennery and Newt was always askin' everybody, 'Where did Cain get his wife?' And one day I bunged up Hennery's eye right here in Jake Smith's barroom for sayin' Joshua didn't make the sun and moon stand still.

"I set right near Hennery while this Miss Carson was preachin', and I seen he was gettin' more and more excited, and whisperin' excited-like to himself.

"'Where did Cain, where did Cain, where did Cain, where did Cain get his wife?' he was mutterin' over and over, feverish and nervous, like he was tryin' to hold on tight to his unbelief; and then all of a sudden he got up and shouted right out loud, with a regular bellow and a scream:

"'Where did Cain get his wife?'

"And the next minute they had him onto his knees at the mourners' bench, a-weepin' and a-flingin' of himself about, something excruciatin' to look at.

"Of course, a revival meetin' that started out by convertin' the village atheist at the very openin' was bound to be a success. If I had been converted then it wouldn't 'a' caused no comment. In the first place, I wasn't an atheist. And in the second place, nobody would 'a' believed I would stick. Nothing I ever do makes me respectable. But with Hennery's conversion the thing warmed up; and by the third night people were coming from miles away.

"It was about the fourth or fifth night I stopped into Jake's place here to get a coupla shots of hooch before I went over to the church, thinkin' to myself if conversion's goin' to happen to me to-night I won't fight it off none, and I might as well be in a receptive mood. What I wanted to do was let it happen as quick as it would, and get it over with. I seen from the start I was doomed to it this time, and the longer you fight against it the harder it hits you. And after it had hit me I would let nature take its course, as at previous times. But while I was gettin' my hooch Al, Jake's bartender here, put me wise to something that give me quite a jolt. When Prohibition first come it derned near ruined Jake. Then he went into the bootleggin' game. And the fellow he got the money from to start into the bootleggin' game wasn't nobody else but old Squire Purdy himself!

"'The damned old whited sepulchre,' I says to myself, as I went along up to the Hill Church. For years a-talkin' temperance, and a-preachin' Prohibition—and then financin' Jake's bootleggin' game on the quiet! It's true he never took a drink himself, nor never smoked, neither, nor even used a cussword—but the derned old hypocrite! And there he would be in the church, testifyin' and exhortin', and pleadin' with sinners to come to the mourners' bench, and tellin' what his religion meant to him, and leadin' in prayer, and spreadin' his moral wings like a reg'lar bird of paradise, the biggest thing in that meetin' exceptin' the Reverend Hoskins and Miss Carson herself!

"And right enough, there he was. It made me contrary-like. Of course, I wouldn't tell on him. I wouldn't do nothing to queer the liquor game, anywheres. And Al wouldn't 'a' told me if he hadn't known I would be silent as the grave. Me and Jake and Al is like brothers; we tell each other everything.

"But it kind o' set me against the idea of gettin' converted that night, somehow. I wondered if he would come round and plead with me to go forward and repent. Probably, I thought, he would consider it his duty, even though him and me hated each other, and both knowed it.

"And he did. The preacher was exhortin' and pleadin' and cryin' out, and they were singin' verses of hymns, and the volunteers were settin' down by the sinners weepin' and exhortin' with 'em personal, and Squire Purdy came and slipped into the pew with me and slid his arm across my shoulders.

"'Brother Hawley,' he says, 'won't you come! Come forward! Come now, Brother Hawley, and give yourself to a better life! Don't fight against the impulse that's stirring in you! Don't fight against your good angel!'

"He's got a powerful voice, but it went into a kind of excited singsong when he spoke to me, and his face was working and twitching. I thinks to myself that this revival meetin' and church work probably means to him exactly what a few good drinks of liquor does to me.

"'Brother Purdy,' I says, 'I don't think I'm really fitten to be settin' here in this church.'

" 'Salvation is for sinners,' he says, 'Brother Hawley.'

" 'I know it, Brother Purdy,' I says humble-like. 'But I'm kinda 'shamed of myself—comin' here, like I have to-night, with several drinks aboard.'

"And I blowed my breath into his face, to show him.

" 'Not,' I said, 'but what it's good liquor. It's the best bootleg liquor that Jake Smith's had for some time.'

"He looked at me quick and suspicious, and I went on.

" 'Brother Purdy,' I says, 'you and me don't think alike about a lot of things; but I could tell the world if I wanted to that you're a kinder-hearted man than you let on to be. You got more sympathy and charity for us fellers that needs our drink, and knows drinkin' ain't really against the Good Book, than you pretend you got. If it wasn't for you and Jake Smith gettin' together on a feenancial plan, I don't know where I'd look for sympathy and charity. It's against your *principles,* liquor is, but you got a *heart* kinder than your principles.'

"He turned kind o' green around the mouth, and got up and left without saying anything more; but it didn't faze him long. In thirty seconds he was down by the mourners' bench leadin' in prayer, and his prayer was a revival sermon in itself.

"And then that revival meetin' really het up. I been to many of 'em. But I never seen nothing like that afore or since. That Miss Kit Carson had got 'em to swayin', and singin', and shoutin', and

388

weepin', all together. And, believe it or not, that church was swayin' and swingin' as the people swayed and swung!

"In time with 'em, I tell you! No, I don't ask you to believe it. I was in it, and I felt it, and I couldn't hardly believe it myself. But it was! It was beating like your pulse beats, that whole church was; throbbin' like you feel your veins a-throbbin', a-throbbin' and a-swayin' and a-swingin', and the people swayin' and swingin' with it—like power and sperrit and archangels had lifted of the building up into their arms, and were rocking it back and forth, and you could almost see and feel and hear the archangels that was doing it. Believe it or not, but I tell you I felt it.

"And then, all of a sudden, right in the midst of this there come a scream—a high, shrill woman's scream.

"It was so loud and so piercin' and so crazy-like that it even cut its way through all that noise and rumpus, and the singin' stopped and the prayin' and exhortin', and everybody turned toward the back of the church, in a sudden dead hush. A hush it was, but it was still filled with swing and pulse.

"But before the complete hush come the tail-end cry of one utterance, that was left for a second going on lonesome when the other voices stopped, came out distinct; and it was Squire Purdy crying: 'Repent, repent of your secret sins!'

"Then come the scream again, and there came staggering down the aisle toward the front of the church Elvira Semple.

"Her head was raised, and her arms was raised, and her hands were groping in the air in front of her, and she walked like a half-blind person, unsteady and faltering. And her hair was flying wide about her head, as if there was a breeze into it, or it was shot full of electricity. Her face was pale, as a usual thing, and she wasn't what you would call a terrible good-looker; but this time her face was flushed, and something made her beautiful.

" 'Moses! Moses! Moses!' she cried out, as she come staggerin' down the aisle.

"My old woman, Matilda, was settin' a couple of pews in front of me, and I heard her say: 'Don't call on the Old Testament, Elvira! Call on the New!'

" 'Moses, Moses is mine!' cried out Elvira, drawing nearer to the mourners' bench, 'Moses is mine.'

"I heard Matilda say to the woman next to her, 'She don't mean *Moses* is hers! She means *Jesus!*'

"But another scream interrupted her, and then Elvira cried out again that Moses was hers.

"She turned, down by the pulpit, and faced the whole church full, and I guess then, when they looked at her face, it came onto the whole church with a shock, just what she meant.

" 'Moses,' she said, 'is mine. I am a sinful woman and a liar! I didn't find him in the bulrushes! For three years I have lived a lie! Moses is mine! I can't stand it any longer. I must confess! I must confess!'

"And then she burst out weeping, and tried to talk through her weeping, but you couldn't understand her; and she went into hysterics.

"Squire Purdy was with her in a minute, and had his arm around her.

"'There, there, Sister Semple,' everybody heard him say, 'you will be pardoned for your transgressions! Let us kneel, and pray.'

"And him and the Reverend Mr. Hoskins made her kneel at the mourners' bench, and put their arms over her shoulders, to pray with her.

"But it appeared Elvira wasn't overly anxious to kneel, and she flounced up off her knees again, and flung Squire Purdy's arm away, and yelled:

"'Don't you put your hand over my mouth, Jonathan Purdy! I must confess! I will confess!'

"It kind o' dawned on me what might be comin', then; and I wondered if that old fox had thought he might be able to get her out of the church while she was still hysterical, and before she spilled everything. The hand over the mouth tipped everybody off.

"She flung her arms over Squire Purdy's neck, Elvira did, and yelled:

"'Let us confess, Jonathan! Let us confess together! The sin was ours, and the child is ours! Let us repent together!'

"Well, Squire Purdy's face was a little green when I spoke to him about Jake Smith a while before. But now it was greener. Maybe you noticed he has got quite a big Adam's apple. While the whole church looked at him that Adam's apple went up and down five times, like he was talking, but not a sound come out of his mouth. That was the minute I spoke of a while ago when I said that oncet Squire

Purdy and his respectability teetered on the verge of destruction. I bet he wished he hadn't been heard makin' that remark about the secret sins just a coupla minutes before. That didn't help the fix he was in, to any extent.

"The sixth time that Adam's apple went up and come down a voice made its utterance.

"'It is true,' said Squire Purdy, 'that once I made a false step. I ask the prayers of the congregation.'

"I draw a veil, as the fellow says, over the next immediate few minutes. There never was a more gorgeous repentin' bee in any church. And I don't need to tell you the upshot of it. So far from hurtin' Squire Purdy's respectability, it's helped it, the whole thing has. For everybody says how noble of him to confess publicly and marry her. Which, personal, I don't see as he had much choice in the matter. But it all goes to show, as I said before, if you're respectable you can get away with anything. And if you ain't, you can't get away with nothing."

The Old Soak paused. Then he chuckled, and continued: "You noticed that dirty look he give me a few minutes ago? He's never forgive me for what I said as he was passin' out of church that night. I took him by the hand and told him how noble he was; and then I says, in a low voice, so's no one else heard, 'Brother Purdy, you needn't be afraid that Jake or Al or me is a-gonna get hysterical and confess about your secret virtues like Elvira done about your secret sins.' He never liked me afore but he's liked me less since then."

"But," I said, "don't you think it is your public

duty, as a good citizen, to show him up as a boot-legger? You said he was a whited sepulchre."

"Mebby," said the Old Soak, cheerily. "Mebby it is. But I *ain't* a good citizen! I'm just a mammal of iniquity! And it's worked into a kind o' special arrangement between him and Jake and me whereby I get my liquor cheaper than most does."

Miss Higginbotham Declines

It was Jehovah's custom, when he came to New York, to put on the material appearance and manner of a member of the Union League Club; indeed, he used the club itself a great deal. Everyone there, doormen, members, servants and all, assumed that he was a member, in spite of the fact that no one knew his name.

"Who is that distinguished-looking elderly gentleman over there?" one member would murmur to another. "Don't look now, or he'll catch you looking."

"I *should* know," the questioner's friend would reply. "I've seen him about here for years, from time to time. But I'm ashamed to say I've forgotten his name, if I ever knew it. I believe he's an artist of some sort, who spends a great deal of his time in Europe."

Or the conjecture might be that he was a railroad magnate; or an international banker, retired from active service to humanity; or a philanthropist who had something to do with rubber plantations. Jehovah (who knew about all these conversations without troubling himself to listen) used to be mildly amused at some of the guesses.

No one ever asked him directly who he was; he was aware that there was a certain awesome quality at his command which prevented such inquiries, when he chose to employ it. But he was usually affable in his personal contacts; he was careful to put people at their ease; there was nothing offensive, either to members or servants, in the occasional condescensions of his attitude.

Young Twiller Van Durden, who was a painter, remarked one day last May when he was lunching at the club as his brother's guest: "There's something almost Olympian in that gentleman's manner."

The brother, Walter Van Durden, a very wealthy man of affairs, looked at Jehovah in silence for a moment, and said: "Almost? I should say, *quite!*" And then he added: "The queer thing about it is that we all seem a bit flattered when he notices us."

"Who is he?"

But Walter Van Durden was prevented from answering by a singular thing, which was afterward quite inexplicable to him: he and his brother suddenly found Jehovah making a third at their table. They did not know how he had got there. The manner of the transition was instantly erased from their recollection, if, indeed, it had ever had a place in their consciousness: one instant, Jehovah had been on the other side of the room, and the infinitesimal fraction of a second later he was seated with the Van Durdens, pleasantly conversing. And this strange thing had happened without any feeling of strangeness whatever. It was all quite right; it was attended neither by any sensation of physical surprise nor by any moment of merely social awkwardness.

Jehovah was taking notice of the younger Van Durden's question.

"You know me," he said, smiling, "better than you have always been willing to admit. You have always known me."

And this, at the moment, seemed somehow satisfactory; the question of a name or a business or a background in the world passed entirely from Twiller Van Durden's mind. It seemed to the two Van Durdens that this personage conversed with them for half an hour or so, but the substance which they carried away from the conversation was a heightened feeling of general well-being rather than any specific idea; and then he was gone. Gone, just as strangely and rightly as he had come. It was only some time later that they perceived the strangeness of it, and then they never commented on it, even to each other.

New York had been rather a problem to Jehovah for some time; a certain type of popular preacher was forever saying that, on account of its wickedness, it would certainly be destroyed (sooner or later) by divine wrath. Jehovah, of course, knew all about these prophecies; and he was aware likewise that he had exposed himself to covert criticism on the part of the more extreme religionists who were forever demanding the most frightful vengeances against peoples and cities with whom they were displeased. New York had a great many wicked people in it; he was obliged to admit the fact. And yet he hesitated to proceed to the extremes demanded by the popular hell-roaring prophets.

He was thinking about this, and about the vexatious problems presented to deity—so much greater in number and complexity than we mere human beings can have any conception of—on the day he lunched with the Van Durdens. He sat at one of the windows, and looked out at the tangle of traffic, and combed his shapely fingers through his carefully parted gray beard, and meditated.

A second flood, such as he had permitted Noah and his interesting family to escape? A flood preceded by a tidal wave, with the great trans-Atlantic liners battering themselves to pieces among the skyscrapers, and the warships from the Brooklyn Navy Yard left stranded on top of the Palisades on the New Jersey shore?

He might have done something of that sort in the old days, he reflected; people had seemed to expect such violent manifestations of physical force then—had seemed almost to *crave* them. Especially his prophets, and he had always liked to please his prophets, when it could be done not too unreasonably. But now, somehow, he shrank from the idea of a flood; he wondered if the change in general public opinion about that kind of thing had been affecting him, the last few centuries, more than he had realized. Certainly, he found himself with a growing disposition to avoid personal participation in anything of the nature of "rough stuff," as it was slangily called in this New York. The recent World War, he was glad to think, had been none of his doing; he hadn't started it, and he had kept away from it as much as a deity could and still not lose his influence entirely on a planet.

There was Sodom and Gomorrah—their destruction had been a terrible affair! He hadn't enjoyed it at the time, he had only done it because it was the right thing to do, and his supporters in that age had demanded it. And if you value your followers at all, you naturally want to do something for the people who do things for you; there is a sort of rough-and-ready politics of that nature in the universe which no anthropomorphic deity can afford utterly to disregard.

But destroying Sodom and Gomorrah, Jehovah reflected, had done no permanent good to mankind; there were plenty of places on any number of planets right now which were in just as bad a fix morally as Sodom and Gomorrah had ever been. And all those cities—he did not trouble himself to recall the names and dates—which he had destroyed, by fire and flood, earthquake and pestilence . . . what good had it done in the long run? People forgot the lesson; or skeptics persuaded them that Jehovah had had nothing to do with the matter.

No, decidedly, he would not destroy New York in that fashion. In the first place, he would get no personal gratification out of it; the picture rather revolted him. And in the second place, even if he were willing to do it himself, he was certain that public opinion would be against it. People might be pretty wicked and vicious in spots nowadays, but in one respect they certainly had improved: they weren't quite as savage in their demands for the complete, painful destruction of entire communities with whom they disagreed—the extreme religionists, and the more fervid patriots, of course, always excepted, and the professional warriors.

"I *wish* everybody would be good," murmured Jehovah, a little plaintively, as he stroked his neat beard and stared out the club window.

And then he fell to considering all the devices he had employed in the last few thousand years in order to persuade, or to compel, people to be good. And after some thought, it occurred to him that the one which had been, on the whole, the most successful had been sending his Only Begotten Son to this planet to give human beings an example of a life lived in consonance with the highest ideals.

Of course, Jesus hadn't been altogether understood. He had been crucified. But the ideas that he had promulgated had, to a very considerable extent, survived his crucifixion; and they had influenced millions of persons throughout several centuries in the most beneficent way. It was true that vast tracts of territory inhabited by enormous populations had never been appreciably influenced by the doctrines known as Christian; and in Christendom itself there was a good deal of lip-loyalty to Jesus that had nothing whatever behind it. The thing certainly hadn't been a complete success, in the sense of inspiring the whole population of the planet to an imitation of Jesus's idealism.

And yet, hadn't it been more of a success than anything else he had ever tried—in the way of spreading notions of kindliness, with here and there some rather notable results in the field of human conduct?

Suddenly Jehovah caught the idea he had been groping for—why not send *another* Begotten Son? It seemed so simple, now that he had thought of it, that he wondered it had not come to him sooner.

And should this one be born of a virgin, also? Jehovah pondered, and decided: Yes. Yes—people were used to that; they would accept it, therefore, the more readily. It had been his experience, in dealing with the human beings for whom he felt so much concern, and such a grave sense of respon- sibility, that a deity must not give them too many ideas all at the same time; it confuses them. Give them an idea and repeat it; repeat it endlessly, with great patience; do not vary its familiar form too greatly or too frequently . . . this is essential to its reception. They had had a Begotten Son born of a virgin; and if they got another Begotten Son, and he *wasn't* born of a virgin, as like as not they wouldn't think he was really a Begotten Son at all! He knew by experience that the idea of begetting juxtaposed to the idea of virginity wouldn't bother the crowds very much; although it was a paradox that had given himself some thought the first time it had occurred to him.

But *what* virgin?

The point seemed to him important. She must be a virgin of the most impeccable virginity; an unquestioned virgin; a virgin of whom it would be believed at once, merely by mentioning her name, that she *was* a virgin. There are a good many unmarried women nowadays who are not really virgins at all, and Jehovah is well aware of this, although some of these women act as if they don't know that Jehovah knows it, or don't care. Jehovah trifled for a while with the thought of an inherited virginity—that is, a virgin who was the daughter of a virgin who was herself the daughter of a virgin; a sort of virginity handed down from mother to daughter for several generations . . . (although, of course, "generations" couldn't be the word for it). But he put the thought from him: a virginal succession of this sort would be as easy for him to bring about as a single virgin birth; but it might have the air of trying to prove too much. He knew he could make it true, but could he make it convincing? No, he would give the people what they had already had, a Begotten Son born from a virgin, and they would accept it readily because they were familiar with the thought.

He thought of the very woman; and taking his light overcoat and hat and his carved malacca stick, he left the club at once. For with him, to think was to act.

"Washington Square," he told his driver, and entered the limousine which was waiting for him at the corner. And in a few minutes the car drew up at the curb in front of one of the good old houses which still stand on the north side of the Square; one of the few private residences still remaining in that block.

A Miss Higginbotham lived in the house; and she would live there until she died, no matter what might happen to the rest of the neighborhood, because she had been born there. She was a person who abhorred change of any sort, and for the most part she ignored it. Her ancestors had come to America in the *Mayflower* and had conspicuously helped in shaping the life of New England. Miss Higginbotham's father had been the first of the line to leave New England. Or, rather, he had attempted to bring as much of New England as he might with him to New York City; he did this because he felt it to be his duty, just as one of his brothers had gone as a missionary to the heathen of India.

Miss Higginbotham, needless to say, had no sympathy whatever with the notions professed by many of the younger women of New York today; but there was very little she could do to combat them—very little except to live her own sort of life with a more determined intensity. And she was upheld by her feeling that her kind of existence tallied with the ideals of many millions throughout America who contrive to make the quality of their puritanism heard and felt in spite of all the flagrant iniquity of the era.

Jehovah was ushered into a bright and sunny sitting room on the second floor at the front of the house, overlooking the Square. And he noticed with satisfaction the evidences of an exquisitely refined taste in the sparseness and chastity of the furnishing and decoration. Not that the mood was bleakly Lacedaemonian; on the contrary, one felt in it what one felt in the woman herself: a delicate selection of the objects upon which it might be worth while to glance and touch with the white flame of puritanism.

Jehovah proceeded at once to state the object of his visit.

Miss Higginbotham lifted to him a puzzled brow, and it was evident from the perplexity which clouded the clarity of her deep gray eyes that she did not really comprehend.

She had known Jehovah instantly; her perceptions were too keen to permit her to believe that any imposture was being attempted; and, indeed, there emanated from the presence of Jehovah a majesty and sincerity which made doubt impossible to anyone. It was plain to him that Miss Higginbotham's perplexity arose from the fact that she could not reconcile such a request with her habitual ideas of deity.

"It is an honor which I intend for you; you are to be rewarded above all other women of your place and time because of your purity and devotion," said Jehovah.

"Honored?" said Miss Higginbotham. And there was the faintest trace of asperity in the tone of her voice and upon her regularly beautiful features.

Jehovah thought he saw her difficulty.

"When I speak of another Begotten Son," said

Jehovah, reassuringly, "I do not mean to imply the necessity of any such communication as is usual between husband and wife. Do you understand me?"

Her blush showed that Miss Higginbotham had understood.

"This matter," continued Jehovah, "can be kept entirely an affair of the spirit."

"I do not see," replied Miss Higginbotham with a tremor of indignation, "that that makes the slightest difference!"

Jehovah regarded her with something like amazement, if it is proper to say that a deity can be amazed.

"Do you mean to say," he inquired, "that you *refuse,* Miss Higginbotham?"

"I mean to say," she replied, "that I consider myself most outrageously insulted!"

"But——" began Jehovah.

"Coming from you," she interrupted with a wail. "Oh, from *you!*" And she burst into tears.

Jehovah was too experienced in the moods of women, ancient and modern, to interrupt her paroxysm of weeping or to attempt to mitigate it until it had spent its force. It was he who had first had the idea of creating women; and even from the beginning, even from the days of Eve herself, he had remarked in them occasional inexplicabilities calculated to baffle deity itself. Moreover, he was not without sympathy for Miss Higginbotham; for he began to perceive that, while he did not as yet understand just *why* she should be so shocked at his proposal, yet the shock itself was genuine and not simulated.

He waited until she had returned to something like her former calm, and then he suggested gently: "You certainly do not think, Miss Higginbotham, that I would *deliberately* insult you?"

"Then," said she, steadying her voice, "why come to me at all with such a terrible proposal?"

She looked at him more grieved than angry now; and Jehovah suddenly realized that her outburst had proceeded from the very simple fact that she had been disappointed in him as a deity, disappointed in the quality of his morality. Disappointed as a child might be in someone he had been taught to trust and revere.

He smiled at her, and as he smiled the remainders of Miss Higginbotham's asperity completely disappeared, and even the tears dried themselves upon her cheeks. Few could withstand the warmth of Jehovah's smile; he was conscious that he had exceptional charm, when he cared to exercise it. And yet he did not feel that he would be altogether justified if he were to gain his point, in this instance, by its exercise. That would make the whole affair seem too much like a seduction—like the rather ordinary romantic seductions which the pagan Greeks used to report so zestfully concerning their Zeus, legends which Jehovah had always rather frowned upon because of their levity and vulgarity. No, he must not "win" this woman with his charm, as a man or a heathen deity might. It was not a question of "winning" a woman, anyhow. A greater thing was at stake: He must convince her intellect, which he respected.

And first he must be sure that he clearly comprehended the nature of her scruples.

"Let us comprehend one another, Miss Higginbotham," he said. "Am I to understand that you have declined the honor for which I destined you because of some obscure moral inhibition?"

"I should think," said Miss Higginbotham, poised and firm and chastely beautiful, "that you would be the last person in the universe to refer to my motive as *obscure!*"

Then she added, with the sublime simplicity of her traditions: "I am a lady."

"I would be the last to doubt it," said Jehovah, with an old-world courtliness. "And," he continued, "it is precisely the fine fragrance of your maiden ladyhood, the rare essence of your pure morality, which I require in making this experiment."

Miss Higginbotham came as near to sniffing as any woman so carefully nurtured might come—as near as anyone would dare in the presence of authentic deity.

"I offer you an equal share," said Jehovah, "in the creation of a being who is certain to redeem millions of your fellow creatures from sin and the errors of the flesh, and you refuse!"

"I am," said Miss Higginbotham, "a pure woman, and the idea of bearing a child out of wedlock is abhorrent to me. I do not consider merely my loss of reputation, for I could bear the scorn of the world for a righteous cause. But the thing which you propose to me is inherently unrighteous."

"Aren't you confusing righteousness," inquired Jehovah, "with your merely local and temporal and human conventions of morality?"

"I am acting in accordance with the dictates of my conscience," replied Miss Higginbotham, ruffling her feathers like a Plymouth Rock pullet.

"But isn't it possible," suggested Jehovah, "that your conscience itself may have been moulded into its shape by men who were themselves apt to confuse absolute righteousness with their merely parochial customs?"

Miss Higginbotham considered before she replied: The idea was new to her, but she was fairminded enough to weigh it seriously before she rejected it.

"Those men," she said, "those Puritans were the spiritual guides given to me: They were fostered and they flowered with the permission of yourself. If they have taught me wrong, I am obliged to ask you why you allowed them to do so. But I have a deep spiritual conviction that they were right, and that I am right in my refusal."

Jehovah looked at her not without admiration.

"Well, well," he murmured, finally, "they certainly got themselves taken seriously in this country, didn't they?"

Miss Higginbotham gave him a look which would have been a frown, if he had not been a deity.

"Wasn't it your intention that they should be

taken seriously?" she asked. If her tone had been addressed to an equal, the equal must certainly have felt rebuked.

Jehovah tried another tack.

"Miss Higginbotham," he said, briskly, "I shall permit you to assume, for the sake of argument, that your ideas of right and wrong are superior to mine. They aren't, Miss Higginbotham—but I am in a lenient mood today, and I am not going to force into your consciousness any conception that might have a suddenly shattering effect upon your ego. As you are now, I shall permit you to remain, until the process of natural growth makes you something other. So, keep on thinking that you are right.

"You are right—for the sake of argument—you are right. Let us go on from there. Let me ask a sacrifice of you. Will you not swerve from your rightness for the sake of saving a world? Will you not be wrong once so that millions of others may be led to righteousness? Will you not permit your morality, and your sense of what is due yourself and your morality, to go by the board, in order that vast numbers of the population of this struggling earth may be led to the joys and securities of salvation?"

"No," said Miss Higginbotham, uncompromisingly, "I am a virtuous woman."

"What is your virtue compared to the possible regeneration of the planet?"

"It is everything to me," said Miss Higginbotham; and she added, with a certain complacency, "I am what I am."

Jehovah meditated over his next remark before uttering it, as if unwilling to wound Miss Higginbotham if he could spare her feelings. Then he said: "When a consciousness of rectitude proceeds to such lengths it is called self-righteousness. It is very evident that your self-righteousness is more important to you than the redemption of the cosmos. Can't you forget yourself and how good you are for one moment in order to make the world better?"

"No, I am afraid I can't," said Miss Higginbotham, "and if I weren't the way I am, if I hadn't the moral fiber which you recognized in me before you came to me, I shouldn't be the woman you want for the mother of your son."

They looked at each other in silence for a moment with this thought between them. Presently Jehovah remarked:

"There are a great many things in the cosmos which seem to be utterly paradoxical to human beings, but which are quite simple to deity because deity has, after all, an opportunity for a broader and more reconciling outlook. I wish you would take my word for it that what I am asking of you will never be counted against you as a sin but rather to your glory. Can't you trust in the breadth of my vision?"

"You have pointed out to me a number of times," said Miss Higginbotham, "that I do not have your breadth of vision. That is the whole point. I must act according to the vision which has been vouchsafed to me. If I am narrow, then I am narrow. If you wanted me broader, you should have made me broader."

"But," said Jehovah, "isn't there any warmth springing up in your bosom at the thought of a divine mothership?"

"Not," replied Miss Higginbotham, compressing the beautiful contour of her lips into a firm straight line, "not at the thought of motherhood out of wedlock. I am respectable."

Jehovah arose and made her a most dignified and gracious bow. "Madam," he said, "permit me to offer myself in marriage to you."

Miss Higginbotham looked at him gratefully. Her self-respect seemed to be somewhat restored by this courtly gesture. Her lips parted; it seemed as if a syllable of eager assent quivered upon them.

And then her lips closed tightly again while the old troubled look came back into her eyes. Slowly she shook her head from side to side. Finally she said: "I do not approve of polygamy."

"Polygamy?" Jehovah seemed genuinely puzzled.

"If your union with the mother of your first son was quite regular," said Miss Higginbotham, "and still exists, it is obvious that another union of the sort must be essentially polygamous."

"Oh, I see what you mean," murmured Jehovah.

"If, on the other hand," continued Miss Higginbotham, "your union was *not* regular, I could not consider uniting myself in matrimony with a person whose past did not conform to my own standards of propriety."

Jehovah sat down again and meditated.

Possibly he was a little displeased. He made a rather impatient movement and plucked somewhat irritably at his beard. Perhaps more of his omnipotence than he intended escaped from him in his passing irritation. For a seismic shock was felt throughout Manhattan Island. The great towers such as the Woolworth Building vibrated and quivered throughout their steel frameworks.

"Am I to understand," he asked, "that you do not approve, Miss Higginbotham, of the former virgin birth?"

"It was all right for those times," said Miss Higginbotham, "but I do hope we have made *some* progress morally in the last 1900 years!"

There was another interval of silence. In the sunny sitting room Jehovah once more considered the situation. His charm, as he had already determined, he would not use; he would employ no arts wherewith to fascinate this woman. Persuasion had failed. He might use compulsion if he chose, but he had a distaste for that method.

He did not even remind Miss Higginbotham that compulsion would be easy to him, that he had but to will the thing which he requested and it would be instantly accomplished. For he was certain that if he spoke to her in this manner she would reply that she *preferred death to disgrace.* And he had had about all he could stand of that kind of talk for one day; all that any self-respecting deity could reasonably be expected to listen to and pardon in a mere human being. More than this, he was aware that Miss Higginbotham, with the candor of her nature, relied on him to play the part of a gentleman and respect her motives; he would not disappoint her in this.

And with this willingness to allow the beautiful and resolute virgin her victory there came also the thought that perhaps after all she might not be exactly the ideal character to mother a new saviour of the world. He arose with dignity.

"Miss Higginbotham," he said to her, "I bid you good-afternoon. You have met Jehovah face to face and given him something to think about. I wish also to leave a thought with you—not by way of criticism but merely as a stimulus to possible spiritual growth. You must consider whether the quality of your chastity does not somewhat resemble a spiritual sterility."

With that he left the room. The neatly dressed maid who showed him to the street door on the floor below, a red-lipped, common person with an appealing liquidity of the eye, could not help but think as she glanced at him: "What a splendid-looking man! I wish——"

But she checked the thought. Nevertheless, Jehovah had caught it. He turned and gazed upon her from the doorstep, long and smilingly, and an ecstatic thrill pervaded the vital creature.

Within a year she gave birth to a son, and this child may be somewhere in the world now, and it is possible that great, saintly things are to be expected of him.

God, the Devil and Old Man Murtrie

Old Man Murtrie never got any fresh air at all, except on Sundays on his way to and from church. He lived, slept, cooked and ate back of the prescription case in his little dismal drug store in one of the most depressing quarters of Brooklyn. The store was dimly lighted by gas, and it was always damp and suggested a tomb. Drifting feebly about in the pale and cold and faintly greenish radiance reflected from bottles and show cases, Old Man Murtrie, with his bloodless face and dead white hair and wisps of whisker, was like a ghost that has not managed to get free from the neighborhood of a sepulcher where its body lies disintegrating.

People said that Old Man Murtrie was nearly a hundred years old, but this was not true; he was only getting along towards ninety. The neighborhood, however, seemed a little impatient with him for not dying. Some persons suggested that perhaps he really had been dead for a long time and did not know it. If so, they thought, it might be kind to tell him about it.

But Old Man Murtrie was not dead, any more than he was alive. And Death himself, who has his moments of impatience, began to get worried about

Old Man Murtrie. It was time, Death thought, that he was dead, since he looked so dead; and Death had said so, both to God and to the Devil.

"But I don't want to garner him, naturally," Death would say, "till I know which one of you is to have him. He's got to go *somewhere*, you know."

God and Death and the Devil used to sit on the prescription counter in a row, now and then, and watch Old Man Murtrie as he slept on his humble little cot back there, and discuss him.

God would look at Old Man Murtrie's pale little Adam's apple sticking up in the faint gaslight and moving as he snored—moving feebly, for even his snores were feeble—and say, with a certain distaste:

"I don't want him. He can't get into Heaven."

And the Devil would look at his large, weak, characterless nose—a nose so big that it might have suggested force on any one but Old Man Murtrie —and think what a sham it was, and how effectually all its contemptible effort to be a real nose was exposed in Old Man Murtrie's sleep. And the Devil would say:

"I don't want him. He can't get into Hell."

And then Death would say, querulously: "But he can't go on living forever. My reputation is suffering."

"You should take him," the Devil would say to God. "He goes to church on Sunday, and he is the most meek and pious and humble and prayerful person in all Brooklyn, and perhaps in all the world."

"But he takes drugs," God would say. "You should take him, because he is a drug fiend."

"He takes drugs," the Devil would admit, "but that doesn't make him a *fiend*. You have to do something besides taking drugs to be a fiend. You will permit me to have my own notions, I am sure, on what constitutes a fiend.

"You ought to forgive him the drugs for the sake of his piety," the Devil would say. "And taking drugs is his only vice. He doesn't drink, or smoke tobacco, or use profane language, or gamble. And he doesn't run after women."

"You ought to forgive him the piety for the sake of the drugs," God would tell the Devil.

"I never saw such a pair as you two," Death would say querulously. "Quibble, quibble, quibble!—while Old Man Murtrie goes on and on living! He's lived so long that he is affecting death rates and insurance tables, all by himself, and you know what that does to my reputation."

And Death would stoop over and run his finger caressingly across Old Man Murtrie's throat, as the Old Man slept. Whereupon Old Man Murtrie would roll over on his back and moan in his sleep and gurgle.

"He has wanted to be a cheat all his life," God would say to the Devil. "He has always had the impulse to give short weight and substitute inferior drugs in his prescriptions and overcharge children who were sent on errands to his store. If that isn't sin, I don't know what sin is. You should take him."

"I admit he has had those impulses," the Devil would say to God. "But he has never yielded to them. In my opinion having those impulses and conquering them makes him a great deal more virtuous than if he'd never had 'em. No one who is as virtuous as all that can get into Hell."

"I never saw such a pair," Death would grumble. "Can't you agree with each other about anything?"

"He didn't abstain from his vices because of any courage," God would say. "He abstained simply because he was afraid. It wasn't virtue in him: it was cowardice."

"The fear of the Lord," murmured the Devil, dreamily, "is the beginning of all wisdom."

"But not necessarily the end of it," God would remark.

"Argue, argue, argue," Death would say, "and here's Old Man Murtrie still alive! I'm criticized about the way I do my work, but no one has any idea of the vacillation and inefficiency I have to contend with! I never saw such a pair as you two to vacillate!"

Sometimes Old Man Murtrie would wake up and turn over on his couch and see God and Death and the Devil sitting in a row on the prescription counter, looking at him. But he always persuaded himself that it was a sort of dream, induced by the "medicine" he took; and he would take another dose of his "medicine" and go back to sleep again. He never spoke to them when he waked, but just lay on his cot and stared at them; and if they spoke to him he would pretend to himself that they had not spoken. But it was absurd to think that God and Death and the Devil could really be sitting there, in the dim greenish gaslight, among all the faintly radiant bottles, talking to each other and looking at him; and so Old Man Murtrie would not believe it.

When he first began taking his "medicine" Old Man Murtrie took it in the form of a certain patent preparation which was full of opium. He wanted the opium more and more after he started, but he pretended to himself that he did not know there was much opium in that medicine. Then, when a federal law banished that kind of medicine from the markets, he took to making it for his own use. He would not take opium outright, for that would be to acknowledge to himself that he was an opium eater; he thought eating opium was a sin, and he thought of himself as sinless. But to make the medicine with the exact formula that its manufacturers had used, before they had been compelled to shut up shop, and use it, did not seem to him to be the same thing at all as being an opium eater. And yet, after the law was passed, abolishing the medicine, he would not sell to anyone else what he made for himself; his conscience would not allow him to do so. Therefore, he must really have known that he was taking opium at the same time he tried to fool himself about it.

God and the Devil used to discuss the ethics of this attitude towards the "medicine," and Old Man Murtrie would sometimes pretend to be asleep and would listen to them.

"He knows it is opium all right," God would say. "He is just lying to himself about it. He ought to go to Hell. No one that lies to himself that way can get into Heaven."

"He's pretending for the sake of society in general and for the sake of religion," the Devil would say. "If he admitted to himself that it was opium, and if he let the world know that he took opium, it might bring discredit on the church that he loves so well. He might become a stumbling block to others who are seeking salvation and who seek it through the church. He is willing to sacrifice himself so as not to hamper others in their religious life. For my part, I think it is highly honorable of him, and highly virtuous. No person as moral as that in his instincts can get into Hell."

"Talk, talk, talk!" Death would say. "The trouble with you two is that neither one of you wants Old Man Murtrie around where you will have to look at him through all eternity, and each of you is trying to put it on moral grounds."

And Old Man Murtrie kept on living and praying and being pious and wanting to be bad and not daring to and taking his medicine and being generally as ineffectual in the world either for good or evil as a butterfly in a hurricane.

But things took a turn. There was a faded-looking blond woman with stringy hair by the name of Mable who assisted Old Man Murtrie in the store, keeping his books and waiting on customers, and so forth. She was unmarried, and one day she announced to him that she was going to have a child.

Old Man Murtrie had often looked at her with a recollection, a dim and faint remembrance, of the lusts of his youth and of his middle age. In his youth and middle age he had lusted after many women, but he had never let any of them know it, because he was afraid; and he had called his fears virtue, and had really believed that he was virtuous.

"Whom do you suspect?" asked Old Man Murtrie, leering at Mable like a wraith blown down the ages from the dead adulteries of ruined Babylon.

"Who?" cried Mable, an unlessened person, but with a cruel, instinctive humor. "Who but you!"

She had expected Old Man Murtrie to be outraged at her ridiculous joke, and, because she was unhappy herself, had anticipated enjoying his astounded protests. But it was she who was astounded. Old Man Murtrie's face was blank and his eyes were big for a moment, and then he chuckled; a queer little cackling chuckle. And when she went out he opened the door for her and cocked his head and cackled again.

It gave Mable an idea. She remembered certain fumbling, senile advances. And she reflected that he took so much opium that he might possibly be led to believe the incredible, and she might get some money out of him. So the next evening she brought her mother and her brother to the store and accused him.

Old Man Murtrie chuckled and . . . and admitted it!

Whether he believed that it could be true or not,

Mable and her people were unable to determine. But they made the tactical error of giving him his choice between marriage and money, and he chose matrimony.

And then Old Man Murtrie was suddenly seized with a mania for confession. God and Death and the Devil used to listen to him nights, and they wondered over him, and began to change their minds about him, a little. He confessed to the officials of his church. He confessed to all the people whom he knew. He insisted on making a confession, a public confession, in the church itself and asking for the prayers of the preacher and congregation for his sin, and telling them that he was going to atone by matrimony, and asking for a blessing on the wedding.

And one night, full of opium, while he was babbling about it in his sleep, God and Death and the Devil sat on the prescription counter again and looked at him and listened to his ravings and speculated.

"I'm going to have him," said the Devil. "Anyone who displays such conspicuous bad taste that he goes around confessing that he has ruined a woman ought to go to Hell."

"You don't want him for that reason," said God. "And you know you don't. You want him because you admire the idea of adultery, and think that now he is worthy of a place in Hell. You are rather entertained by Old Man Murtrie and want him around now."

"Well," said the Devil, "suppose I admit that is true! Have you any counter claim?"

"Yes," said God. "I am going to take Old Man Murtrie into Heaven. He knows he is not the father of the child that is going to be born, but he has deliberately assumed the responsibility lest it be born fatherless, and I think that is a noble act."

"Rubbish!" said the Devil. "That isn't the reason you want him. You want him because of the paternal instinct he displays. It flatters you!"

"Well," said God, "why not? The paternal instinct is another name for the great creative force of the universe. I have been known by many names in many countries . . . they called me Osiris, the All-Father, in Egypt, and they called me Jehovah in Palestine, and they called me Zeus and Brahm . . . but always they recognized me as the Father. And this instinct for fatherliness appeals to me. Old Man Murtrie shall come to Heaven!"

"Such a pair as you two," said Death, gloomily, "I never did see! Discuss and discuss but never get anywhere! And all the time Old Man Murtrie goes on living."

And then Death added:

"Why not settle this matter once and for all, right now? Why not wake Old Man Murtrie up and let him decide?"

"Decide?" asked the Devil.

"Yes—whether he wants to go to Hell or to Heaven."

"I imagine," said God, with dignity, "that if we do that there can be no question as to which place he would rather go to."

"Oh, I don't know," said the Devil. "Some people come to Hell quite willingly. I've lived in Heaven myself, you know, and I can quite understand why. Are you afraid to have Old Man Murtrie make the choice?"

"Wake him up, Death, wake him up," said God. "It's unusual to allow people to know that they are making their own decision—though all of them, in a sense, do make it—but wake him up, Death, and we'll see."

So Death prodded Old Man Murtrie in the ribs, and they asked him. For a long time he thought it was only opium, but when he finally understood that it was really God and Death and the Devil who were there, and that it was really they who had often been there before, he was very much frightened. He was so frightened he couldn't choose.

"I'll leave it to you, I'll leave it to you," said Old Man Murtrie. "Who am I that I should set myself up to decide?"

"Well," said God, getting a little angry, perhaps, "if you don't want to go to Heaven, Murtrie, you don't have to. But you've been praying to go to Heaven, and all that sort of thing, for seventy or eighty years, and I naturally thought you were in earnest. But I'm through with you . . . you can go to Hell, Murtrie."

"Oh! Oh! Oh!" moaned Old Man Murtrie.

"No," said the Devil, "I've changed my mind, too. My distaste for Murtrie has returned to me. I don't want him around. I won't have him in Hell."

"See here, now!" cried Death. "You two are starting it all over again. I won't have it, so I won't! You aren't fair to Murtrie, and you aren't fair to me! This matter has got to be settled, and settled to-night."

"Well, then," said God, "settle it. I've ceased to care one way or another."

"I will not," said Death. "I know my job, and I stick to my job. One of you two has got to settle it."

"Toss a coin," suggested the Devil, indifferently.

Death looked around for one.

"There's a qu-qu-quarter in m-m-my t-t-trousers' p-p-pocket," stammered Old Man Murtrie, and then stuck his head under the bedclothes and shivered as if he had the ague.

Death picked up Murtrie's poor little weazened trousers from the floor at the foot of the cot, where they lay sprawled untidily, and shook them till the quarter dropped out.

He picked it up.

"Heads, he goes to Heaven. Tails, he goes to Hell," said Death, and tossed the coin to the ceiling.

Murtrie heard it hit the ceiling and started. He heard it hit the floor, and bounce, and jingle and spin and roll and come to rest. And he thrust his head deeper under the covers and lay there quaking. He did not dare look.

"Look at it, Murtrie," said Death.

"Oh! Oh! Oh!" groaned Murtrie, shaking the cot.

But Death reached over and caught him by the neck and turned his face so that he could not help

423

seeing. And Old Man Murtrie looked and saw that the coin had fallen with the side up that sent him to——

But, really, why should I tell you? Go and worry about your own soul, and let Old Man Murtrie's alone.

Satan Goes to Church

Dr. David Bentley enjoyed a lucrative position as pastor of the church to which belonged one of the richest men in the world, Mr. Jefferson Pettigrew. One Sunday during the Lenten season, Mr. Pettigrew proceeded up the aisle arm in arm with no less a person than the Devil himself, and they sat down side by side in the Pettigrew pew.

Satan on this occasion had not even taken the trouble to disguise himself as an ordinary citizen, although he was considerate enough to hold his long spiked tail in such a position that it would not catch and snag the clothing of any of the other members of the congregation. He listened to the sermon in a decorous manner, and when the services were over lingered with Mr. Pettigrew to shake Dr. Bentley by the hand.

Everyone in the church had seen the Devil with Mr. Pettigrew and had recognized him for what he was. But each person kept up the pretence before all the other members of the congregation that it was not the Devil at all, but merely some eccentric human friend of the great financier's. Some of them even claimed to know that he was a distant cousin of Mr. Pettigrew, who was, unfortunately, a bit off mentally, and who persisted in putting on strange costumes and going about in them. He loved to "dress up," and Mr. Pettigrew humored him in it; that was the story. The legend ran that the church service had a soothing effect upon this cousin's nervous malady, and that Mr. Pettigrew, out of his boundless charity and good-will, conducted him to church careless of what form public criticism might take. Mr. Pettigrew was much praised for his piety and his courage and his kindness in the matter. These things, the congregation said, were characteristic of him.

And yet, while the members of the congregation were whispering this story to one another, they knew well enough that it was really the Devil who was with Mr. Pettigrew.

The press was deep in the deception also. Towards the end of the service Satan nonchalantly, but nevertheless in an irreproachably polite manner, and with a tea-table smile, reached over into the pew in front of him and caught a young woman by the throat and strangled her to death. He was thirsty. He twisted her head off, quite calmly, and drank her blood, and threw the body into the aisle, and then picked up his hymn book and turned to the song which had just been announced, which he sang in a pleasing and sympathetic baritone.

The young woman, who belonged to a very good family, might have so far forgotten herself as to scream while she was being killed; but her mother's eye was on her, warning her silently and eloquently that it would never do to offend Mr. Pettigrew, and so she permitted herself to be strangled quietly as a well-bred girl should. Two gentlemanly ushers, while the hymn was being sung, carried the body to the street and told a policeman, who had looked into the door of the church and seen the whole thing himself, that the girl had been run over by an automobile. The policeman rang for an ambulance, and so reported the matter. Five newspaper reporters, who had also seen the Devil drink the blood, wrote it for their papers as an automobile accident, since the girl's family was of such prominence that something had to be said.

Mr. Pettigrew did not tell any of these people what to say or do. He did not have to. He knew they would find the right explanation.

But when the rest of the congregation had filed out and Dr. Bentley and the Devil and Mr. Pettigrew were alone together, Dr. Bentley made a protest.

"Mr. Pettigrew," he said, "I think this is going a bit too far! I have submitted to you in many ways with regard to the management of the church, and I do not think it either kind or polite that you should inflict upon me the bodily presence of this person. Mr. Pettigrew, you have cut me to the soul. There must be a limit to what even a clergyman is expected to countenance!"

"Don't blame me," said the old man, raising his feeble arms and speaking in a thin, piping voice. "I'm as helpless in the matter as you are, Dr. Bentley. He *would* come! What could I do?"

"But," objected Dr. Bentley, scowling darkly at the Devil—with whom, to do Dr. Bentley justice, he had never liked to associate unless it was absolutely necessary to further the material interests of his beloved church—"but, Mr. Pettigrew, if you never associated with him at all, if you were strangers, he would find no pleasure in your society, and would not insist on accompanying you."

"Dr. Bentley," said the aged magnate, a little angrily, "I resent your insinuations that this person associates with me because there is any spiritual affinity between us! But, indeed, if there *were* any, whose fault would it be but your own? Are you not my spiritual mentor? Do I not employ you and pay you for moral guidance? And when have I ever failed to rise to the heights indicated by you? Dr. Bentley, during ten years of association with me, have you not repeatedly, in public and in private, pointed out that I am the perfect flower—or as near perfect as a human being can be—of a perfect social system?"

The Devil, still feeling a bit thirsty, no doubt, looked from Mr. Pettigrew's scrawny neck to Dr. Bentley's fat one. But perhaps he wished to hear this conversation. For he wrung neither one. He found the sacramental wine and drank a quart or so of it, instead. And he said nothing.

"I have felt it my duty," said Dr. Bentley, "to

hold you up as an ideal to the youth of the land. The public must understand that our really great men are on the side of Christianity, law, order and the stable interests of society. I do not say even now that I have praised you too highly, Mr. Pettigrew. But I do feel that it is quite within my rights to protest against your continued association with this person."

Mr. Pettigrew looked meditatively at the Devil, who was examining a stained-glass window which depicted the crucifixion, with his head on one side, and with all the affectation of an amateur artist.

"I've told you," said Mr. Pettigrew, "that I'd like to get rid of him. But how can I? He's always intruding—in a business way, you know."

"Yes," said Dr. Bentley, a little sadly, and dropping his more clerical manner, "yes, quite so! I can understand that. He would!"

Dr. Bentley sighed. "You have your material problems, Mr. Pettigrew, just as I have my spiritual ones."

"And in order to reform the world," said Mr. Pettigrew, "you must have many great philanthropic institutions and foundations which take a deal of money. Christianity costs a lot, Dr. Bentley, if it is run right."

"It does," said Dr. Bentley. "It does. If it is run right. I can understand how difficult your position is! I am sorry if I appeared heated in my protest a moment ago. But the shock was great. . . . Yes, I have always held that the money was sanctified by the use to which it was put."

428

"He says," said Mr. Pettigrew, indicating the Devil with his long forefinger, "that he only intends to come in person once a year. . . . Somewhere around Easter, he says. . . . Really, Doctor, I think we'll have to stand for it! He could wipe all my financial interests out with a wave of the hand, you know. Yes, we'll have to stand for it."

"For the good of the church," said Dr. Bentley, thinking how badly the church needed the money in order to carry on its widely beneficent work.

"For the good of the church," said Mr. Pettigrew.

They passed down the aisle together, in complete brotherly accord once more, leaving the Devil in the church.

The Devil smiled. "I knew," he said, "that I wouldn't need to say anything. They always work around to the right point of view if you leave them to themselves!"

The Golden Legend

Jesus had been going about New York for more than a year, and the rumors of his various quiet activities had come to the ears of certain persons who liked them none too well.

It was not the occasional miracles which he had

been performing; the offensive and dangerous thing was the way in which he sometimes talked with people. These conversations frequently had the most disturbing results: people would listen to him, and then go and do the most extraordinary things without any respect at all for the established social order.

The miracles were nothing. To know that Jesus, or anyone else, is able to walk on the water, or cure hardened arteries, or restore to his pop-eyed family some poor simpleton who has fallen into a new subway excavation and broken his neck, is very interesting indeed; but it does not necessarily strike the overlords of our complicated society as overwhelmingly important.

A miracle is a miracle: there it is, and that's that; you can take it or leave it, believe in it or not; you can call it supernatural or supremely natural; in any event, it need have very little effect upon general human conduct.

There was a Gadarene swineherd one time who witnessed Jesus transfer a legion of devils from a maniac to a herd of swine. The hogs ran down a steep place to the sea and were destroyed. The swineherd was impressed for the moment, and afraid; but later he became angry. Here were 2,000 hogs gone, which he was supposed to be in charge of, and he was out of a job, and his reputation as a responsible swineherd ruined for life.

It was all very well for him to go about explaining that the hogs were destroyed through circumstances which were quite beyond his control. People either would not listen to him at all, or disbelieved his story when they heard it.

The more he thought about it, the angrier the swineherd became, and he later joined the mob in front of Pilate's palace and bellowed for the crucifixion of the Galilean prophet. He never had the slightest suspicion that there was any great truth involved in the matter; and, indeed, after nineteen hundred years, what great truth does emerge? The thought that it must be very unpleasant to be a devil, or to be possessed of devils, and that it is unlucky to be a hog, is one that humanity in general might very well be trusted to grasp without all the spectacular trimmings. The thing is picturesque, and there is about it the grotesque humor of folklore. And of course the picturesque and the humorous are always welcome; but the only thing that need be taken seriously is the act of kindness towards the man possessed of the devils. And it seems that the man might possibly have been relieved, as Jesus relieved so many others, without all this fuss.

But ethical ideas are different. They are loaded. They are always dangerous. Under the influence of an ethical idea any meek little rabbit of a Long Island commuter is apt to get off the eight fifty-seven train and run down to the Wall Street district and bite the fiercest financial bulldog there. There had been enough of that sort of thing going on in New York—enough of these attempts on the part of rabbits and guinea pigs to bite bulldogs and wolfhounds—since Jesus had been coming to the city, to make the rulers of the metropolis uncomfortable. Something would have to be done about Jesus, or there might be a good deal more of it, with very far-reaching results.

Something would have to be done . . . but what? It was to consider this question that three or four dozen men prominent in the life of the city met one evening in a building in uptown New York. To be specific, they met in a large new church, which was being built in imitation of several important European churches—although no one was quite able to tell *which* particular European church it imitated. It was commonly said to combine the best features of several of them.

There were politicians, bankers, commercial magnates, newspaper proprietors and editors, representatives of several Christian denominations, in the solemn assemblage—in short, the Best People of the community, the solid people, the people interested in seeing that the current system of civilized society should suffer no overthrow at the hands of idealistic radicals.

Several Jews were present, both Jewish religious leaders and men of affairs. It was notable from the beginning of the meeting that these were less forward in their demand that some drastic action be taken than were the Gentiles. The Jews were, in fact, worried and anxious; and seemed to have come less from any spontaneous interest in the proceedings than from the motive of proving that they were patriotic Americans, and conservative New Yorkers, concerned to give evidence of their solidarity with the best thought of the community.

One queer thing about the meeting was, that while all of those participating knew well enough that the man with whom they were concerned was really Jesus of Nazareth, they seldom referred to him by that appellation. They called him "Josephson," and "Joshua ben Josef," and several other names, as if they were willing to hide from themselves his identity; as if, indeed, an acknowledgment of his identity might go far, in itself, to weaken their case against him in their own minds.

"This Josephson," said one of his self-constituted judges, "is a charlatan. He claims to be a prophet of some sort; and to my mind this stamps him as blasphemous and sacrilegious."

This was a lie, for Jesus had made no claims whatever. He had just said what he had said, and done what he had done, and allowed people to draw their own conclusions.

"He is an anarchist," said another one, who had a prominent place in municipal affairs. "He was clubbed by the police down in Union Square the other day, and that proves that he is an anarchist. For if he hadn't been an anarchist, he wouldn't have been clubbed, would he?"

There were those present to whom this seemed irrefutable logic. And when the speaker went on to say that anarchy must be stamped out at any cost, he received a round of applause. "These people," he said, "if they don't like our American system of government, should go back where they came from."

A Jewish rabbi observed mildly that there had always been a certain amount of controversy as to just where Jesus came from. Perhaps nobody caught the rabbi's drift; at any rate, there was no comment on this.

A well-known radical, who was frequently described as a Philosophical Anarchist, got up and denied that Jesus was an anarchist; repudiated him, in effect. In the following two minutes he was also repudiated by a Communist, a Socialist, a Bolshevist sympathizer, a Holy Roller, a Theosophist, an International Banker, a Prohibitionist, and a Vegetarian. He was In Bad, in the current slang of the era; it was felt that something was going to happen to him, and they were shying away from him. Just a week or two previously, before public sentiment had begun to crystallize against him, all these people, and a good many more, had been eagerly claiming him as one of themselves, trying to gild their Causes with his fame.

"He isn't orthodox," said a Protestant minister who had been making himself conspicuous for years as a thundering Modernist.

"Orthodox—you make me laugh!" This was from a priest of the Greek Church. "I shouldn't say anything about Josephson's orthodoxy one way or the other, if I were you. As far as I can see, there's no one here at all, except myself, who can lay the slightest claim to being an Orthodox Christian."

A Roman Catholic priest who was present demurred to this, and the revival of a classic controversy was imminent, when another Jewish rabbi arose.

"Gentlemen," said he, "before we go any further

with this inquiry, I should like to have one point cleared up. This man Josephson is a Jew. Whether he is what he is said in some quarters to be, Jesus of Nazareth, or a reincarnation of Jesus of Nazareth, he is still a Jew. For Jesus of Nazareth was one of our people——"

"What's the point you want cleared up, Doctor?" interrupted an impatient international banker.

"Just this," said the Rabbi. "Josephson is a Jew, and I want to know whether the animosity I discover against him in this meeting does not have a trace, a tinge, of racial antagonism—whether it is not, in fact, an anti-Semitic feeling."

Loud cries of "No! No!" from every part of the church answered the Rabbi.

A well-meaning liberal got up and said: "Rabbi, it is really an anti-Christian feeling."

Whether he said it satirically or sincerely, it was instantly felt that the utterance had not helped matters any, for there was an indignant chorus of "No! No!" once more; in which joined Roman Catholics, Episcopalians, and every variety of Protestant; the Protestants being the most vociferous, through sheer numerical strength, for they include, like a certain well-known brand of pickle, fifty-seven varieties.

The Christians, Roman Catholic and Protestant, made it evident that they were shocked and distressed by Josephson's imposture—by the claim, made for him, if he had not made it himself, that he was Jesus of Nazareth, back on earth once more.

Just at this moment Jesus himself came into the

church. He was guarded—escorted, in fact, by two policemen. Twiller Van Durden followed along behind, at a discreet distance, because Twiller had been present at his arrest. Like another disciple, on a previous occasion, Twiller wanted to see what was going to happen to his friend, and whether it was possible for him to do anything about it himself.

One of the first persons Twiller saw in the church was his brother Walter, sitting proudly among the big business men. And then Twiller realized that something dreadful was probably going to happen. For Walter was stupid, and the men among whom he was seated were stupid; and dreadful things are just as apt to happen when stupid people control a situation as when definitely ill-natured people are in charge.

Jesus had been arrested in a restaurant on East Forty-fifth street, between Third Avenue and Lexington. It is a very pleasant place, with a big back yard, run by an Italian named Tony. Twiller was there having his dinner, and presently Jesus came in and sat down at the same table, and the two renewed a pleasant former acquaintance. The big kitchen of the place is also the dining room, and Tony and his wife and children cook the food on a range in the corner and carry it right to the plates of the patrons, hot and flavorous.

There was an Italian wedding party having dinner at the large central table, and when Jesus came in they had just been thrown into consternation by Tony's announcement that they could not have any red wine with their dinner. The pretty little dark-eyed bride, and more especially her parents, were aghast; they expostulated. A wedding party without wine? Who ever heard the like? It took the shine off the party; it made the wedding itself seem almost illegal.

There was no help for it, Tony explained. He simply did not dare to serve wine tonight. He had poured every ounce in the place down the sink an hour earlier. This was a few months before the repeal of the Eighteenth Amendment made drinking legal once more in America. Tony, it seemed, had been caught between two rival gangs of racketeers. The Blarney gang and the Spaghetti gang were making a fight for the lordship of the district in which his restaurant was located, and if he purchased supplies from one of them, the other would shoot up his place or turn him in to the cops.

Twiller regarded the wedding party and their disappointment with sympathy—happy, innocent people, with a native gayety of disposition, their humble festival was spoiled. While he was wondering if he couldn't find a way out for them, suddenly a way was found—or seemed to find itself, as if by magic.

The water in the glasses before them surprisingly became wine. There were no histrionic effects attendant upon this sudden change. Indeed—and it was the queerest part about the whole affair—nobody seemed to know that there had not been wine there all the time. The disappointment, the whole series of antecedent events, seemed to be wiped completely from their consciousness; a pleasant harmony prevailed, with no recollection of anything else before.

And when the police came, and found wine on the premises, actually being consumed, how was it that they had connected Josephson with its presence? Twiller, for the life of him, could not remember. There seemed to have been a sort of haze enveloping everything between the events at Tony's place, and the entrance of Jesus—or Josephson—into the church, and his arraignment before this solemn, deliberative body which sat there in judgment, eagerly awaiting some pretext for action against him.

"Josephson," said Walter Van Durden, "it seems you are a bootlegger!"

Jesus made no reply. Perhaps he knew perfectly well that Walter had had a couple of highballs himself before coming to the meeting. He said nothing to the effect that human laws are all nonsense when they get in the way of divine laws.

"Josephson," said an international banker, "you are an anarchist. Only the other day you said, down in Union Square, that it is as easy for a camel to pass through a needle's eye as for a Rich Man to enter the kingdom of Heaven."

Jesus said nothing; but Twiller Van Durden suddenly spoke up: "He said that a couple of thousand years ago; not down in Union Square the other day. But maybe you just heard about it the other day." Twiller had been reading the New Testament. He added: "In my estimation, it's just as true as it was two thousand years ago."

"Do you mean," said the international banker, "that the possession of great riches *always* connotes wickedness? Irrespective of how they were acquired or how they are used?"

Jesus said nothing. The assemblage seemed impressed for a moment. And then a tactless radical asked the international banker:

"Would you like to tell us, in detail, how yours were acquired and have been used?"

There was a moment of undignified levity in the church, and the international banker sat down without pressing the point.

"Josephson," said a Bishop, "you are an atheist."

"Josephson," said another man, "you are a blasphemer."

Jesus said nothing at all. And the charges went on . . . and on and on . . . the company gradually working themselves into a heat of rage with the vehemence of their own denunciation. Twiller judged that they were getting more and more angry, really with themselves, because they knew that the charges they were making were not true. They thought that they were angry with Josephson, and only later would they perceive that their hatred and ill-nature had been lacerating themselves.

But angrier and angrier they were getting. There was no doubt of it. Everyone in the church, except Jesus himself, shook and quivered with the agitation.

At the very crest of this wave of anger, a Jewish rabbi got up and said:

"Gentlemen—I think we Jews had better leave this meeting! We don't want to have any part in what is evidently going to happen to this man Josephson."

He looked around the room and gathered up the eyes of his fellow Jews present. Then he continued:

"This man came before one of our meetings a good many years ago, and what happened then did not turn out to be so fortunate for the Jewish people. It wasn't the Jewish people as a whole who got him crucified, but only a meeting of the best citizens. But the blame was put upon the whole Jewish people. And I know perfectly well what you are all getting ready to do now—you are going to do the same thing over again, and you're getting ready to blame it upon us Jews! Yes, it's going to be put onto the whole Jewish people again! Come—let's get away from here!"

And all the Jews present marched out in a compact little body.

There was a heavy silence for some moments, and then the charges and denunciations broke out again, with renewed vigor.

Finally, another hush fell; a strange hush. The editor of an important paper got up, after this silence had lasted for some time . . . got up slowly, as if he were somehow impelled to rise.

"Listen, gentlemen," he said, "what we are going to do is in everybody's mind, although none of us has phrased it yet.

"And none of us has phrased the real reason why we are going to do it, either.

"We might as well get some honesty behind this thing; come down to brass tacks with regard to our motive. All these charges of law violation, blasphemy, and sacrilege are nonsense, and we know they are.

"We want to get rid of this Josephson for one reason, and one reason only; and to my mind it is a sufficient reason in itself, and needs no lies nor apologies to bolster it up.

"We want to eliminate him because he is an idealist, and because he really means, sincerely and effectively, the application of the Christian ideal to our current society. And if we permit him to go on talking to people and convincing them, he will bring it about, too.

"There's this about idealism, and particularly about Christian idealism—some people are able to take it, undiluted, and practice it. But most people are not. They can go a certain way with it, and they can't go any farther; and the attempt to make hundred per cent Christian idealists out of them leads to all manner of distressing circumstances, embroils them with the facts of the universe as they feel and know them, and with the established order of human society. Humanity is not yet ready for a thorough-going Christian ethic. Something like a new species will have to be evolved. We are in an intermediate state, and we can't stand too much spirituality—at least, all the time. Prophets of an *absolute* idealism confuse us, and earn our enmity. We can't live with them, and we can't live in a state of society dominated by them. After all, we are largely flesh, and they are practically all spirit. It is our instinct to conform in action to a division which we find throughout the universe. We simply *aren't* all spirit, and we can't act as if we were; and if we try to act as if we were, it leads to a disintegration of what we *really* are. It tears us to pieces. We feel this absolute idealism, this absolute spirituality, as an enemy. This man said once, years ago, that he brought a sword into the world; and he did, and now he has come back here again to sharpen the sword. We've got to get rid of him, or go ourselves.

"There is the issue, squarely joined.

"Do you want the world to go on very much like it is going on now, as it always has gone on; or do you want it changed in accordance with the Christian ideal?

"For my part, I don't want it changed. I couldn't stand it if it were changed. The Christian ideas and ideals, if they were really put into practice, instead of being merely talked about, in churches and elsewhere, would burst the world asunder. Cover them up with any sort of talk or clever explication you like, attempt to explain them away if you will, the fact is that if they are really put into effect it means a revolution in every department of human life, an overturning of all our cherished institutions. Do we believe in these ideals enough to follow through with them to the limit, to face all that their sincere practice connotes? I don't, for one!

"Let us be candid about it. If we eliminate this man, we do it because he is a sincere idealist, and not because he is any of the things we have called him tonight—because he is that, and we can't stand it. It's too perturbing. It's too dangerous to us."

He sat down. Jesus got up and spoke for the first time. He went to the end of the nave, where a statue of Christ on the cross faced the main body of the church. Directly opposite it, blazoned on the wall in prodigious gold lettering, were the words THE GREATEST OF THESE IS CHARITY.

He looked at the letters. He looked at the statue.

"Gentlemen," he said, "I am minded to save you a certain amount of trouble. At the same time, I cannot allow you to dodge your share of responsibility."

With these words, the Christ upon the cross was suddenly gone. An instant later, Jesus himself had taken its place; and an instant after that, he seemed to have turned to stone there. He backed up to it, with his arms spread wide, and crucified himself. It all happened so quickly and so strangely that most of those in the church thought that nothing whatever had happened.

But a good many persons who were familiar with the stone figure, which had been carved by a famous sculptor, began to see a look on the face of the statue which they had never noticed before—a faint smile, too good-natured to be really satirical, although partaking somewhat of the nature of satire, too. This element of satire, perhaps, having something to do with the fact that the eyes of the statue are fixed all day long upon the golden legend at the opposite end of the church: THE GREATEST OF THESE IS CHARITY.

Country Doctor

It was still raining; the water had been flung turbulently down out of the sky all day long. And now it was early dusk, an October dusk, and the world outside the Doctor's windows was a chaos of cold, wind-driven rain and lowering gloom and mud, the sticky black mud of northwestern Illinois which clings and clogs and overwhelms. Dr. Stewart peered out at the village street, or as much of it as he could see through the wind-slashed crevices in the murky wall of storm, and drew the heavy shawl tighter about his shoulders, and took another sip of his hot lemonade spiked with whiskey, and breathed a little prayer that he would not have a call; especially a call out to the Swamp.

He shuddered when he thought of what the Swamp would be like tonight. Green River, which drained the vast tract westward to Rock River and the Mississippi, would be up and roaring and tearing at its low clay banks: and the swamp roads—if you could call them roads at all when the Spring and Autumn floods were in spate—would be roiled and brawling creeks themselves in places, almost rivers. And here and there would be a melancholy twinkle of light, flickering through mists and scrub timber across the bogs and bayous, from some lonely farmhouse perched on a wooded island. For scattered over the district, forty miles or so in length and half as broad, were many farmers; and even when the freshets left them only a third or a quarter of the crops they had planted they still could live, for the land was incredibly rich. Dr. Stewart knew the Swamp and its people, none better; for day and night, winter, spring and fall, sick or well, he had had a good many years of it.

"Always ague, malaria and influenza," he murmured. And then, with grim self-irony: "I've dumped enough quinine into that hole myself to pave a solid road from Dante's frozen hell to Timbuctoo, and still it shakes, shivers and shakes."

He shivered himself, for he had the flu, and put another lump of soft coal on the grate fire. His office was in the front part of his residence on the main street, and presently he noticed a bedraggled object bogged down in a lake of mud across the way, and chuckled. A feeble glimmer from the post-office windows illumined its dejected contours.

"Young Dr. Hastings' horseless carriage," grinned Dr. Stewart to himself. People still called them horseless carriages in the late nineties of the last century.

"I can see how Hastings might break his arm cranking the damned thing," he mused, "but how the deuce did he manage to break his leg? He's got no right to break his leg and leave all the work on Jones and me . . . and Jones just a kid out of college last spring, and me sick, and the whole damned country down with flu and pneumonia!" He snorted indignantly. "Horseless carriage! Hell!" he said.

Then he reflected: "They'll be all right, when there are some decent roads for them to run on."

For he was not against progress, far from it. He had seen too much of it not to believe in its continuity. Born in Ohio the same year the British burned the White House in Washington, he had seen the country grow up, and opined that it had a healthy constitution. Ohio had been "out west" when he was a lad; he was now past eighty, and Illinois had long been "an old settled country." Nearer sixty than fifty years of practice of medicine lay between his student days and this present evening.

He shook himself, as if to shake off the sense of the gloom outside, and something of the dread that had settled on his spirits—the dread of a call, in his present condition.

"I haven't got time to be sick!" he said. "People need me." For he was a country doctor, and he did not know what it was to spare himself. He had been going hard all last winter and spring—battling through prairie blizzards, battling through flooded spring swamps, to some remote house of suffering, battling all night to save a life, and reaching home again in the dawn to gulp down a pot of boiling coffee and take up the new day's work without an hour of sleep. His hands and feet had been frozen again last winter, but no frost had reached the stout old heart within. But now, he faced a new winter—and before it was fairly begun, here he was, sick!

He hadn't time to be sick, he told himself again, rebelliously. So *many* people needed him! There were the Simpkins children, down with the measles, for instance: and nobody knew the Simpkins constitution, or how to bring out measles on the reluctant Simpkins hide, as well as he did.

And there were the Rays, and the Tuckers, and the Prices and the Smiths—sickness in all these families, and what did the two young doctors, Hastings and Jones, know about them? Good doctors, no doubt; fine conscientious boys—but boys. They had never fought through more than half a century of chill midnights hand to hand with death. And these were *his* people that were sick, in the village, on the prairie farms round about, out in the Swamp—*his* people, and they needed him, and what right did he have to be nursing himself here at home? It wasn't natural.

Nobody ever heard him say anything about loving these people. Nor did they talk about loving him. Nor did anybody ever hear the word "service," so popular since, from his lips. The nearest thing to an expression of affection on either side would be something like this: "Don't you love to rile Old Doc Stewart, just to hear him cuss?" But there was a pretty good understanding between the Doctor and his people. He had helped bring more than one generation of them into the world; and helped to make a little easier the way out of it for some of their fathers and grandfathers. They took him as naturally as they did sunlight and rain and the change of seasons, and, some of them, as thoughtlessly. He was the last man they paid, after settling with the grocers, the implement dealers, and for the interest on the mortgage.

A mud-splattered man on a mud-splattered horse walloped through the mire, and came to a stop in front of his house. A second later the man hammered on the outside door.

"It's come!" groaned Dr. Stewart. He had known it would, had "felt it in his bones." He let the man in himself, for his housekeeper was nursing a case of pneumonia in the village, and, save for her, he lived alone. He was a childless widower.

He opened the door, and one of his own Swamp Angels, as he called them, stood dripping mud and water in the entryway.

"Jason Tucker, isn't it?" said the Doctor, peering at him.

"Uh-huh," said Tucker. "Howdy, Doc?" A manner of apology, as well as mud and water, oozed from his dishevelled wetness.

There was an instant's silence, while the two regarded each other by the gleam of the kerosene lamp in the narrow hallway; and the Doctor read his doom in Tucker's earnestness and anxiety.

"Is it Myra, Jase?"

"Uh-huh; her time's come," said Tucker.

"Yes; it would be about now," nodded the Doctor, reflectively.

"First baby, too," said Tucker, twisting his drenched cap in his nervous fingers, till a little rivulet of water was squeezed from it and ran down to the floor. He gulped, and added: "She was an old maid when we was married. And she's got this here *la grippe* on top of everything else, Doctor. What I'm scared of is it turnin' into pneumonia, if it ain't turned already."

Then, with a quick look at the Doctor: "You're sick yourself, Doc?"

"Not so sprightly, Jase," admitted Dr. Stewart.

There was another moment's silence. Then Tucker cleared his throat, and murmured: "Doc Hastings, he's got a busted leg. His shin bone. Twixt his ankle and knee. It's in a splint."

He gulped again, and added, anxiously: "I seen it myself, Doc—his leg's really broke."

"Of course," murmured Dr. Stewart.

After another moment, Tucker said: "And Doc Jones, he's out on the Swamp somewheres himself, and I can't get into touch with him." He paused, and drew a long breath. "It's a turrible imposition to come to you, Doc, and you sick like you be."

The thought took shape in the Doctor's mind, though he did not utter the words: "It's more than an imposition; it's probably my death."

For he was running a temperature, and he was weak: it meant, almost certainly, pneumonia. And then there was that pain in the cardiac region, which, he had been telling himself, was only *pseudo*

449

angina pectoris. Well, pseudo, or the real thing, it didn't make much difference at his age: the fact was that the heart had been strained and enlarged, last winter. Oh, damn it! He didn't have time for all this self-diagnosis!

These were the thoughts that ran through his mind. But what he said was: "I'll go, Jase."

"Thanks, Doc, I knowed you would," said Tucker. "How you goin'?"

"Come in," said Dr. Stewart. He scribbled on a prescription pad. "Take that over to the drug store and get it filled. Get back home as quick as you can with it, and give her the dose that will be marked on the bottle." Then he answered the other's question. "Buggy," he said.

"Green River's up and a-rarin' tonight," said Tucker. "Don't trust the wooden bridge, Doc—take the iron one. It's a mile further, but it's safer."

"I've seen it up and a-rarin' before," said Dr. Stewart, grimly.

The men exchanged a brief glance. Neither of them said a word of the thought in their minds, but both were thinking of the same thing. Myra Tucker was, in a way, one of Dr. Stewart's artistic creations. She had been a country school teacher; and four or five years before she had been kicked by a horse, and fallen down, and the horse had then trodden upon her face, breaking her nose and her cheekbones and her jaws. Dr. Stewart had practically built a new face for her, feeding her through tubes until she got the use of her jaws again, and grafting skin from her arms and legs—and this in a day before skin-grafting was generally practiced. Myra had been a pug-nosed girl of no beauty; and it had pleased the Doctor, when he made her face over, to give her a bold aquiline nose.

This was in the days before hospitals in the country regions, or district nurses: he had done it all himself, without help. Myra had some fine, thin lines, scars, on her face after it was healed. But the new nose made a different person of her. Dr. Stewart always said he was responsible for her improved profile and, indeed, for her marriage to Jason. That made him responsible for this baby that was trying to get itself born out there in the Swamp in the midst of such difficulties.

He chuckled under his breath at the thought, and murmured to himself: "I wonder if the baby will inherit the Roman nose I gave Myra, or her natural one?"

"What say, Doc?" asked Tucker.

"Nothing—except that Green River was up and a-rarin' the night Myra was born herself, Jase."

"Yep," said Jase, "you borned her, Doc, didn't you?" And he disappeared into the gloom.

Dr. Stewart put on his overcoat, and a raincoat over that, and went to the stable, lighted a lantern, and hitched up his horse.

"Two miles north to the county line," he said to himself, "and then four miles west to the iron bridge . . . Here! Damn your hide! How'd you like to get lashed in the face yourself with a wet tail? Huh?"

This was to his horse, the latest of a long line of

animals familiar with mud and dust and snow. "If you don't get over that trick of using your tail like a windmill every time I try to put a crupper under it, I'll . . . I'll . . ." he paused to think up a terrifying threat . . . "I'll sell you to a circus, where they'll make you walk a tightrope and feed you on barbed wire."

He was always making terrible promises to his horses, that they should go to the treadmill, or be manufactured into bologna sausage, or the like; but as a matter of fact he never even carried a buggy whip. His horses perfectly understood the oratorical nature of his threats. Animals worshipped the man. Stray dogs gravitated to his office in the village with such regularity that he had a theory that they must have the house marked, as tramps are said to mark houses where they receive human treatment for the benefit of the next vagabond; and some of his surgical triumphs had been in the field of canine treatment. "The dogs pay me about as well," he said once, with an affectation of cynicism, "as some of my human patients." All about the place he had nailed up tin cans to trees and posts, which he kept filled with water for the birds in hot, dry weather.

For several years a pet crow had insisted on accompanying him on his professional calls, perched on the top of his buggy, or even on his shoulder. This bird now solemnly fluttered down out of the hay mow and watched him hitching up the horse.

"You can't go," said the Doctor to the crow. "I don't trust you any more—you black thief, you."

The bird made a grating noise with its vocal apparatus, as if it knew what he was referring to. A few weeks before, astonished at the number of things he was missing from his office, he had instituted a search of the premises. In a cache under the eaves he had found a favorite lancet, a gold watch with which he had been presented on his seventy-fifth birthday, a fountain pen, a thermometer, two hypodermic syringes, and, surprisingly, a set of false teeth.

"If you'll confess which one of my patients you stole those teeth from, Jim," said the Doctor, "you can start going around with me again. And if you don't reform, I'll have you stuffed and mounted on a plaque as a warning to malefactors."

The bird looked at him incredulously, with its head on one side, hopped to the stable door and looked out at the rain; and then fluttered back to the hay mow, with the secret of the teeth still intact.

In spite of his coats and lap robe, the Doctor was wet to the skin before he was well into the area where muddy prairie began to merge with drowned swamp, for the wind, so to speak, showed a diabolical cleverness in taking the rain in hand as if it were a weapon, and slicing and slashing with it, thrusting it like a fencer through and around and past all defences. Half an hour of this soaking—for the Doctor moved slowly over the wretched roads— and he was sure that his temperature was rising.

He stopped, and thrust his thermometer under his tongue, and read what it registered by the light of his lantern. It was as he had suspected. But he went on; he was bound for Jason Tucker's, and he would get there, he told himself, in spite of hell and high water. He only hoped that he would arrive before the baby did . . . or, to put it that way, before the mother . . . was gone.

Thickest night came presently, and he and his horse had difficulty in keeping to the road. Not that it made much difference. The going when the animal stumbled off it, with the buggy lurching after, was about as good. The sense of sight was practically blocked off; and the sense of hearing brought to him little more than a mingled tumult of waters, far and near, where creek and rivulet met, and swelled the roadside ditches, or dashed against and bit into and tore at the gravel-surfaced road itself.

He had been travelling something more than an hour, perhaps, when the sound of these random streams began to be merged with a steady roaring . . . Green River was ahead of him and it was, as Jason Tucker had said, "up and a-rarin'."

He paused at the road which branched off to the wooden bridge, and got out of his buggy, leaving the horse standing in the road; he could trust the animal to stay quietly until he returned. He wanted to look at the condition of the wooden bridge himself. He splashed through the mud to the bank of the stream, holding his lantern ahead of him, and . . .

And paused just in time. There wasn't any wooden bridge! It had gone down stream. A line of willow trees, which he remembered as having marked the entrance to it, was not thirty feet from shore.

He had still cherished a hope that the bridge might be there and might be passable, for it would save him a mile or so of mud and ruts . . . half a mile to the west, and half a mile back east again, after he had crossed the new iron bridge, to get back into the road which passed the Tucker house.

"Rarin' is right!" said the Doctor, peering out at the flood, on the surface of which his lantern cast a few dancing yellow gleams.

He looked for only a few seconds, but it was long enough to see a chicken coop, part of a straw stack and a dead pig with all four feet sticking stiffly up in the air, go whirling by.

When he got to the iron bridge he stopped and got out of his buggy once more, for an examination. The water was boiling and shouting over the road-way on the bridge itself, but the structural iron-work looked solid and unshaken. He walked out a few yards on the bridge, stamping on the planks: there was more than a foot of water swirling over the planks: it lashed him nearly to the knees.

"Drenched from toenails to tonsils," said the Doctor to himself. And then, ironically: "The thing to do with this influenza, or grip as they call it, Dr. Stewart, is to stay warmly in bed, with your feet dry, and avoid violent exertion of any sort; for the heart at such times is particularly susceptible to strains."

Something banged against the eastern and up-stream ironwork of the bridge, as he made this facetious recommendation to himself, and then crashed into splinters. The air in front of him was suddenly filled with broken timbers, and, strangely, out of the debris was propelled a speckled hen, who cried shrilly to earth and heaven and flood that she was wet and outraged because of it, and then disappeared into the howling night. The major portion of some farmer's barn had slammed into the bridge, and the impact shook the structure. But still it seemed able to withstand the shock.

Nevertheless, it was nothing to drive out upon gaily and blithely, with all that water whirling over it. The Doctor went back to where he had left his horse.

"I'll lead him across," he said to himself, and started off, his lantern in one hand and the horse with the lurching buggy following. Although the flood rushing across the bridge was not deep, it was swift, and plucked and sucked at his feet. But he went on, and the horse patiently splashed along behind.

In a few moments he paused. Where the hell *was* the west end of this bridge, anyhow? He must be nearly across it and . . .

By the Great Horned Toad of Mithridates! There wasn't any west end to it! Nothing ahead of him but water rushing across his path! He reflected on this phenomenon of a bridge unanchored at one end and still standing sturdily, for a moment, and then the solution came to him. The ironwork was stout enough, but between the west end of the bridge and what had been the shore the flood had cut a new channel, narrow, and he did not know how deep.

He would have to cross that, and it was nothing to be got through in a buggy. Nor, he suspected, on foot either. He unhitched the horse from the buggy, tied up the traces to the horse collar, shortened the driving reins. He'd have to mount and ride the horse through. The buggy he would leave where it was, and it could either sink or swim.

"Damned old worn-out buggy anyhow," he said.

He took from the vehicle, not his bag, but a smaller, leather-bound pocket case, with a dozen vials in it . . . morphine tablets, strychnine tablets, a couple of small bottles of brandy, a hypodermic syringe, a thermometer, digitalis . . . other things. He put this case in the inner breast pocket of his overcoat. The larger bag would be in the way on horseback. The lantern he left, lighted, on the buggy seat.

As he made the effort, and mounted the horse, a sharp pain in the region of the left breast took his breath; and for a moment he closed his eyes, and hung onto the horse's mane.

"Damned old worn-out Doctor, too, I guess," he breathed, when he could breathe again. The pang passed. He pulled himself together on the horse's back, and then said, with a resonance in his voice: "But by God, I'm going through!" It was a challenge to the night and the storm and the treacherous swamp and the wind and all the physical elements; the challenge of the old man's undaunted spirit. There were people ahead who needed what he could do for them, and he was going through! He had always gone through: for more than fifty years he had been going through.

There was a cramp in his left arm. It kinked and twisted. He knew what that meant. He clung to the animal's mane with his right hand, and dug his muddy heels into its flank. To hell with the angina! He didn't have time to stop for that. Probably it was only pseudo angina anyhow . . . gas pressing up . . . indigestion . . . it was time, at his age, he was getting a little sense about what he ate and when he ate it . . . he was strict enough with other people's diet . . .

The horse walloped into the cut at the west end of the bridge; and if there was a shore on the other side, neither horse nor rider could see it. The Doctor felt the water about his knees . . . about his thighs . . . it was up to his seat . . . the horse staggered . . . and then . . .

A black choking . . . a frantic, lashing struggle . . . where was the horse? A strained, instinctive muscular reaction . . . a blankness . . . and Dr. Stewart found himself clinging to the roots of a willow tree. The rushing water still pulled at his feet and legs and sodden clothing. But he clung. He strove to pull himself up the slippery bank. But the pain . . . the pain in his chest . . . it was terrible . . . but he held on to his willow root . . . he lay, half in and half out of the water, and was lifted and threshed about by the insensate, brute flood . . . but he held on . . . he was going through! Another agonizing effort, and he felt the flood release his legs. He would lie here in the mud awhile and rest . . . it was soft, the mud was. But that pain in his chest. It was as if it were filled with hot ashes, that shifted back and forth and burned and burned when he tried to breathe. No . . . hot snuff . . . more like snuff than ashes . . . it burned and burned . . . burned like hot snuff would burn, if you had snuff in your lungs.

Presently he managed to get his hand into his overcoat pocket, and draw out the leather-bound little case. The morphine tablets were in the first vial. He took one, and lay back in the mud. The rain was in his face . . . But after while the rain was not in his face any more.

"Must look like a goddam old white-whiskered muskrat," said Dr. Stewart to himself. He stared up at the sky. And presently he noted something. The storm had broken. The wind was blowing a section of the heavens clear of clouds. He took another morphine tablet. A corner of the moon was clear of cloud. There was a star near it. There was something he wanted to say to that star . . . he couldn't quite remember what it was. His chest was a little easier . . . a good deal easier . . . oh, yes, what he wanted to say was, if you stuck it out long enough the mud got a little warmer after while . . . the tension in his chest was relaxed; that was a little warmer, too . . . No; that wasn't what he wanted to say to that star! What he wanted to say to it was: "Damned funny you didn't get drowned . . . neither one of us got drowned . . . damned funny!" He lay back; he felt almost comfortable . . . although his mouth did taste like he'd swallowed a raw catfish . . . damned funny animal, the catfish . . . especially the variety known as the bullhead. He knew how a bullhead must feel in the nice warm mud in the summertime, and it wasn't so bad.

Then, suddenly, thought returned, in its complete and cruel lucidity, and he struggled to a sitting posture, and then to his feet! Jase Tucker's wife was sick, and he had to get there! He stumbled up the bank to the road. Something was moving up there: some animal. He stood, staring, trying to penetrate the night. It came nearer to him, and stopped. It was his horse, marvellously escaped from the torrent, which had scrambled free from the river and waited in the road. The animal nuzzled at his elbow, as if in relieved welcome. And his own relief was boundless—thank heaven, he wouldn't have to walk that last half mile to the Tucker house! He doubted if he could have walked that far.

He could see the lights of the farmhouse, gleaming through the roadside trees, in the distance; and he tried to mount the horse again. But the effort brought another sharp pang in his chest, and he desisted.

He put his right arm over the horse's neck, and twined his fingers in the mane. His left arm was . . . not so good.

"If you've got sense enough to let me guide you," he told the animal, "we can still make it." He had started out to go to Jase Tucker's place, and that was where he was going. And, supporting himself in this fashion, he made it, partly walking and partly dragged along through the mud.

"And none too soon," said the Doctor, as he pulled himself wearily up the crunching gravel path from the road to the front door. For the screams of a woman in the vital anguish of childbirth stabbed his ears.

He opened the front door without ceremony, and stood within the little living room—the parlor, as they called it. Myra was in the best bedroom, just off the parlor. The door was open, and he went in. Jase Tucker sat in a corner, his hands among his dishevelled hair, sweating. Bending over the bed where the woman lay groaning and writhing was a young man with black circles under his eyes and a two days' stubble of beard on his face; he lurched and stumbled strangely towards Dr. Stewart as the latter entered the room.

"Hello, Doctor," he said. "You got here!"

And then he finished giving Myra a hypodermic injection in the arm.

"She'll come through, Hastings?" enquired Dr. Stewart.

"If the heart lasts," said Hastings.

"Hearts are hell," said Dr. Stewart.

They delivered the baby, and not until then did Dr. Stewart's consciousness fully take note of the fact that this was, indeed, the young Dr. Hastings who was supposed to be back in the village with a broken leg.

"How the hell did *you* get here, Hastings?"

"On a horse. I told Jase I couldn't come. And

then I got worried for fear *you* couldn't make it
. . . bad night, and everything, you know . . .
and so I came anyhow. I must have passed you on
the road somewhere."

"I was in the mud," murmured Dr. Stewart.
"Quite a while, I guess."

Hastings repeated, almost apologetically: "I
thought you might not get here." His leg was giving
him great pain, now that he had time to notice it.
He started to speak again.

But he paused. A change had come over Dr.
Stewart's face. Hastings supported him, or Dr.
Stewart would have fallen. Hastings eased him to
a sofa in the living room. Dr. Stewart tried to roll
up his sleeve.

"Heart, Hastings," he muttered, as he fumbled
with his sleeve. The younger man slid it up for him,
and the needle went beneath his skin. But, oh,
Christ! . . . that choking agony . . . the hot ashes
. . . the hot snuff . . . hot sand . . . his chest
was full of it. But he tried to sit up.

"Hastings!" he said. "Keep me alive . . . for a
while. I haven't *got time* to be sick! I haven't *got
time* to die! Not till this goddam flu epidemic is
over . . . people need me . . . keep me going!"

Pretty soon the drug began to take effect; again
came the warmth, the relaxation, something more
like easiness. But no strength with it. He seemed to
himself to be swaying, drifting, falling, floating;
carried on by a full tide. Why, he was in Green
River again, he thought, and it was rushing him on

. . . down stream . . . on and on . . . carrying him away.

It was not so unpleasant now, either. But he must get through. He mustn't let himself drift like this, pleasant as it was. There were people on the other side; people who needed him. He must make an effort.

Clarity returned for a moment, and he tried to sit up again.

"Hastings," he said again, as if he were just now seeing the young man for the first time that night, "you got here, broken leg and all!"

And then something of resonance returned to his voice; and he sat fully upright on the couch and spoke loudly—spoke as a commanding general might, in brevetting a younger officer for gallantry on a field of battle, with pride and authority and affection in his tones:

"By God, boy," he said, *"you're a Doctor!"*

He sighed a long deep sigh, and relaxed. He let the tide carry him on down stream, with no further effort at resistance. He had time now; time to let himself be carried away. He was leaving his people in good hands. There was the wail of a baby from the bedroom.

"Another dam little Swamp Angel squawking," said Old Doc Stewart, and smiled; and, smiling, went on with the rushing waters.

The Crack of Doom

"No," said Mason Bridges, "I don't play poker."
There was something about the manner in which
he said it that made his friend Tom Ackley look
sharply at him. They had been in college together,
had been friends for more than fifteen years, and
this was the first time Ackley had ever heard just
that note in Bridges' voice. He had never thought
of Bridges as fanatically puritanical—indeed, now
that he remembered it, hadn't Bridges been one of
the very eagerest of the devotees of chance, in their
college days?

"Just a little fifty-cent-limit game, Mason," said
Ackley. And the other men in the group regarded
Bridges and his frowning face with curiosity. They
were in the cardroom of the club, and everyone had,
temporarily at least, grown tired of bridge. They
needed Mason to make a good seven-handed game.

"I wouldn't play if it were a twenty-five-cent-
limit game or a ten-cent-limit game," said Bridges.
And after a moment's pause he added: "No; nor a
one-cent-limit game." And with that he got up and
left the room. His companions, all good friends of
his, gazed after him wonderingly. One of them
turned a face full of inquiry to Ackley, who was
Bridges' oldest and best friend.

"Don't ask me," said Ackley, in answer to the unspoken question. "I've never seen Mason like that before." With a facetious remark or two they settled down to the cards.

It was a week later that Ackley asked him outright about his aversion to poker and Bridges, after some urging, told him the story.

You think of me (said Mason Bridges) as an honest man; and so does everybody else. And I am an honest man. I have always been an honest man except——

Except once. Once, for a few hours, I was a crook; and knew myself for a crook; felt myself a crook. And what I suffered in the way of strain and anguish during those two or three hours . . . well, Tom, I don't want to go through with it again. It is by the mercy of a printed symbol upon a piece of pasteboard that my life was not ruined permanently. No; that's not exactly right either, for the printed symbol wasn't even——

But I'm getting ahead of my story. Ten years ago I was a partner in a promising little business in Clifford Hills, which is, as you know, one of the most exclusive suburbs within a thirty-five-minute ride of the central district of New York City. There were four of us, all active, hustling, ambitious young men, all felt to be assets to the community, if you know what I mean, and all with a taste for sports and social shindigs, when we had the time—which did not hurt us at all in our business. We dealt in real estate—sold and leased property and collected rents—and we dealt in insurance, both life and fire;

we also placed a good many bonds with cautious local investors, and acted in an advisory character in a good many ways. One member of the firm was a lawyer, also.

There was but one bank in the village, and the people who ran it were asleep where their opportunities were concerned; and we gradually and unofficially took over some of its functions. That is to say, although we did not have much capital of our own, we made financial connections which enabled us to lend money on mortgages, and all that sort of thing. The bank closed at three o'clock in the afternoon; we discovered that there were a dozen of the local tradesmen who occasionally needed to have money changed after that hour, and just as an accommodation, and to increase our popularity in the community, we made a point of keeping currency on hand in our big safe. What with currency, bonds, securities of various sorts, there was always a rather considerable amount of money in our large steel-and-concrete structure, some of it the assets of the firm, and some of it entrusted to us.

I was the inside man, the office manager, with one very efficient woman assistant, and no other help. All of the partners had a loose and easy way of taking from the safe, upon occasion, anywhere from fifty to a couple of hundred dollars, and putting in its place a personal I O U, or a memorandum of some sort, which was always made good to the firm within a day or two. We all trusted each other —why not?

You know why not, without my telling you, Tom.

Poker. I was a poker fiend in college. And in Clifford Hills there was a game; the same bunch met twice a week. When I started in with them it was a mild dollar-limit affair, which hurt nobody. Three years later it had grown to a most prodigious game, considering how gradual the growth was, and how mildly it had started. There were about ten of us implicated; but commonly not more than six or seven got together for any one session. Of that number, I suppose four or five could really afford to lose ten or twelve hundred dollars in one week without being greatly hurt by it—and the game had grown to those proportions. I couldn't afford it; but for a time I was lucky, and, like a fool, I stuck. None of my partners strung along with the poker-playing crowd.

One man particularly annoyed me in the game—Sam Clinker, his name was; and he was a politician with some vague connections with "the Street." From the moment he entered the game he began to "bull" it, brutally. The old pretense of neighborly friendliness went out of it. As you know, a man with a large bank roll has a terrific advantage over players who have to be careful. The very weight of his money wins for him. And the more money I lost to Sam Clinker, the more I resented his existence, his presence in Clifford Hills; I told myself he didn't "belong" with our crowd anyhow. Within six months after Clinker's advent it was a no-limit game, usually stud poker; with sometimes as much as five or six hundred dollars bet on a single card; and an opportunity to drop several thousand in the course of an hour. I couldn't afford anything like it. The queer vanity of the poker player kept me telling myself I would "get" Clinker in spite of his bank roll; like a fool I stuck.

There came a night, one that I will never forget, when I realized that I was more than $4,000 in debt to the firm. It was a very great deal more than any of us partners had ever permitted ourselves to leave paper and memoranda for, and it was all the result of my two last poker games. My position as office manager made it easy enough for me to carry even this comparatively large sum along unnoticed for four or five days; and I was not in the slightest worried about my ability to make it good. My wife and I had $9,000 worth of negotiable securities in a safe deposit box in the bank across the street, from which I could make good what I had borrowed at a moment's notice. But that very evening there was to be a game in Sam Clinker's apartment at the inn and I wanted to get into it.

"If I win a couple of thousand back tonight," I told myself, "I'll quit this damned foolishness." Poker players, you know, Tom, tell themselves that again and again.

But I had no assets with which to enter the game that night. My account at the bank—such had been my losses recently—was down practically to nothing. We usually started nowadays, since Sam Clinker had "bulled the game," by purchasing a thousand dollars' worth of chips when we sat down. It was a cash game . . . we took checks, but they were supposed to be as good as cash, and up to this time they always had been. I felt that premonition of winning which comes to every confirmed poker player . . . and which so often treacherously deserts him . . . but how was I to get into this game tonight?

"This last time will put me somewhere near even," I said to myself, "and then I *am* through."

I was sitting alone in the office, where I had come after dinner, to wait for the time when the clan would be quietly gathering at Clinker's rooms. Suddenly I remembered that Clinker had been in that afternoon, and had left with us $10,000 in U.S. four per cent bonds, of an issue then listed at par. He was to have made the closing payment on a parcel of land and to have taken title, but the seller had failed to meet him, phoning that he had been unavoidably detained.

The appointment had been postponed until ten o'clock the next morning, at our office, and Clinker, the bank being closed, had asked us to keep the bonds in our safe overnight. They were unregistered —they were, in effect, ten one-thousand-dollar bills. Clinker hadn't even had their numbers, I remembered, for when my office assistant had asked him, and had started to copy the numbers down for him, he had said, indifferently: "Oh, what's the use? It's $10,000 cash."

I put two of the bonds in my inside coat pocket, left a careful note of the transaction, and went over to Clinker's apartment, where I found the game beginning. I was idiot enough to feel amused at the idea of getting back some of my own from Clinker by using his own bonds. I didn't feel the slightest sense of dishonesty—for there was the $9,000 worth of my own bonds in the safe deposit box across the street, to make everything good with, if the game went wrong. But I felt an imbecile confidence that it wouldn't.

It did. I rose from the table at eleven o'clock trying to absorb as quietly as I could the first great jolt of that night—and there were other jolts to come. Clinker, who was banking the game, had his $2,000 worth of bonds; he had in addition my check for $2,500—and on top of that I already owed my firm $4,000. The check wasn't worth the paper it was written on, and wouldn't be until I got my own $9,000 worth of bonds from the safe deposit box as soon as the bank opened in the morning, cashed them, and made everything good. But I *would* be there when the bank was opened and make everything good.

Thank heaven for that $9,000 worth of bonds in the safe deposit box!—I said that to myself a dozen times in the walk of a dozen blocks to my home. Thank heaven for those bonds. They were all that kept me from being a defaulter! There was the $4,000 which I owed the firm; there was the $2,500 check to make good, there was the $2,000 worth of bonds which I had taken from Clinker's deposit, of the same series as my own bonds—but I wasn't dishonest. My own bonds kept me from being dishonest—I would make all good at one minute past nine o'clock in the morning!

I was a fool, an utter fool, a vain idiot; I had lost in less than two weeks between eight and nine thousand dollars, practically all my liquid assets. An idiot, but honest, I kept telling myself. And oh, what a lesson I had had! Off of it, off of it forever!

Thank heaven for those bonds in the safe deposit box! Still saying this, I went into my wife's room to wake her up. A pretty hard thing was before me—I had to tell her that I needed those bonds the first thing in the morning. The safe deposit box was a joint affair; each of us had a key to it—and I remembered with a pang that about $2,200 of the money that had gone into the bonds had been her own: They were lying there, on agreement between us, waiting for an opportunity for some very attractive investment. And they were all we had in the way of capital, irrespective of my business; we had both been rather extravagant. But Jessie, I told myself, would be a sport about it—she was always that, a loyal little sport. Debating in my mind as to how much of my situation to tell her at once, I waked her.

She sat up in bed.

"Jessie," I said, "I'm going to need those government bonds of ours the first thing in the morning—as soon as the bank opens."

She murmured something inarticulate. I thought she had not understood. I repeated my statement.

She slowly turned in the bed, and put her feet out, and sat on the edge of it. Then she turned on the pink-shaded reading lamp at the head of it. One of her hands clutched at the jacket of her sleeping suit over her breast—but it was not really the jacket

471

she was clutching at; it was the sudden fearful leap of her heart that she was trying to still with a shaking hand, as I realized a moment later.

She tried to speak, and could only gulp. I noticed then that her face, ordinarily high in color, had gone gray—it was gray even under the added color of the night lamp.

"What's the matter?" I said, alarmed at her appearance—alarmed for her as well as for myself.

"They're . . . they're . . . gone!" she gasped.

"Gone?" I felt as an ox must feel when he is struck on the head by a butcher's mallet.

She flung herself upon me in a passion of weeping. "Oh, Mason," she sobbed, "I don't . . . I don't know how to tell you. . . . Oh, don't be hard on me . . . don't . . . don't. . . . I've been trying to tell you for two weeks. . . . Oh, what I've gone through . . . what I've gone through!"

I held her closely to me, while the story sobbed and shook itself out of her; held her in a growing, numb despair. I suffered with her and for her; and with an added suffering that she could not comprehend—for her story was, in its essence, my own. She had lost twelve or fourteen hundred dollars at bridge; she had been ashamed to tell me. She had tried to recoup by taking a flyer on the stock market —and had lost. And had tried to make back her losings, and had lost again. They were gone, all gone, the whole $9,000 of them—and the poor girl had been feeling like a criminal for two weeks.

"Oh, Mason, don't be hard on me!" she kept saying. I thank heaven that I wasn't—and I wished that there was someone to whom I could make a similar plea. I tried to comfort her; but I couldn't say much. I couldn't find any comfort in my own situation. She felt my despair, for suddenly she writhed free from me, and held me at arm's length, and studied my face for a moment in the dim light with a fresh access of alarm.

"Is it something . . . something terrible . . . something I don't know about yet?" she cried. "Is it some terrible emergency you need them for?"

Whatever might be going to happen to me the next day, I couldn't let her have the full force of it now, on top of what she had already gone through.

"It's pretty serious," I said woodenly.

"Oh, Mason, forgive me, forgive me!" she wailed.

If she only knew how much she had to forgive me! But I couldn't tell her, right then.

"Have I ruined us?" she asked.

"Listen, old dear," I said, "whatever happens, *you* haven't ruined us. If I'm ruined, it's my own doings, not yours. You took securities that you had as much right to as I did, and invested the money hoping for a profit for both of us—and whatever happens you're to blame for nothing. Now go to bed and get to sleep."

"But it *is* my fault," she said. "The gambling—the gambling that led up to it—that's the *wrong* part of it; the gambling and not telling when I lost, is what led up to it!"

"Yes," I said—and as I spoke I felt a kind of grimace twist through my whole being—"yes, gambling isn't always so good!"

I couldn't say anything more, and I started out of the room. But she caught me, and clung to me, wanting to know . . . everything. I couldn't tell her, then. She was thoroughly frightened by my manner, especially as I wouldn't tell her why I must have the money the first thing in the morning. She was afraid I was going to kill myself. I got away at last, with a promise to do nothing so idiotic—told her I *must* go.

I had to be alone to think. And almost the first thing I thought, when I sat down in my office—for my feet had taken me there almost without my volition—was that I might as well kill myself. That was nonsense, of course . . . but what way out was there?

I had gone into my wife's room knowing myself to be a fool, but feeling an honest fool. I had come out of it feeling a thief. Maybe you are enough of a moralist, Tom, to put your finger on the line of demarcation; I'm not. Was it dishonest to use money not mine when I knew I could return it at nine o'clock in the morning? Not strictly businesslike, of course—but we all left memoranda for the small sums we took, and made good at our early convenience; and if the principle of the thing was not wrong, not dishonest, where a small sum was concerned, how was it wrong just because a larger sum was concerned? And the larger sum had been at my command.

"No," I said to myself, "I wasn't crooked when I had the $9,000 in bonds to make good with; I wasn't crooked when I *thought* I had that $9,000, even

474

though I didn't have it. But now that I haven't got it, I am a crook!" That's the trouble with gambling, Tom—it lends itself to a kind of moral confusion; it creates a fog in which the nicer points of honor become imperceptible.

You may be astonished at the intensity of my despair over a matter of $8,500. Well, we're both fairly well to do now, and $8,500 wouldn't make us or break us. But in those days it was a considerable sum. I made a good income, for my age and the time and place, but I lived up to it. All of us in the firm were rather popular young fellows, hustlers, active; but careless spenders. And while it wouldn't ruin the firm, it would ruin me personally. Even if I didn't go to jail—as I well might—I was finished as far as that community was concerned. And these things follow a young man from place to place. I was an idiot—an idiot whom unforeseen circumstances had turned into a thief—and I was finished.

My partners might rally to my support, in spite of my—I hated to say it, but I had to—in spite of my stealing from them. But Sam Clinker and I detested each other, and if he could jail me, he would do it; and he would gloat over it as he did it. He had my bad check; but he had worse than that against me— he had the actual abstraction of two bonds which were his personal property, and their use. He had the political influence to have me railroaded. And if I estimated the man correctly, and his feelings toward me, he'd lose no time about it. We loathed each other with one of those intense personal animosities that grow out of poker games. I had finished myself.

An unbusinesslike habit, pardonable so long as its consequences could be easily met, had been turned into a felony the instant its consequences could no longer be met! And that's the fruit of gambling, Tom. Forgive me if I seem to labor the point—but as I tell you of it there comes back to me something of what I suffered that night.

None of us four young fellows in the firm was a heavy drinker; but there was generally a quart or two around the office at that. This was shortly after prohibition went (in a manner of speaking) into effect. It wasn't a bad thing, now and then, in a business way, to be able to give the right customer or prospect a nip of good stuff. I suddenly wanted a drink—I told myself, desperately, that it would help me think. What I really wanted it for, I guess, was to help me *not* to think for a few minutes. I opened the safe, and took out a bottle of Scotch. I sat there in the gloom for some time thinking about what Sam Clinker was going to do to me next day, and every few minutes I took a nip from the bottle.

I suppose a man who is born a crook, or who has been at it a long time, doesn't mind being one. But I did. It was new to me. It had come on me suddenly. A few hours ago I wasn't one. Now, those bonds were gone, and I was one! I sat there and stared into the open door of the safe, and thought of Jessie at home, and thought of jail, and what my life might have been, and what it would probably be now, and took a drink, and another drink, and another one. The drink didn't appear to me to intoxicate me; it seemed to contribute to the coldness of my despair. The longer I sat there, the more I hated Sam Clinker—not only for what he had done, but for what he would surely do to me tomorrow. I hated him almost as much as I hated myself, and that was as much as anyone can be hated and live.

Suddenly, either out of my despair, or out of the Scotch, or both together, an idea came to me. I put it from me at first. But it came again and again. And finally I extended it a welcome, which had in it a kind of grim humor.

I took from the safe $5,000 more of Sam Clinker's bonds, locked the safe, and went back to the poker game. It was between one and two o'clock in the morning, but they were still going strong, and Clinker was, as usual, the big winner.

"Give me nine of the yellows, and ten of the reds," I said to Sam Clinker, who was banking, and tossed $5,000 of his own bonds at him. Clinker had succeeded in getting the game up to the place where the yellow chips were worth $500 each, the blues $100 each, the reds $50 and the whites $10—and this, Tom, is in itself a great commentary on poker! This was the game that had started three years before as a friendly game at a dollar limit!

Clinker glanced at the bonds, and handed over the chips.

"Those bonds were listed at exactly par in the afternoon paper quotations," I said to him.

He stared at me, as if he found the phrase reminiscent. Indeed, he might well have. He had used almost exactly the same words when he had handed those same bonds over to one of my partners to put in the safe nine or ten hours previously. But he had no way of knowing—or, at least, of proving—that they were the same bonds.

On the inside, I was all fever and chills and wild, illogical hope, and wilder despair. And mixed with this, and perhaps due to the Scotch I had drunk, a kind of queer, jeering humor—a humor that jeered at myself, sneering at me: "Well, fool, if you're going to jail for using $2,000 worth of Sam Clinker's bonds, you might as well take a chance on $5,000 more of them; if you lose, it won't get you any longer prison sentence, probably."

I had only been a crook an hour or two; but you see, Tom, I was already thinking like a crook! Gambling! I don't want to talk to you like a tract, Tom—but there it is; the confirmed gambler does not gamble merely with money; he eventually gambles with the very essence of honor and life.

On the inside of me was this queer jumble and turmoil of emotion; but the outside must have been cool and quiet enough. Nevertheless, the other men in the game seemed to catch something of the inner feeling, for they looked at me strangely and with a certain gravity. It was only now and then that a few of the yellow chips got into the game, in spite of Sam Clinker's forcing methods—and I had come in and bought $4,500 worth of them. They all knew that I couldn't afford it, or anything like it. It was an announcement, in itself, that I intended to "bull" the game. And I had sense enough left to realize that if I were to be ruined I was already alienating the sympathy of several very influential citizens by my present attitude.

I could see in the faces of three or four of them—there were eight of us all told at the table, and the game was now exclusively stud—that they didn't want to win my money, but I was the big loser, and they were more prosperous men than myself, and they felt in honor bound to stick on and play to give me the chance to get something back. That wasn't Sam Clinker's idea. There was a deep and deadly animosity between him and myself; he would delight in my utter ruin. I had never told him what I thought of him; but he knew it; he knew it as deep as the marrow in his bones, and returned the sentiment with interest.

I won. I lost. I won. I lost. I bulled the game. I drank Sam Clinker's Scotch. I got as low as $200 worth of chips. I got as high as $4,000 again. I bulled the game. I drank more highballs. I was not myself. Outwardly I must still have been deadly quiet. Inwardly I was burning flame. My vision was blurred. I played rotten poker. Then I would make myself settle down and play good poker and hold myself to it.

The disconcerting thing was that when I took the wildest and most idiotic chances with the cards I was as apt to have good luck as when I played sensibly. I can't tell you the details of the last hour of that game, because I don't remember them; they were a whirl, a blur, to me, a shifting madness, an unreality, an insanity, a whirl and blur of colored cards and chips.

But I can tell you the details of the very last hand —the last hand of poker I ever played, or ever will play.

Clinker and I faced each other across a board piled high with stacks of blue and red chips—with a few of the yellow ones worth $500 each mixed in with them—and he had three tens and a king showing.

And I had three queens and a king showing.

He had got his third ten to show, and I my third queen, on the last card.

Three other men, who had had possibly winning hands, had gone along with us until the last cards to fall had destroyed their chances, and then had dropped out. But there was at least $5,000 in the pot in front of us.

He looked steadily at me, and all the partially hidden animosity he had long been feeling flared into his eyes. And this permanent animosity was intensified by the fact that twice before I had bluffed him out of pots with $2,000 bets, and then had let him know it afterwards.

"Five hundred dollars," he said; and tossed a yellow chip upon the table.

I read him for four tens, the three showing and one in the hole—and oh, how I hoped that I read him correctly! For I was betting on four queens. That is the essential brutality of stud poker; you know, at times, when you have an antagonist at your mercy.

"I'll raise you five hundred," I replied, and tossed in two yellow chips.

He did not hesitate an instant—and I realized with an accession of fever that must have shown in my bloodshot eyes, although my face was quiet, that he thought I was trying to repeat my former bluffs and get away with another pot without the goods.

"Five hundred more," he said, without hesitation; and then I was certain that I had read him correctly—read not only his hidden card, but his thoughts about myself.

Inwardly I gloated. I had him! I would play him for all it was worth. I raised him $2,000 in one bet, and it took the last chip in front of me.

According to the way in which we had been playing, all he could do was to call—a man who had put in his last chip was entitled to a "sight" for what he had bet, and no one could buy more chips from the bank during the actual playing of a hand. But he was as sure that he had me out on a limb with a foolish attempt to steal the pot—to repeat my previous successful raids—as I was that I had him where I wanted him. My whole maneuver arose, to his thinking, from the desperation which he could not have helped but notice in me. And Sam Clinker was the man to take advantage of it. I saw in his face the fierce desire to ruin me.

"Don't you," he said provocatively, as I announced my $2,000 bet, "want to buy some more chips?"

Without waiting for me to answer, he raised my bet to the tune of $1,000. This, as I have said, was irregular, by the rules of the game we had been playing. But he was so sure he had me hooked! There was no reason why I should not take advantage of the irregularity which he had started, as we were the only two players in the pot. I was so sure I had him hooked!

"Yes," I said. I hastily scribbled a check—with not a penny in the bank to meet it! I tossed it to him. "Five thousand dollars' worth of yellows," I said.

My voice broke with sheer inward hysteria. There was a cackle of laughter in it that must have sounded like utter imbecility. It confirmed Sam Clinker in his estimate that he had to do with a sucker gone mad. He took my check and passed me over the $5,000 worth of chips.

I shoved the entire pile into the pot. "I raise you $4,000," I said.

There was a murmur from the other men around the table; they shifted uneasily in their chairs; they were not enjoying this, nor my manner, nor Sam Clinker's. I felt their unspoken sentiment that this ought to be stopped. I felt their unspoken conviction that I had departed utterly from my senses; they were estimating my desperation, my hysteria, my vain idiocy, just as Sam Clinker was.

Sam looked at me frowningly. He was sure I had gone temporarily mad. I saw it in him. And he was the man to take advantage of it.

He shoved into the pot the $7,000 worth of bonds which he had brought to our office in the afternoon, and on top of them he laid the check for $2,500 which I had given him earlier in the evening, and on top of that he laid the check for $5,000 which I had just given him—$14,500 in all.

"I raise," he breathed. And the whisper was as malignant as the hiss of a snake. He thought he had me!

It amounted to a raise of $10,500. I began to wonder if he really had his four tens, or was trying to steal the pot from me by this prodigious bet—or if he rated me at four queens, and was still trying to beat me down. Never mind which! I had him! I wrote a worthless check for $20,000 and tossed it on the heap that lay between us.

"I raise," I said—and how I hoped he would call me! For I had him; with my four queens I had him.

There was a period of intense silence in the room, except for the hard breathing of the others who were now but astonished onlookers.

Clinker bent up the corner of his hole card and looked at it. He looked at me. He looked at my three queens showing. I had him stopped—and I was sorry for it; I wanted him to go on.

"Of course you know, Bridges," he murmured, "that I've got four tens."

"I don't know anything of the kind," I said provocatively. "I think you're trying to steal this pot with three tens and a big bank roll—the way you've been stealing good pots for six months!" I was trying to goad him into another bet; at least into calling me. I was as sure that he had four tens as that I had four queens.

"It begins to look to me," said Clinker, "as if you really have four queens."

"It will cost you another ninety-five hundred dollars to find out for sure," I taunted him.

And still gloating mentally I turned up the corner of my hole card.

It was not a queen. It was a jack—the jack of spades. The queen of hearts, the queen of diamonds, the queen of clubs, lay exposed before me, and I——

My bloodshot eyes, and my eager and fevered brain, had misread the hole card on my first blurred and hasty glance. I had been playing it for a queen —and it was a jack!

The man had me. My enemy had me. My life was over. It was ruin. Disgrace. Prison. For me. What for my wife? God knows! I did not dare to think of Jessie. I turned cold, in an immobile, dumb agony. I stared at the J on the corner of that jack that should have been a queen. My folly. My idiocy. My—yes, my crookedness! They had brought me to this.

I think my breath stopped. I lost all count of time. How I sat upright I do not know. My mind was in a black whirl. No thought, but only jumbled fragments of thoughts, swung round and round in the dark eddy . . . a thankfulness that my father and mother were dead, and I had no child nor relative . . . a flash of Jessie bringing me a book and handing it to me through iron bars . . . a flash of myself standing before a judge. I was through.

I lifted my face, and it must have been blank with my utter suspension of life to the cruel eyes of Sam Clinker, as if he were the judge I stood before . . . as indeed he was! I held up the dead head on my dead spine and waited sentence. Was it seconds? Or minutes? Or hours? I don't know. Time was gone. It meant nothing. Do you wonder that since that night I have never touched a card, Tom? I wouldn't bet a soiled lump of sugar against a burnt match. I know what agony is.

Time, I say, was through. I lay on one of the grids which eternity has waiting for idiots and crooks. I waited for the shattering blast of the last trump—for Sam Clinker's voice. Finally it came.

"I guess you got 'em, kid," he said. He flung his hand into the discard, and pushed the pile of chips, checks, and bonds toward me.

I did not move. I could not. I had stood upon the trap of the gallows. And a reprieve had come. Heart, lungs, brain, nerves, were not functioning yet. Slowly I came back to life; I drew a breath. I felt the blood begin to move in me. Then I let out one wild yelp of insane laughter—the utter irony of it! I would not have had the nerve to try to bluff Sam Clinker again, to make such a large bet, unless I had known that I had four queens—and I had won the pot, and I didn't have them! My own mistake had saved me from a disgrace that I deserved. My career, my fortunes, my future, my good name, the stuff of my honor itself, the sweetness of my life, had come back to me because my blurred eyes had misread one face-card for another.

The hideous unreality of gambling came home to me in that instant more poignantly because I had won, through that idiotic mistake, than if I had lost and paid the penalty for my folly. Never again would I put myself at the mercy of a symbol on a slip of paper.

I rose, and tore up the checks I had made out. I stuffed the $7,000 worth of bonds into the inside pocket of my coat. I shoved the pile of yellow and red and blue chips to Sam Clinker.

"Cash these; I'm through," I said.

He counted them and wrote me a check, silently. I put it into my vest pocket. Then I tossed my hand into the discard. One of the men made a sudden snatch for the hand, and turned all the cards over.

"Cripes!" he said.

"Mason stole that pot!" breathed another, with incredulous admiration in his voice.

It is impossible to describe the look on Sam Clinker's face. It was mottled. His jaw dropped. And then, with a sudden flash of complete comprehension, he glanced at the pocket into which I had placed the bonds and said, with conviction in his voice:

"Yes; and I'll bet you it's not the first thing Bridges has stolen tonight."

"You'll never know, Clinker," I said, and left the room and went home to tell Jessie not to worry about bridge losses or stock markets. And that, Tom, is why I'm such a stickler for complete business regularity today—and why I would not even join you in a game of penny ante.

The Referee Says——

"One!" says the referee, a second after my shoulders hit the floor.

And, believe me or not, the instant he said it I could have been on my feet again and lacing into Kid Mike Jackson. I wasn't hurt. It wasn't a knockdown. It might have looked like it to the crowd, but there was an elbow between the old solar plexus and Kid Mike's wallop. What he had done was to catch me off my balance; my feet tangled and I fell.

"Jack's hurt bad," I heard Bugs Baker say.

"Always wrong," I says to myself. This Bugs was the wrongest sports writer in New York; not a bad guy, only cuckoo, and thought it a great laughing point that I was always a gentleman. My head was under the ropes at the edge of the ring right above the press table where the reporters sat getting things wrong. I could hear this Bugs Baker's squeally voice piping misinformation to one of his newspaper pals, not three feet from my head.

"Two!" says the referee.

"Fair enough," I says to myself. "I'll lie here and get me a nice little rest, and when he says 'Nine' Kid Mike is going to think a volcano jumped up and erupted on him."

I took a good long breath all the way from the back of my nose to my ankles, and felt contented. It was about half a minute before the end of the seventh. We'd been going fast. Kid Mike was staring at me from a neutral corner with his mouth open and gasping like an orphan catfish that's lost its mud puddle. He'd nearly fought himself out against my defense. I could see his ribs heave, and almost hear him breathe; and if that gorilla knew any prayers he was making them then that I wouldn't get up. I could take him any minute now. I thought I'd stagger to my feet pretty soon, and act goofy, giving the fans a little theatre for their money, and then when he came in to finish me he'd connect with a couple of pineapple bombs.

It tickled me to come back and cinch the welterweight title that way—I'd had it once; Kid Mike had it now; in a couple of minutes I'd have it again. I'd never been a popular fighter. I had a press agent once that made me read too many books, overworked the highbrow stuff on me, played the gentleman racket so stiff it got me joshed.

"Three!" says the referee.

"You see," squeals this Bugs Baker, not more than a conceded putt distance from my ears, "this fight means everything to poor Jack there! If he loses, that settles his hash with his wife!"

"Yeah," I thinks—"you know a lot about that, Mr. Bugs Baker." It was all I could do to keep from lifting my head and giving him the razz.

"How's that, Bugs?" pipes this bird he's talking to. "I thought she made him quit the ring."

"Yeah," says Bugs, "and left him when he come back to it. But now——" The crowd was yelling, so I lost his next words.

"Four!" says the referee. And I hear the man at the mike passing out hooey to the radio customers about how placid and quiet poor Jack is on the canvas.

"Jack couldn't really make the grade with the gentleman stuff after he married Old Man Masters' daughter," says Bugs Baker. "Four-flusher with that stuff . . . four-flusher with the book stuff, too . . . got to be a bad joke with the Masters crowd, especially after he gave that dumb lecture on Homer at Harvard."

I'd have walloped Bugs right there if the circumstances had been different—there were no flies on that Harvard lecture; I had it lined out by the flossiest press agent in New York for me, and a Rhythm Teacher with Greek duds on drilled me in the gestures. But what he spilled about the Masters crowd had some truth in it.

The fact was, I *had* sort of over-married myself. I could get away with the clothes in the Masters crowd, O.K., and got hep to the right fork quick enough—but the life I led! Oh, that continuous applesauce! Dorothea, my wife, bullying me to quit the ring. Really ashamed, after the first excitement of marrying a champ, that I was a boxer. Old Man Masters detesting me. Patronizing me. Her brothers and mother the same. Humiliating me. The friendly treatment like I was a nice trained seal. The underhanded kidding of the whole outfit. And me knowing all the time I was really over-press-agented on the highbrow stuff. Was it any wonder I lost my goat one night at a swell party and soaked her brother and three of her pals and walked out on the whole side show, done with society forever?

"Five!" says the referee.

Over in my corner Red Clancy, my second, was pretty nervous and I tried to wink at him but he didn't get it.

"But things have taken a turn," squeals this Bugs Baker to his friend. "I interviewed her today. Well, women are the queerest outfit! Believe it or not, but she wants him back now—is going to take him back if he wins this fight. Oh, kid, the story I got out of that girl! It makes this fight front-page stuff!"

I turned as chill inside as if Kid Mike had really landed the wallop him and everybody but me thought he had. For the first time I got a real slant on Dorothea's psychology, as the sports writers put it—she liked me being a champ even when she hated me being a boxer. And she'd try to kidnap me again when I got the title back. Cripes! I'd have to go back and be a freak lion again in that den of culture and hooey!

"Six!" says the referee.

Listen, I don't want to knock anybody, especially a woman, especially the girl I married—BUT! She was born to be an iron hand under a velvet glove, O.K. She'd never had anything in her life but her own way. If she said she'd get me back, she'd do it, too. I never been afraid of many men, but I was afraid of that girl. She had my number. Go back to her! And be bossed as I was for a year once more! Managed. Made to jump through and over again. I got my feelings, too.

Go back! I turned into a cold sweat from a dry chill. And Old Man Masters—for one thing he'd given me a bum steer on the stock market, and when I lost my bank roll had got me a job in a broker's office, and the whole outfit had tried to bully me into taking it—me! Back to that Gehenna I'd walloped my way out of!

"Seven!" says the referee.

"She's here tonight," says this Bugs. She was. I moved my head a little and saw her eight rows back standing on a chair between her father and that brother I'd knocked for a loop. Maybe she was yelling for me to get up and kill Kid Mike, but she looked like she always did when she give me Hades for not taking the dogs out to walk at regular hours. The referee says: "Eight!"

"Old Man Masters has got a hundred thousand on this fight," says Bugs.

Yeah? Huh? Must have had another straight tip, thinks I, like the one he give me on the stock market, the old coot! I squinted at Dorothea again, and turned sicker—she'd do it, if she'd set her mind to it! I knew that girl! I felt iron bands tightening on my arms and legs. And then the thought come to me how fine it was I was my own manager now, and had got a fifty-fifty split on the purse and fifty-fifty on the gate with Kid Mike, win, lose or draw.

"Baker," I says, out of a corner of my mouth, "is this stuff you been spilling on the level?" He was startled; but he gasped, within a foot of my head: "Yes, Jack; it's straight." And then: "Are you hurt badly?"

"Nine!" says the referee.

"Can't move hand nor foot, Bugs," I says. "Partial paralysis."

I thinks just for once I'll fool that forty-will-power dame!

"Ten!" says the referee.

"Out!" yells the crowd.

"Yes, and how!" says I to myself.

Homer O'Meara and Helen of Troy

"It's a queer thing, as many singers as the Irish have had," Terence O'Meara said to his father, "that they have never produced a very great singer, such as Shakespeare or Dante!"

His father gave him a glare of contempt.

"Don't ye ever give utterance to such ignorant words annywhere ye might be overheard by a real scholar," said the senior O'Meara. "The greatest poet of all time—famed, noted and renowned the wide world over wherever poetry is read—was an Irishman. Homer, he is called."

"Homer?" Terence's tone was incredulous.

"Homer he is called nowadays," said Mr. O'Meara

solemnly, "but there shouldn't be anny letther H at the beginning of it—that H was put there by the English, like as not, for they're always putting H's where they shouldn't be and laving thim off where they should be. This name Homer is a diginirate corruption of the name O'Meara—he had the same name as me own, who am discinded from him. A great warrior he was, too, though he says nothing about that in his songs, being a modest man, as all us O'Mearas have ever been."

Mr. O'Meara loved to dwell upon the ancient glories of Ireland, although he had been born in America and had never even seen the green island of his ancestors. He had spent most of his life in Brooklyn, where he had been a prosperous building contractor for many years. His sons had found they could stimulate him into strange narration by pretending to underrate Irish prowess, and that was what Terence was at now. After a little more goading, the old gentleman jumped into his tale.

The history books don't tell ye where the Greeks came from—said Mr. O'Meara to his son—but I can tell ye. For the story has been handed down in the O'Meara family from father to son for thousands of years. They originated as sicond-string Irishmen, thim Greeks did.

In all the old mythologies, as ye would know yoursilf if ye were not uneducated because of your indolence towards learning, there is always the story of some green and golden island far in the western seas that is the land of the blest. And thim stories was not fables entirely; thim stories was legends that had truth in thim, and the land of heroes they had reference to was Ireland.

In the young days of her early glory there came a time whin Erin found hersilf terrible thronged with surplus population, and the kings and chiefs says there must be either more emigration or less propagation. So they put wan of these referindums up to the peasantry, and the peasantry voted as wan man to increase emigration and not diminish propagation. A couple of millions of the lower classes emigrated to the mainland of Europe, and afther wandering hither and yon for a thousand years, went down over the hills and streams and took possission of the islands and peninsulas of Greece. They was the inferiors of the betther classes in Ireland, but at that they was the superiors of anny wan else they met.

And that's how the Greeks got started. Somehow changed they was in their migrations, by contact with thim Scythians and bohunks and other furriners; but the memories of the heroes of ancient Ireland was still in thim, faded and dim afther manny centuries, and they carried with thim the story they was discinded from the gods. The warriors and sages and minstrels left behind in Ireland was pagan deities to their minds. Thim Trojans was a similar people. Indade, wan of thim Trojans in particular comes to me mind who called himsilf Æneas; he wasn't nothing but wan of the Innis boys who'd forgot his right name.

Wan day the High King of Ireland—Timothy

O'Meara was his name, the same as me own—was thinking how the country was being overrun by peace and prosperity to a disgraceful extint; whin wan of the O'Neills says to him:

"Tim, Your Majisty, you're not giving us anny of your songs these days."

"There's no great deeds anny more to be singing about," says King Timothy. "Thim Scots and Britons and Gauls has been subjugated and civilized and dicimated ag'in and ag'in by me and you lads, till there's occasion for nayther song nor slaughter left in thim."

"Seaumas O'Kelly passed through yesterday with the tale of a ruckus down around some place called Troy," says The O'Neill. "I thought I might get a gang of the lads together and go see what 'tis all about. It has been a long time," says this O'Neill, looking at his fist, "since The Red Hand of Ireland has had anny action. Maybe ye would like to be coming along with the rest of us lads, Your Majisty."

"Come along with ye, O'Neill?" says King Tim, getting off his throne and hitching his sword near to his hand. "If ye go, 'twill be under the King's command, and 'tis well ye know that, O'Neill. Or if ye doubt it, O'Neill, do ye and that Red Hand of yours step out on the front lawn and I'll convince ye."

For at that day and date, if ye was going to be a king in Ireland, 'twas a continual necessity to be showing anny wan in the world wide ye was the better man. Were ye not a real leader and chieftain, soon there was another King in Ireland. O'Neill of the Red Hand looked King Tim in the eye and kept his own fist away from his sword hilt.

"Fair enough," says he; "and whin do we be sailing?"

The upshot of that was that within a few weeks King Timothy O'Meara and a score or more of his best men dropped anchor and took possission of an island seven or eight miles off the coast of Troy, where thim so-called Greeks and Trojans was bickering. There was The O'Keefe, with his blue shield that had the golden hands and the prancing lion on it; there was The Hennessy, The McCarty, The O'Dwyer, The O'Toole; there was Seaumas O'Kelly, whose jaw was ever like blue steel with the beard under the skin, and the anger of his eyes in battle was like the thrust of spears; there was The O'Reilly and The O'Rourke; there was The O'Neill, with the two red beasts and the three red stars above the green sea with the white fish in it; there was The Hickey and The Caroll, The O'Donnell and The Rooney; The O'Brien with his motto, Lambh laidir an nachtar; The Ryan was there and The O'Sullivan and The Cavanagh; The O'Connel flaunting his shamrocks and his deer and the cry of C'eall agus neart; The Regan came along and The Nolan; there was Duffy with his golden lion against the green; there was Keogh with the wild boar for his crest, and wan of the mightiest of the Murphys with his legend: To Conquer or to Die! Men and mottoes known, noted and feared wheriver the yells of battle and the ring of steel resounded. Bright green was Tim's twenty-oared ship, which he had named the *Shamrock,* and she had a sharp bronze beak; and all thim heroes' shields along the gunnels made her the gay sight going through the wather.

"Now thin, me lads," says Tim, whin the anchor was down, "there's the war over there in front of us. Which side is it your notion we should be coming in on?"

"Which side would be the most Irish?" says Duffy.

"Which side would be needing us the most?" says O'Neill.

"Arrah, the side that would be needing us the most," says Murphy, says he, "would not be the side that was the most Irish."

"There's logic in that, Murphy," King Tim says, "and it makes the choice difficult."

"Which side is in the right, and which is in the wrong?" says O'Rourke.

"Now don't ye be codding us," says O'Donnell. " 'Tis not nicessary there should be anny right or wrong to it; 'tis just a war."

"Mesilf," says McCarty, "I'm always for the under dog."

"How could we be for the under dog?" says Hickey. "The instant we join wan side or the other, that instant will it cease to be the under dog."

"Well, lads," says King Timothy O'Meara, "I've brought ye down here for the frolic, and ye'd betther be making up your minds—here's a war will be going to waste right forninst us, and us not in it."

"Did but wan side or the other insult us," says Cavanagh, "the choice would be aisy."

"They're both afther insulting us," says O'Brien, "by ignoring us—here's a war going on, and we've not been asked in by annybody."

"But both sides has aquelly insulted us that way," objicted Regan, "and that laves us where we was."

"Seaumas O'Kelly," says King Tim, "what is this war all about, annyhow? Ye've been in these parts before, and ye should know."

"Some quane or other," says O'Kelly. "Some wan stole her away from some wan, and so the trouble started. But don't ye lads be underrating this war, nayther. There's wan of me own distant relations in it is a divil with edged tools; O'Kelly is his right name, but it's been corrupted to Achilles. And there's a fella by the name of O'Day—Odysseus they are afther calling him in these ignorant parts —is a strong man of his hands and a crafty fella for strategy. There isn't annything the matther with this war excipt these Trojans and Greeks is superstitious beyond all belief. Ivery now and thin they'll get to fightin' like divils, and the rumor will start as wan of the pagan deities they believe in has joined on wan side or the other, and with that they'll scuttle away like hares."

"Such superstitions is beyond the comprehinsion of me mind," says O'Sullivan.

"Ye must remimber that these people is not altogether enlightened people," says O'Kelly. "The learning they brought away from Erin ages ago is

498

diluted and contaminated by Asiatic communications."

" 'Twould be great sport," says O'Reilly, "for us lads to pretind we was some of thim deities oursilves!"

King Timothy O'Meara was doubtful about this. It somewhat appealed to the mirth of his amusement, but 'twas not entirely a dignified procedure, to his mind. The wise prophets of Erin had foretold that there wasn't going to be anny religion in the world worth the trouble of an Irishman's attintion for a couple of thousand years yet, and the Irish was soberly waiting for its appearance and kaping thimsilves free of all manner of heathen foolishness in the meantime. But the more he thought of it, the more it struck him that O'Reilly's suggestion might hilp cure these people of their terrible superstitious belief in thim pagan deities of Olympus, who niver existed annywheres—the lads might pretind to be deities, and wallop them about a bit in that character, and thin get thim together and lesson thim in the foolishness of such ignorance.

"Well, well, boys," says Tim, considering, "so ye do not let the sport diginerate into mere horseplay, I have no objections to a little fun of that nature, for a week or two annyhow."

But 'twas all too aisy, that jest, and it worked all too well. There worked with it the ancient, age-long memories of thim Greeks and Trojans. O'Kelly or O'Brien or wan of the others would come ashore from their island in a small boat and disembark in wan of the numerous coves screened by sand dunes, and suddenly appear in the midst of a combat, and thim pagan Greeks and Trojans would cry out 'twas a heathen deity in their midst. The appearance and bearing of the heroes from Erin, their superior craft and courage, made thim just like the tales of the gods had been going the rounds for centuries. They'd say, the Greeks or the Trojans would, that Zeus, the chief heathen, had joined the battle, or maybe Ares, the god of war, or Phoebus O'Pollo, and whole troops and squadrons would flee from wan Irishman.

Tim's lads would sit around their own camp fire at night and shake dice to see who would be on which side the next day; and Tim used to call that the council of Olympus, and put it all down in that poem he wrote about the fracas, which he called the *Iliad*. Now and thin contintions broke out amongst Tim's lads.

"That Hector," Duffy would say to O'Kelly, "could wallop ye to a fare-ye-well, Seaumas, was he not firmly convinced ye are an Olympian. Ye have nothing on him at all, at all, excipt for his superstitions."

"Ye lie, Duffy," would be the natural answer of blue-jawed O'Kelly; and Tim would have great ado to prevint the sudden death of wan or the other. Within a week there was a score of rows like that started.

And the war itsilf, beneath the city walls and

along the plain, got to be less and less of a war between human Greeks and Trojans and more of an
affair where, if the so-called deities did not urge
wan side or another forward, there was nothing
doing. So King Timothy O'Meara, out of patience
with the situation, sat down wan day with a quill
pen and a sheet of parchment and drew up an ulti-
matum which went like this:

PROCLAMATION

To All Ye Greeks and Trojans

*Oyez! Oyez! Oyez! Hereafther and from now on
us deities from Olympus will take no notice of the
brawls and contintions of ye Greeks and Trojans
unless so be ye make thim snappier.*

*Ayther ye are at war, or else ye are not. If ye are,
us deities would like to see some action we don't
have to be starting oursilves. If ye are not, 'tis time
ye dropped the foolish pretince of it.*

*'Tis our intintion to hold oursilves aloof for the
space of three weeks and give ye the final chance
to fight to a conclusion as real warriors should,
without fear nor favor from anny of us deities. If so
be ye have not the guts to take up with this fair
offer and go through with it, at the end of the three
weeks us deities will gang up and utterly destroy
both armies.*

*A word to the wise is sufficient, and ye can take
it or lave it.*

*Who do ye think ye are, annyhow, that ye should
monopolize the exclusive attintion of us deities that*

*may have important business elsewhere that ye
know nothing about?*

Signed, ZEUS, Head Heathen
ARES, deity of battle
HADES (X) his mark
POSEIDON, deity of the sea
HERMES
PHOEBUS O'POLLO
et al., and company.

*Olympus, Greece
June seventeenth
1589 B.C.*

"Now thin," says Tim, "we'll make a couple of
dozen copies, and me and some of you lads will slip
into town tonight and post some of thim up on the
street corner, and others we will take to the Greek
ships."

But instead of inspiring thim to action it seemed
to paralyze the Greeks and Trojans. Day after day
wint by and nothing started. The truth was, they'd
niver got anny communications from Olympus in
black and white before, and they was perturbed in
their minds.

Wan day Tim went ashore alone from his island
where the *Shamrock* was moored, and sat down in
a nook of rocks fronting the beach. His harp was
with him, and above him and behind him to landward was the dunes of sand. He was thinking this
whole expedition was a failure, and he'd be hard
put to it aven to get a good ballad out of it all—for

502

Tim niver thought much of that stuff he called the *Iliad* himsilf—when he heard the padding of horses' hoofs muffled in sand, and the soft slur of wheels, not very far away.

He judged a chariot had driven by on the sandy plain on the landward side of the barrier of dunes, and thought no more of it. But afther a few minutes a woman emerged from behind a hill of sand, not thirty yards from him, and ran down to the sea to bathe.

A bit of a scrap of a wan-piece bathing suit she was wearing, and a gleam of brightness she was as she raced and plunged into the sea and battled through the surf. Had it been early dawn instead of afthernoon, ye might have thought she was a ripple of the rose-and-golden morning moving on the dark blue wathers.

"By the powers," says Tim to himsilf, he says, "it may be there's something in the heathen superstitions of these parts afther all; for ayther that's a goddess swimming there or else me eyes need the expert attintion of a physician."

And his hand fell upon the strings of his harp, though he scarcely knew it, and his harp began to talk. "Are ye but a crest of golden foam upon a green-blue wave?" says the harp. "Come hither, foam upon the wave! Are ye goddess, are ye woman, are ye creature of the sea? Have all the tides of all the wathers of the world gathered their gleaming beauty to wan point, to thrust it like a spear's point through the heart of me? Come hither; here is my heart, point of the spear of beauty! All the seas of life are breaking in me soul and all the surf is beauty; and all the seas of all the world are ringing all the coasts with song; and all the waves of all the seas are an army of strong warriors, and ye are the sharp sword they have plunged through the heart of me! Come hither, woman, if ye be woman! Goddess, come hither! Gleaming arrow from the curved bow of the ocean, bright arrow from the twanging string of ocean, ye are sped to pierce the heart of me."

'Tis such nonsense as that a harp will be speaking when 'tis left alone with a young fella under such circumstances—and always 'tis "Come hither!" will be the burden of its speech.

Out in the wather the woman heard. She swam farther out, as if to be beyond the reach of it. Thin she turned and floated and listened ag'in. For a minute the music stopped; betwixt his lifted finger and the strings a moment's silence gathered, and farther out ag'in she swam. And thin the song—for Tim had no consciousness that he had annything to do with it himsilf personal—the song, like a queer fisherman, reeled her slowly in, and she drifted ashore like wan in a dream.

Straight up to him she walked, and he rose; and the dream and bewilderment of the music was on both of thim.

"Are ye a god?" says she. Considering the looks and bearing of the man, and the woman's superstitions, 'twas an entirely logical question. "Are ye a god?" she says, simple and frank and in all good faith.

504

"Do ye judge of it," says Tim, aquelly simple and direct, and dropped an arm about her and kissed her.

"Ye are!" she says, says she, afther a moment or two, with a long breath.

"I've had me moments of feeling like wan," says Tim, quite sincere, "but niver before a moment like this."

"I niver knew before," says she, sizing him up in wonder and admiration, "that there was anny red-headed gods. Are ye Pan—ye with your music —or are ye O'Pollo?"

"Which would ye rather, mavourneen?" says Tim, always anxious to plaise the ladies, and this wan in particular.

"If ye're not a god," says she, looking a little worried, "'tis terrible unconvintional and indiscreet me kissing ye like this, for I'm a married woman mesilf. I'd rather ye was O'Pollo."

"Thin ye can call me O'Pollo, mavourneen," says Tim, with a smile.

"Oh! Oh!" she cries, alarmed by his smile and his tone of voice. "Ye're not a god at all! Ye're a man! And ye've tricked me by your music into a most unconvintional situation! What will ye be thinking of me? Oh, I hate ye for it!"

"Arrah, now, mavourneen," says Tim, he says; "make your mind aisy. I'll prove to ye agin that I am wan."

Which he did.

"Yes, oh, yes!" she says, says she, with a sigh. "Ye be wan; I know ye must be wan now—and the most convintional woman is hilpless entirely agin the gods!"

"Of course," says he; "let your mind be at rest."

"It is," says she. She gave him a wondering look. "I'm sure ye are wan," she says, "but 'tis strange that, too. 'Twas always in me mind a god would be a little different from this, somehow."

"How?" says Tim.

"More like a ghost, maybe, some way," she says. "More kind of loose and misty-like in the material he's made of," she says. She wiped her lips where he had kissed the salt wather from thim, with the back of her hand. "Ye're not misty at all, at all," she says. "Ye're more like a god would be if so he was a man at the same time," says she.

"Tell me about yoursilf, colleen," says Tim, charmed with the childish simplicity of the creature. "Are ye maybe wan of the goddesses of these parts?"

"I'm related to a number of thim," says she, so solemn that Tim saw she really believed that ignorant superstition. "I came from over there," says she, pointing across the wather in the general direction of Greece. "But at prisint," she says, "I'm living in the city down yonder." She motioned towards the towers and walls of Troy, swimming in the sunlight half a dozen miles down the coast.

Tim O'Meara had a sudden mind.

"And next," says he, he says, "ye'll be coming with me to Erin! Get yoursilf dressed and we'll be off at wance!"

"Dressed?" And thin she cried: "Oh, ye're not a

god at all, at all! 'Tis a man ye are! No god would be afther noticing the kind of clothes I was wearing!"

All wan blush of anger and confusion she was; and whin he tried to speak ag'in, she snatched up his sword which he had unhooked from his belt and laid on the ground, and banged him across the face with it. Lucky for Tim, 'twas in the scabbard. "I hate ye!" she cried, and flung the weapon at him and turned and ran. She was up and over the line of sand dunes in an instant, and him feeling of his face and wondering was his nose broken.

"The wild cat!" he says. But he liked thim like that. He stood for some minutes looking towards the town of Troy in the distance, and already forming a plan to take it. Of a sudden a pebble rolled from the top of a sand dune and bounced and pinged agin the strings of his harp. He turned and looked up. There she was, in her proper street clothes, gazing down on him with a countenance all lighted up with curiosity.

"Where is that Erin ye spoke of?" she says.

Before he could give her that lesson in geography she had vanished ag'in. Tim struggled to the top of the dunes, but she was scampering towards a chariot with two attendants that was waiting fifty yards away. She jumped in and the horses was off at a gallop towards Troy. 'Twas ayther the breeze of their gallop or her own hand that waved a bit of a bright scarf back at Tim.

That night Tim reconnoitered. And the next day at dusk he was in the town of Troy himsilf, in the

507

guise of a profissional minstrel. There was a canal cut inward from the sea through which the Trojans got the greater part of their supplies; and this entry was definded by great ballistas and catapults. The Greeks had sea force enough to harry and discommode this commerce, but not enough to stop it entirely. Nor had the Trojans the superior naval force to sally out and destroy the entire Greek fleet. The war had been a queer kind of a stand-off. The Greeks controlled the plains in the near vicinity of the city, and had destroyed all the crops there and taken all the livestock, but at a distance the allies and countryfolks of the Trojans still carried on and slipped materials into the town in barges.

'Twas through this wather gate to the city that Tim entered, with his harp and in a small boat. He played some chunes to the guards and cracked thim some jokes, and they passed him on from station to station. Whin he had tied his boat to a wharf and begun to wander through the streets wan of the first things he noticed was long lines of people waiting at the wells of the town. Officers were rationing out wather very carefully.

Terrible thronged was that big town, and ivery male person Tim saw from fifteen to sixty was bearing arms. The city was laid out like a great wheel; at the center, where the hub would be, was King Priam's citadel. It stood upon a height of rocky land and was both a palace and a fortress. Terraces led up to it from the city streets, and ivery terrace was capable of definse. Long streets, splendid, and so broad that six chariots might drive abreast, radiated like spokes of the wheel from the citadel to the gates in the walls; and at each gate was a watch tower. Tim judged the price of real estate in that town was high, for the tindincy in building had been to go up in the air. Ivery building had its tower, or became a tower itsilf, like we're putting thim up in New York and Brooklyn today; and manny families lived in each building.

In the blue dusk, with lights flaring high above in the manny windows, and the whole city crowned and adorned by King Priam's lofty citadel with its own flares here and there upon its scarps and battlemints, and billows of shadow and cloud rolling in from the sea, perhaps the town seemed taller than it was. For to Tim's mind it seemed to thrust itsilf up towards the yellow moon and early stars that hung above it; 'twas hard to tell where city left off and sky began, and that gave it all a touch of shifty magic to his eyes. Indade, wance or twice he had the feeling, as he took his way towards the citadel, that he had built it all himsilf out of the music of his harp, for the amusemint of his own fancy, and could tumble it into nothingness ag'in with a slam of discontented discords. The dream of that woman was strong upon his soul, and the mood of his intellect glimmered with the extravagance of poetry and love.

"I'm the minstrel that King Priam sint for," he said to the guards, and all of thim was impressed by the port of the man and the conquering glamour that walked with him, and into the citadel he went.

He was sure that the lady he'd met on the seashore would be somewhere about the King's palace, for there was quality in ivery line and look of her.

And she was the first thing Tim seen whin he entered the King's council hall. A great and lofty room that was, with a high vaulted roof. At the far end was a dais, with a great fat man upon a throne and a fat woman upon another throne near him. A group of half a dozen others stood or sat near King Priam and Quane Hecuba; and this woman of Tim's was by Quane Hecuba's throne. A man's voice said, as Tim entered and strode up the hall:

"Your Majisty, suppose we lave that point to Helen hersilf."

Tim's colleen opened her mouth as if to speak. Thin she seen Tim and recognized him. She closed her mouth ag'in, and stared at Tim and said nothing. With that, all prisint turned and stared. Tim stepped forward boldly.

"Your Majisty," he says, says he, bowing mannerly to King Priam. "I'm the minstrel was brought the word ye wanted me at the palace here this night."

King Priam opened his eyes wide and rubbed his forehead. "I don't quite remimber ye," he says, "but sit down somewheres, minstrel, and I'll spake to ye prisintly."

Tim sat down quietly and pretended to be studying the condition of his harp, and they all give him a long look. Calm and placid he received it, and prisintly they wint on with their hot argumint ag'in, and ignored him—all excipt Helen, and kape her eyes from him she could not.

They was all so heated with the business in hand, excipt King Priam himsilf, that in a minute they forgot Tim. King Priam was robed in fine white wool trimmed with purple and clasped with gold. Tim, as the argumint wint on, might have thought most of the time that the King was aslape; for his eyes was mostly shut and his head drooped forward so that his crown was tilted crooked on his white poll. But his hands was clasped over his enormous stomach and now and thin ye could see he was twiddling his thumbs. And now and thin he opened both his eyes and mouth and aimed at a golden cuspidor was set convenient to the throne; for the King was chewing betel nut—a most unroyal habit he'd picked up from a wandering Hindu sage. Quane Hecuba was a red-cheeked ould dame like a dumpling, with manny gems that twinkled and a blond wig was all awry. With a pair of bronze knitting needles she was clicking away at a stomach band for wan of her numerous grandchildren.

By the look on Helen's face, where she stood near Quane Hecuba's chair, she was wondering wance more was Tim a god or not. She was pale and red by turns, and her breath was quick. She was in a bad enough jam before Tim strolled in, as he seen whin he realized who the others were. There was Paris, whom she had eloped from Sparta with. There was Menelaus, her former husband, whom she had run away from. There was Hector, Paris' brother. There was King Agamemnon, Menelaus' brother, with his ferocious visage and the yellow fangs that showed whin he opened his mouth.

"Helen should come back and mind her house like an honest woman," says this King Agamemnon. "If she does not come back, we must have an indimnity in place of her. Is that not right, brother?" he says to Menelaus.

This Menelaus was a boyo with a bull neck set on heavy shoulders, and a twirl of hair on his forehead was altogether like a bull's. He glared at Helen and nodded to his brother.

Tim had walked in on an attimpt to settle the whole war.

"Ye've not been able to take her, ye dog face!" says Hector to Agamemnon. And Paris laughed and trifled with a golden-plated spear.

"Now, boys, don't be afther calling names!" says King Priam, with his eyes closed. "Remimber this is a peace parley, and not wan of your famous contists of strength and skill."

"Himsilf there," says Quane Hecuba, nodding towards Priam, "is getting nigh his dotage, or he would tell ye that the gods is tired of all this strife —'tis themsilves has said as much. For me own part, does Helen go or does Helen stay, it matthers little to me. The wan thing I want is the end of this war."

" 'Tis well I know ye'd be glad to be getting rid of me, Quane Hecuba," says Helen, with a glance at Tim.

"Sorrow came with ye," says the Quane, still knitting and placid, "and the divil can take ye, for all I care. I'm not the kind of woman has trouble with

512

anny of me daughters-in-law as a rule, but afther ye strife follows, as plague follows drought. Howiver, if 'tis so decided we kape ye here, kape ye I will, and spake ye civil whin ye spake me so."

"Nobody loves me," says Helen; and ag'in her voice was for Tim. "Nobody wants me!"

"I do!" says Paris and Menelaus in wan breath.

"Ye do not, nayther of ye!" flares Helen. Maybe she was anxious Tim should get the rights of the story. "The only reason Menelaus wants me back is because I'm Quane of Sparta in me own right, and he'll niver feel aisy on his throne unless so be I reign beside him! He was niver the man to come storming across the seas for the love of anny woman, not him. And as for ye, Paris," she says, says she, turning on that handsome lad; "'tis often ye say ye love me, but whin did ye ever have the nerve to face Menelaus here and fight for me with your own hand?"

"Always there was wan of thim Olympian deities on his side," says Paris, smiling and waving his hand, airy and graceful. "Ye know full well, mavourneen, I'd fight anny man in the world for ye, so none of thim Olympian deities comes meddling into the matther."

Menelaus says to Paris, with a scowl, dropping his hand to his sword: "All thim Olympian deities is laying off this war right now, and you and me can sittle this affair in wan minute."

"Ye spake so bold because ye know I can't fight ye now," says Paris; "and ye here under word of honor and flag of truce."

513

"Now thin," says Agamemnon; "it's got to the place where ye can no longer sittle it personal—ye two. Too manny others has become involved. King Priam, here is me terms to ye: Give us Helen and ten thousand head of good cattle and fifty of your best ships, and we go in peace. Or kape Helen, and give us twinty thousand head of cattle and wan hundred ships."

" 'Tis exorbitant, dog face," says Hector, "aven if ye were in a military position to demand it, which ye are not. The walls of this town is still intact."

"And the wells is all but dry," says Agamemnon.

"And your own people back in Greece is half of thim rising in revolt agin ye," retorts Hector.

King Priam nodded and took a little golden box from the bosom of his royal robe and hilped himsilf to another chew of betel nut.

"Himself here does nothing all day long but sit and chew and let the world go by," sighs Quane Hecuba. "Ye fools all!" she cried suddenly, and laid down her knitting. "Stop this war!" she says. "Both the human sinse of mortal intellect and the warnings of the gods tells ye the wan thing—stop this war!"

"There's something in what hersilf here says," King Priam remarks, his chew in his cheek and his thumbs twiddling. "I didn't want anny war, nor anny Helen nayther—there was none more surprised than whin Paris comes councing home with her, expicting iverywan in Troy to be as plaised as he was himsilf. And now there's no doubt the gods is all stirred up inimical to all of us. Agamemnon, I'll settle with ye on the basis of the status quo ante—take Helen, and be off with ye, and be damned to ye!"

"No!" cries Hector, jumping to his feet. "Our Trojan honor demands we keep her!"

"We'll take her, and we'll have ships and cattle too!" says Agamemnon.

"I hate ye all!" cries Helen, so vehement that Quane Hecuba dropped her knitting and King Priam swallowed his betel nut. "All of ye I hate! Ye pass me back and forth, and bargain for me with cattle, like I was a prize cow meself—and me a quane in me own right! I hate ye all!" And with that she turned and ran from the room through a door was back of the thrones, and slammed the door afther her. But before she slammed it she give wan look at Tim.

The discussion rose high and loud ag'in, promising annything but peace, and Tim watched his chance and slipped unnoticed from the hall. He had the intuition she'd be making for the open air. And 'twas on wan of the terraces he found her, high above the flare and rattle of the city. She was at the base of a bronze statue, leaning agin it; and whin Tim came up to her she was beating her head against the bronze and weeping—maybe she'd seen him coming, and annyhow, the thick hair on her head protected it from real injury.

Tim slipped an arm about her.

"Lave me die, Redhead," she says, says she;

"niver before was woman or quane humiliated as I have been, and there's nothing left but death!"

And she give her head a real bang, and maybe it hurt her more than she intinded, for she left off that diversion.

"There's me left," says Tim. "And there's Erin left, mavourneen."

"Is it like Olympus?"

"Practically the same," says Tim.

"And which wan of the gods are ye?" she says. For the certainty he was wan had returned to her in full force. "Are ye O'Pollo?"

"Listen, mavourneen," says he; "I love ye so much I must be truthful with ye. I ain't anny deity at all, at all. I'm an Irishman."

"That must be the same thing, darlint," she says. "'Tis no use your telling me ye're a mortal man; for mortal men I have been married to, and I know the difference. Oh," she says, all wan blaze of rapture from head to foot, "'twas the dream of me girlhood to be abducted by a deity, and now the dream's come true! All us girls in Greece used to talk about it," she says, "but I'm the only wan it's happened to! Whin do we start for Erin?" she says.

"Now," says Tim.

But 'twas not to be that aisy. Wan of the palace doors had opened soft behind thim and Quane Hecuba came out, walking fat and quiet-footed in her sandals. There was half a dozen respectful guards behind her, and wan of her grandchildren was suffering with the colic laid stomach down across the muscle of her left arm. The Quane looked at thim two lovers and chuckled scornful, and the child she was jiggling gurgled in a most knowing way, and the Quane said to Tim, very skeptical and pointed:

"So ye're a minstrel, are ye? Minstrel! Huh!"

Tim looked at her guards, and he looked down the slopes toward the city streets. A company of a hundred spearmen was coming up the terrace toward their barracks in the citadel. 'Twas too manny, aven for Tim O'Meara. He did not reply to the Quane; he murmured, quick, to Helen: "Be at this spot two hours before daybreak."

With that he was off through the dusk before Quane Hecuba could make up her mind to shout to the soldiers to stay him.

Tim was out of the canal with his rowboat and back at his island with his Irish lads in but little more than an hour. He told thim the situation, and they got their gear and arms in shape as quick as might be, and 'twas not long afther midnight the *Shamrock* was under way for the shore. 'Twas Tim's idea him and his Irish would presint thimsilves at the Skian gate as deities, and as deities march to the palace and carry off the girl.

But things had took a turn. Whilst they was still five miles out at sea, Seaumas O'Kelly cried out: "By the powers, Tim, Your Majisty, there's something doing yonder!"

A fire was burning by the Skian gate. While they looked, from the top of the watch tower at the gate there suddenly spouted a burst of flame; 'twas on fire inside. And thin a flame within the town leaped higher, so that they saw it above the walls. In a few minutes more they began to hear a confused great noise and the shouts of men and the clanging of arms.

"The Greeks are in the town!" cried Tim, and they all bent to their big oars.

The parley had broke up in a row. 'Twas scarcely over before that Greek O'Day, who called himself Odysseus, appeared at the Skian gate with a big wooden horse on wheels, and the tale that 'twas intinded as a prisint to Quane Helen from her loving Spartan subjects overseas, who continued to regret her absence—and for all he knew what 'twas for, says this O'Day, she could use it to dry clothes on or something. Whilst he parleyed with the doubtful guard, his men wheeled it agin the gate itsilf, which was made of great oaken beams braced and re-enforced with bronze. Thin this wily O'Day sets fire to its tail, which was made of tow soaked in oil, and steps back. In a minute there was an explosion like ye had thrown a torch into a room full of culluloid collars; for the inside of that wooden horse was filled with hundreds of gallons of naphtha and oil. The burning fluid was flung all over the beams of the gate thimsilves, and they was dry as tinder, for 'twas a hot, rainless summer. The Skian gate was a good mile distant from the salt-wather canal, and the only well near was almost dry. Whin the charred beams weakened, a thousand Greeks crashed thim and forced their way through the flaming breach; and thin they rushed a long row of wooden barracks near the gate and set fire to thim. The alarm was given in all quarters of the town, but the Greeks were pouring through the Skian gate by the hundred, and lancing deep into the city, and fires climbing and spreading iverywhere, long before Tim and his Irish beached the *Shamrock* and made their own way into the doomed capital.

'Twas a mad town that Tim and his Irish entered, with bells clamoring and trumpets screaming and the shouts of warriors and the shock of arms and the yells and squeals of chariot horses and the whirl and roar of reaching fires. For the Greeks carried fire to ivery house they took and ivery street they assaulted, and the Trojans had to fight agin both the Greeks and the fires. The wather shortage licked them from the start. Some of the buildings was masonry, and some tile with stucco over it, and some made part of wood and plaster, but whativer the outside material, the inside of all was braced and lined and floored with wood. Tall towers they was, and that was their undoing; for whin a building caught inside, it became just wan terrible high and roaring chimney.

Tim, as he entered, mixed up with a streaming tide of Greeks and unnoticed amongst thim for the moment, saw a company of Trojan cavalry flanked by chariots trying to form in wan of the broad streets for a dash at the thick of the Greeks. But just as the horsemen got the word to charge, a big tower came roaring down right across the street and the whole company disappeared amidst the smoke and thunder. Out of the crash squirmed wan hurt horse with its hind quarters smashed, and Tim himself put his sword through its heart out of pity, for 'twas screaming like a woman. More and more Trojans was hastening from ivery quarter, and more Greeks surging through the gate; and 'twas a terrible street-to-street and house-to-house struggle, with aven the girls and women flinging down crockery and brass kettles upon the invaders, and iverywhere a most eruptive tumult like hell, saving your prisince, was sick at its stomach.

In wan compact body like a steel fist, Tim and his Irish hammered their way straight across the turmoil toward the citadel—not that they had to do much hammering at this stage of the game, nayther. For iverywhere they was seen, under the heave and swing of those fiery skies, the cry would go up: "The gods! The gods!" And whether 'twas Greeks or Trojans, all men that saw thim scampered from before thim.

'Twas through strange scenes they approached the citadel. Horses raced loose and riderless, cattle milled and clashed their horns and bellowed, dogs ran here and yon, singed cats wailed and scurried, and rats from the falling houses, red-eyed and insane, kept pace, fearless, with the cats—all these, and men and women no less mad, were before thim, and behind thim the main strife of battle and the Greeks advancing and the jumping fires. Wan small boy Tim saw astride a white bull; he'd nothing on but his undershirt, and was blowing a trumpet and having the time of his life. And there kipt pace with the Irish for a mile or more an old woman gone mad, who'd saved a mattress from her burning home. A drunken trooper came from a wine shop and took it from her; he stood befuddled-like with it for a moment and thin cast it to the pavement and laid down on it. And the old woman reached down and took the drunkard's sword and plunged it in hersilf, instead of him, as if with the loss of the mattress the world was at its end.

And madness was in the citadel itsilf. Tim and his men slashed their way through a moil of broken regiments that was trying to re-form in the plazas and parks and open spaces at the foot of the citadel, and up and into the hall he'd left but a few hours before; and there he came on a dozen of the Trojan leaders in a council. Paris was there, and Æneas and Hector, and Helen, sitting dumb at the foot of King Priam's throne, and ould Priam himsilf, sprawled in fat slumber with his kingdom toppling.

"We'll make a stand below," Hector was saying, as Tim came in; "and if we lose, we'll burn the palace oursilves, and perish with it. And Helen too!" he cried, with an angry look at her who was the author of all their woes.

"Helen too!" says Æneas. And Paris said nothing, but looked around him, running his tongue along his dry lips, as if seeking his own way out.

With a gust of gray smoke from the burning town, and the red fires behind thim, the Irish swept into the hall.

" 'Tis the gods! The gods!" cried a Trojan chief, and all the warriors shrank back. But Helen jumped up with a cry, and was in Tim O'Meara's arms.

"Gods or not," cried Hector, beside himsilf with desperation, " 'tis me own hall and me father's!" And with that, with a most magnificent bravery, he loosed a javelin at Tim O'Meara—a courage more than mortal was his, for he thought 'twas more than mortal man that he assailed.

The spear glanced from Tim's shield. It swerved and laid open the blue jaw of Seaumas O'Kelly. The red blood spurted. There was a roar wint up.

"Not gods but men!" cried the Trojans. "Not gods! They bleed!"

With that, the fight was on.

"There's some satisfaction in this!" says Mc-Carty, hanging sword and sword with that Æneas. " 'Tis no fun at all, at all, unless they stand up to ye!"

"Right ye are, Mac," says O'Reilly, putting ten inches of steel through a Trojan's neck. "There's the makin's of a sweet little brawl here!"

Tim drove straight at Hector; and that splendid warrior whirled up his sword and met him halfway. The most distinguished swordsman the world iver saw was Timothy O'Meara—me ancestor he was, and your own, but ye are not worthy of him! 'Twould have been pleasant pastime for Tim to have given him a fencing lesson before he disposed of him, but 'twas no time for mere diversion now, and Tim regretted the necissity for haste, aven as he laid him low with a thrust under the arm.

"So ye'd burn the lady, would ye, Hector?" he says, as the toughest Trojan of thim all fell clashing to the marble floor. But aven as he spoke an arrow pinged agin his breastplate, and an instant later another wan splintered on his helmet. 'Twas that Paris, peering from behind his father's throne and shooting with a horn bow. Helen had located him before Tim had, and as Tim cut down two spearmen and strode toward him, she slipped a spear through him.

"That's me sicond husband, Tim," she says, looking down on him. "He was niver anny good, and I'm glad to have me freedom back nice and legal."

"Arrah, darlint, here comes your first wan!" says Tim. 'Twas so. For into the hall burst Menelaus, and Agamemnon was with him, and Ajax and Achilles, and a score more of thim Greek lads. The vanguard of the Greeks had lanced through the Trojans in the streets below, and up into the palace, seeking Helen hersilf. What Trojans was left was still shouting: "Not gods! Not gods but men!" and the Greek lads took the tip at wance, and came rushing at the Irish.

What had gone before was child's play to what happened now, for the Greeks was wild with victory and crazy with the wine of blood-letting. 'Twas a strange fight. All about the palace the wild city reeled and roared, and the great slashing blades of fire tore at the dark heart of the night; thousands of the Trojans still battled in the courts and streets below, and there was the constant thunder of the falling buildings; all up and down the terrace the warriors strove, and all up and down the sky blue shadows and yellow flame twined about each other like serpents and bit and struck. The citadel itself was afire now, and smoke and flames was within the great hall—and that queer fat king huddled in his throne and sleeping through it all.

With the Trojan leaders trampled under foot, the Irish turned to meet the Greek rush.

"This was worth waiting for," says Duffy to Regan, smiling happy as he took that big Ajax to pieces, neat and scientific.

"Give them the point; they ain't used to it," advised Cavanagh to O'Brien.

"Hark to King Tim singing!" says O'Neill to Murphy. "That means the boss's blood is getting up, indade!"

Tim was. 'Twas a way he had whin he was happy in battle; and happy he was now, for Menelaus was in front of him, and he hadn't liked that man from the first minute he set eyes on him. He pleasured himsilf in the job, and took pains to make the combat interesting—for was not Helen hersilf looking on?

"Don't fence wide, Tim," warned Keogh; "that boy ye have there is not without the rudimints of the art himsilf."

"King Tim's showing off," laughs O'Toole to O'Connel, as he freed his blade from the throat of Agamemnon.

"King Tim's in love!" laughs O'Donnell to Nolan. "King Tim's in love!" laughs Nolan to Rooney, and Rooney laughed and lifted the head from a Spartan prince with a backhand sweep; and Hickey and O'Sullivan laughed, and all the Irish laughed—and a terrible thing for their foes to hear is that Irish laughter whin it rises from the din of battle.

"Gods afther all!" said Menelaus, whin he heard that laughter. Thin Tim killed him quick, lest his superstitions come back on him and spoil the fight.

"There's your first husband, mavourneen," he says to Helen. "And we'll be out of here quick." For parts of the citadel itsilf was beginning to crash and fall.

"I'm glad both thim fellas has passed on," says Helen to Tim, looking from Paris to Menelaus. "It makes no doubt of me being a legal widow, darlint. I've always been a convintional woman," she says, says she, "and discreet."

"I admire ye for it," says Tim, proticting her with his shield, as he slashed his way at the head of the Irish towards the outer door. 'Twas just at the door itsilf that O'Kelly put the finishing touches to Achilles.

"I could have made something of that man, with a month's tuition," says Seaumas O'Kelly, looking down on him regretful. "Well, good-by, cousin," he says, says he; "'tis too late now!"

Down the slope the Irish cut their way, and through the blazing town, with Helen in their midst. Plunderers and drunkards was abroad in the burning ruins, and there was the cries of women and all the hell of a sacked and taken city. Three or four times Tim had to stop and face about and fight off bands of Greeks that hung upon their flanks or disputed the way; and of more than a score of Irish that wint into the town that night there was but twelve came out ag'in, and all of thim was hurt.

'Twas dawn whin they reached the seashore and found the *Shamrock*. Red dawn came up out of Asia behind the red city, for now the citadel itsilf was blazing high, and 'twas like two terrible red roses of destruction was flaring in the heavens.

"Ye have fine flowers for yer wedding day, Helen," says Tim, pointing to thim.

"Yes," says she, contented-like; "aren't they beautiful? Oh, Tim, darlint, I'm so happy! And it all goes to show," she says, says she, "that does a girl cling to her ideals, and always seek for the finest and the best, she'll be rewarded in the end," she says.

Just thin they seen ould Quane Hecuba, sitting on the sand, staring with queer eyes out at the wather; and she was alone, excipt the child she'd comforted the night before was sleeping in her lap.

"'Tis wan of Hector's little boys, Tim," says Helen, good-natured. "Let's take thim along with us."

But the ould Quane gave her a glare of hate, and rose and clasped the child to her bosom, and stumbled off along the sand.

"Well, Dad," said Terence O'Meara to the narrator, "that shows where our ancestor, Homer, got the material for the *Iliad*. But how about the *Odyssey*?"

526

The old gentleman reflected for a moment. Then: "Two or three years later," he explained, "comes that O'Day, that called himsilf Odysseus, to Ireland. He'd been wandering here and yon, and got himsilf mixed up with a woman somewheres, and he was afraid to go home, for he could not think of annything to tell his wife. So Tim, he sits down wan afthernoon and writes him the *Odyssey*, so he could go home with a good story for Mrs. O'Day."

V Prefaces

Preface to a Cook Book

An elderly gentleman who found me a bore once asked me desperately, "Are you fond of literature?"

"I dote upon it," I said.

He was a painter; we had met at a kind of tea where every one was talking of art and literature and things like that; we hated each other at once because each had been told that the other was interesting.

"Oh, you *dote* on it!" he said, after a moment of venomous silence.

"I do!" I replied firmly.

He sneered; it was evident that he wished me to understand that he was incredulous.

"Sir," I said, striving with all the rancor of my nature to be offensive, "sir, are *you* fond of literature?"

"I am," he said, putting on a pair of eyeglasses, and looking as if he might look like Whistler if he thought me worth wasting the look on.

"What *sort* of literature are you fond of?" I asked.

"I am fond of Lord Tennyson's Poems," he retorted insultingly.

I permitted myself a faint, superior smile. It maddened him, as I intended it should; his nose turned a whitish blue as the blood receded from his face.

"Did you ever read any of Meredith?" I asked.

"I did!" he replied.

I turned toward the fireplace, as if willing to veil a doubt.

He took off his glasses; he pointed at me a long, bony digit that trembled with anger.

"Did *you?*"

"Yes," I said.

"What?" he demanded.

"For one thing," I told him, " 'The Egoist.' "

I dwelt upon *The Egoist* as if I tasted a subtle, ulterior jest in mentioning it to *him*. I hoped that would puzzle him.

"One of Meredith's lesser known pieces, no doubt," he said.

"Oh, no!" I affirmed.

"Not so well known as 'Lucile,' " he asserted.

" 'Lucile'?"

"What—you do not mean that you have never read Owen Meredith's masterpiece, 'Lucile'!"

"Owen!" I gasped; but before I could do more than gasp he quoted:

" *We may live without poetry, music or art,*
We may live without conscience, and live without
  heart,

532

We may live without friends, we may live without
  books;
But civilized man cannot live without cooks.'"

The next instant our hostess was upon us, mur-
muring with a bright, arch smile: "Ah! Locksley
Hall! Those old Victorian things were wonderful
in their way, after all . . . were they not? I *knew*
you two dear men would be just simply wild about
each other!" . . . She was that sort of hostess.

Those lines were printed in blue and gold, with
a red border around them, in the front of a Cook
Book that was one of my grandmother's wedding
presents. Above them was the picture of an ample
and dimpled young woman in a white apron, who
was smiling and mixing something in a bowl. I
cannot remember the time when I was not aware
that this young woman's name was Dorcas. No one
ever told me that her name was Dorcas, but the
knowledge somehow came to me while I was still
in kilts, and it is as Dorcas that I think of her to
this day.

One glanced at her and knew at once the sort of
things that Dorcas would cook, that Dorcas was
born to cook. Never, in later life, have I sat down to
dinner without saying to myself, "Ah! things look
Dorcassy to-night!" or, "Alas! there is nothing Dorcassy here."

Do not mistake me; my affection for Dorcas was
(and is) based upon nothing so simple as her air
of bucolic wholesomeness. I am no advocate of
plain cooking. Dorcas was not a Plain Cook. She

was the mistress of seven hundred complications, and in them she rejoiced. If there was an apparent simplicity in the result, that appearance proceeded from the excellent art of Dorcas which subdued many ingredients to a delicious unison. For she was an artist.

But she was not a scientist. Dorcas had never studied culinary chemistry. If you had tried to talk seriously to Dorcas about her gastric juices she would have been as shocked as if you had mentioned her legs. Dorcas cooked for the sight and smell and soul and palate of Man; his digestion did the best it could. She betrayed Man's duodenum, and he loved her for it.

And suppose the richness of Dorcas *did* ruin one's digestion. What then? Is the digestion a god that we should regard it reverently? To my mind there is something base in considering one's digestion as if it were one of the higher attributes. I like to see a reckless, adventurous, headstrong, romantic, dashing sort of eater. I like the vaunting spirit that proclaims, "By heaven, I will conquer that plum pudding or die!"

Let us be sensible about this thing. . . . An Average Man may eat the Dorcas Cooking from infancy on to the age of forty years before he becomes an incurable dyspeptic. Suppose, then, he must retire to poached eggs and malted milk—what memories he has to look back upon!

I once had a second cousin, a prudent boy, who thought a great deal of his digestion; Dorcas could not tempt him; he knew all about his alimentary canal and gave himself as many airs as a bumptious young anchorite who has just donned his first hair shirt. He exasperated me; if he had been deliberately saving his digestion for the first thirty-five years of life in order to enjoy it to the full and with more mature discrimination during the latter thirty-five I could have understood him. But no—he intended to eat poached eggs and malted milk to the frugal end.

But the universe is not on the side of frugality; the stars were hurled broadcast from the hand of a spendthrift God. . . . Cousin Tom, going back to his office after a lunch of oatmeal crackers on his twenty-eighth birthday, was killed by a brick which fell from the chimney of a chop house in which I sat eating a steak *en casserole* with mushrooms and thinking sentimentally of Dorcas. He died without issue, and carried his gastric juices unimpaired to the grave. In a way I took a certain satisfaction in his death, as it proved the folly of prudence; and yet I wept at the funeral, for the thought struck me, "What could I not do with Tom's practically virgin digestive organs if he had but contrived to leave them to me!"

There was a stomach that had never really lived . . . and now it never would!

It is better to go swaggering through the cates of life loose-lipped and genial and greedy, embracing pleasures and suffering pains, than to find one's self, in the midst of caution, incontinently slain by chance and eaten by worms.

Preface to a Book of Fishhooks

This little book of flies and hooks and guts and hackles, which was presented to us by a friend who heard us say we liked to go fishing—we may as well admit at once that it is full of riddles we cannot rede. We know nothing about trout, and have no great ambition to learn. Fishing for trout has too much exertion and bodily effort about it to be attractive. One tramps about over rough country and gets one's self wet in cold water, and tangles one's hook in one's hair and ears, and all that sort of thing.

Our idea of fishing is to put all the exertion up to the fish. If they are ambitious we will catch them. If they are not, let them go about their business. If a fish expects to be caught by us he has to look alive. We give him his opportunity, and he must make the most of it.

Most of our fishing, and the only fishing we ever really enjoyed, was done with a worm, a hook, a leaden sinker, a line and a willow pole. We wouldn't know what to do with a reel. We expect a fish to eat the hook very thoroughly, to persist until he gets it well down and then to signal us that all is well by pulling the float under water; a reel is superfluous; one flips the pole over one's head and the fish lands somewhere in the bushes behind.

A little quiet river or a creek, with low banks and plenty of big trees along the banks, is the only place to fish; and the fish should be mostly bullheads. Bullheads know their business; they hook themselves more completely and competently than any other fish. A bullhead will swallow the worm, the hook, and the lead sinker, a part of the line, and then grumble because he hasn't been able to eat the float and the pole. And you can leave it all up to him. You can sit in the shade and watch the float bobbing and jerking about in the serene consciousness that he will do a good job. When he pulls the pole itself out of the socket of earth into which you have jabbed the butt end of it, then is the time to interfere and bring him to land. Don't hold the pole yourself; it is too much trouble.

Being out of the water doesn't make much difference to the average bullhead. We don't suppose he could stand it more than two or three days, unless there was a damp wind blowing, but a few hours more or less are nothing to him. After having eaten as much of your fishing tackle as you will permit him to have before interfering, you might think that he would be a little dejected. But not so. You go to take the hook out of him, and he rushes at you and horns you, with a queer purring noise, and shows every disposition to fight it out on land.

And he seldom knows when he is dead. Often in the course of a day we have caught a bushel or so of bullheads and thrown them into the back of the buggy and driven home with them, five or six miles, maybe. Arrived at home we would find them stiff and caked with dried mud and dust, and to all appearances dead, having been out of the water and jogging along in the hot afternoon sun for a couple of hours. But throw them into a barrel of water, and in a few minutes they were swimming around as if nothing had happened, grinning over the top of the barrel and begging for more worms and hooks and lead sinkers. Refreshed by his cool plunge, the beast was ready for another romp. The bullhead is not a beautiful fish, and has no claims to aristocracy, but he is enduring.

We never liked to fish from a boat. You have to row the thing about, and that is a lot of trouble. Select a big, shady tree that bends over a pool in some little inland stream and lie down under the tree, and lie there all day and fish and eat and smoke and chew tobacco and watch the dragonflies and spit into the water. If you feel like swimming a little, all right—it doesn't particularly bother the bullheads. But it is a mistake to go to sleep.

If you go to sleep while you are loafing, how are you going to know you are loafing? And if you don't know it, what satisfaction is there in it? And it is also a mistake to think too deeply. If you do that, about the time you begin to get on the track of the secret of the universe some fool fish will hook himself, and you will have to attend to him.

Lie with your hat over your face and watch thoughts carefully from under the brim of it as they come toward you out of the woods or up the creek. And if a thought that seems as if it were going to be too profound or troublesome tries to crawl up on you shoo it away and wait for an easy thought. And when you get an easy thought hold on to it and think it for a long time and enjoy it.

The best thoughts to have when you are fishing are the thoughts about what you would do if you had a million dollars. After a while you get sort of lenient toward the world, and unambitious, and think it's a little selfish of you to want a whole million, and say "Shucks! I'd be willing to take a hundred thousand!" And you think maybe if you roused up a little and looked over the edge of the bank you would see a streak of gold in the soil, and then you would go and buy that land of the farmer that owns it and get rich off of the gold. And then you remember that you don't know who owns the land and it would be considerable trouble to have to ask questions around and find out. So it doesn't seem worth while to look over the edge of the bank and see whether the gold is there after all. And, anyhow, would it be fair, to whatever farmer owns the land, to buy it knowing there was gold on it and never tell him? And what would you buy it with? If you borrowed money to buy it with the fellow you borrowed the money from would likely get the biggest part of it, and you would have all your work and worry for nothing, and so you don't look to see if the gold is there. And then you get to thinking that probably there aren't many people honest enough to pass up a fortune like that just simply because somebody else owns it and you admire yourself for being that honest.

You can find more things to admire yourself for,

lying around fishing like that, if you pick your thoughts properly. Everybody ought to do it all the time and not work at anything else.

Several friends and literary advisers to whom we have shown the foregoing preface have taken the trouble to intimate that they do not believe what we have said concerning the fish known as the bullhead; namely, that he can live out of water for several hours. This only shows how little some people know about bullheads. We might have told a story of a particular bullhead far more incredible, and equally true, but that we are aware of this general lack of exact information concerning bullheads and did not care to have our statements questioned by the ignorant.

This particular bullhead we caught and tamed when we were about twelve years old, and named him Mr. Hoskins because of his facial resemblance to a neighbor. Mr. Hoskins—not the fish, but the fish's godfather—had fallen from a windmill in youth, upon his head, and his head had been getting larger ever since, until he seemed all head, with a few wiry spikes of beard and mustache around his mouth. His intellect had not grown as his head grew; the poor man used to go about calling attention to his large head, saying: "I fell off a windmill and the hogs ate me, all but my head—see my head!" He was pathetically proud of it. The fish looked like him, and with the heedless cruelty of boyhood we named the bullhead Mr. Hoskins.

Mr. Hoskins (the fish) dwelt in an old wash

boiler under a maple tree. And it was beneath this maple tree that we used to feed all our other animals every morning—a black dog, a crow, a black and orange cat, a brown dog called Gustavus Adolphus after the Terrible Swede of that name and an owl known (for we had been reading Dumas) as the Duchess de Montpensier. At that time, and in that place, the village butcher would give one a whole basketful of scraps and bones for a dime; the dogs, the cat, the crow and the Duchess would range themselves, solemnly expectant, in a row under the maple tree and catch the bits of meat we tossed to them in their mouths or beaks, no animal stepping out of his or her place in line and no animal offering to bite or peck its neighbor.

Mr. Hoskins, the bullhead, would come to the surface of the water and peer with one eye over the rim of the boiler, watching these proceedings closely. At first he watched them grouchily, we thought. A bullhead, however, is somewhat handicapped in the expression of the lighter and gayer emotions; his face is so constructed that even if he feels otherwise than gloomy and ill-humored he cannot show it. But as the spring wore into summer it seemed to us that Mr. Hoskins was getting friendlier, somehow. One day we tossed him a piece of meat and he snapped at it. After that we ranged the other beasts in a circle around the wash boiler, and if Gustavus Adolphus or the Duchess de Montpensier missed a piece of meat it fell to Mr. Hoskins. In ten days Mr. Hoskins could catch as well as any of them.

One morning we were alarmed to see that Mr. Hoskins's boiler had been overturned during the night, no doubt by some thirsty cow. He seemed dead when we picked him up and we dug a hole in the ground and threw him into it. But before we had him covered a sudden summer rain came up and we sought shelter. It was a drenching rain; when it was over, a couple of hours later, we returned to Mr. Hoskins to find the hole filled with water and him flopping around in it. He was evidently feeling quite chipper, and was contentedly eating an angleworm.

We put him back in his boiler.* And then we began to experiment with Mr. Hoskins. If he could live out of water for two or three hours, why not for a whole day? Every morning we took him from his boiler at a certain time, and each day we kept him from the water ten minutes or so longer than the day preceding. By September he was able to go from seven in the morning until eight in the evening entirely out of water without suffering any apparent ill effects except a slight loss in weight. At first during the hours when he was out of water he would seem rather torpid, in fact almost comatose. But by giving him frequent cool drinks from a bottle with a quill in it we found that he became livelier. By autumn he could go until sunset on not more than two drinks of water.

He became a jollier companion, joining, so far as he was able, ourself and the other animals in

*The star marks the exact spot at which the more skeptical sort of person will likely cease to believe.

542

all our sports. One of the most pleasant recollections of our boyhood is the memory of Mr. Hoskins flopping genially about the garden while Gustavus Adolphus and the other dog dug angleworms for Mr. Hoskins and the crow.

When the chilly weather came in November we moved his wash boiler into the house and set it behind the kitchen range, as we did not care to run the risk of having him frozen. But with the cold weather his need for water grew less and less; he began to manifest something like pride in his ability to do without it; it was in January that he began to experience, or at least to affect, a repugnance toward being in water at all. Then we substituted for the boiler a box full of sawdust. Still, however, even during January he would sometimes awake during the night and cry for a drink, and we insisted on a weekly bath.

At seven o'clock on the morning of St. Valentine's Day, 1890, we went into the kitchen and found that Mr. Hoskins had leaped from the floor to the hearth of the kitchen range, and had succeeded in working himself in among the warm ashes. He had felt cold during the night. After that we always put him to bed with a hot water bottle, and we remember well his cries of peevishness and discomfort on the night when the stopper came out of the bottle and drenched him.

We linger over these last days of February, hesitating to go on, because they were the last days in Mr. Hoskins's life. It was on February 28 that he went out of doors for the first time that year. Some one had left the cistern uncovered and he fell in. We heard his cries. We put a ladder down and plucked him from the black water. But it was too late. If he had only remembered how to swim, if we had only had the presence of mind to fling down a plank to him he might have kept himself afloat until we reached him with the ladder. But it was too late. We suppose that when he felt himself in the water a panic struck him. Those were days before every family had a pulmotor. We worked over him, but it was no use. It is silly perhaps to feel so badly over a little animal like that, but from that day to this we have never eaten a bullhead.

Preface to the Prospectus of a Club

Brooklyn is getting to be a devil of a place. They are organizing a club over there, and the name of it is to be La Bohème . . . just like that: La Bohème! With one of those rakish, foreign looking accents over the È. One of those sassy accents that make you think of Trilby and the Latin Quarter and . . . and . . . oh, you know! All that sort of thing!

They have been having oyster fights at the church parsonages and elocutionary teas at the Pouch Gallery and hearing it hinted that they are staid and conservative, long enough, and now they are going to show they have some *vie* over there, if you get what we mean. Greenwich Village isn't the only place in Greater New York that can get away with this *vie* stuff. There has always been plenty of *vie* in Brooklyn, but people in Manhattan and the Bronx have pretended not to believe it.

People in Greenwich Village wouldn't act as if they owned all the *esprit* and *verve* and *vie* in the five boroughs if they only knew more about Brooklyn.

Walt Whitman used to live over there and edit the *Eagle* and go swimming in Buttermilk Channel, two points off the starboard bow of Hank Beecher's church. Once an old Long Island skipper sunk a harpoon into Walt's haunch when he came up to blow, and the poet, snorting and bellowing and spouting verse, towed the whaler and his vessel clear out to Montauk before he shook the iron loose. Is there a bard in Greenwich Village that could do that? Not even Jack Reed, who writes like Byron and swims like Leander, could do that.

Walt was a Brooklynite; Ben De Casseres was born there; Newell Hillis and Jim Huneker and Laura Jean Libbey live there now, and we moved away ourself only a few months ago. And now that the *vie* over there is getting more organized, and more Bohème-like, so to speak, we're going to move back when our present lease runs out.

There have always been *literati* and *vie* in Brooklyn, if you know where to look for them. Ed Markham is going over there and recite "The Man with

545

the Hoe" when this La Bohème Club opens up, out on Washington avenue, halfway between the Pouch Gallery and the place where the Battle of Long Island was fought. And speaking of the Battle of Long Island, Mr. Higgins, the ink manufacturer, once offered a prize for the best piece of poetry about the Battle of Long Island, which gave quite an impetus to the efforts of all of us younger Brooklyn *literati*. The winning poem wasn't written in his brand of ink at all, but he was game and paid the prize just the same. If Mr. Higgins isn't asked to join this new La Bohème Club it will be a darned shame.

Mr. Eugene V. Brewster—undoubtedly Eugene Vie Brewster—who is considerable *litterateur* himself, a patron of all the arts, and quite an authority on Bohème, both here and abroad, we understand, is starting this new La Bohème Club; and his own house on Washington avenue is to be the clubhouse. There's nothing of the short sport about Eugene Vie Brewster! To give you some idea, we quote Rule 5 of the House Rules from the prospectus:

The freedom of the whole house is conceded to all guests and is desired by the host and hostess. The books in the library, the engravings in the dining room, the paintings in the salon, the photos in the hall, the pen and inks in the den, the piano, the pianola, the harp, the guitar, the curios, the portfolios—everything—are to be freely utilized. Please don't all congregate in one corner of one room.

There's nothing takes the *vie* out of a Bohème party like everybody bunching together in one corner, or sitting around the walls not saying anything. They used to do that at spelling-bees back home when we were a kid, before the spelling actually started; and Julius Chambers, in his department in the Brooklyn *Eagle*, mentioned that he noticed a tendency toward the same thing at Windsor Palace when Queen Victoria was presented to him. E. Vie Brewster is right to speak out plainly and firmly about that corner stuff at the start.

We might as well give all the rest of the rules while we are about it:

This organization shall have only one officer, a vice-president. It shall meet every now and then, but usually on Sunday, from five to eleven. There shall be no dues, no elections, no formalities, and no business. It shall have no constitution nor by-laws. Membership shall consist of attendance. Any person may call a meeting at any time or place and all may attend who are invited. Any person is eligible who can do something, or who has done something, in science, arms, letters or any of the arts. Members may dress as they please, but semi-formal dress is preferred. Every person attending must expect to be called upon at any meeting, without notice, to do his or her bit, and to do it—if convenient. Hence, please come prepared. The purpose of this organization shall be to promote social intercourse; to bring together agreeable people of talent; to encourage social, political, domestic and national economy; to give receptions to distinguished people; to exchange ideas, sift them and make public the best ones; lastly, but not leastly, to encourage early hours—early hours for retiring and rising, and hence early hours for beginning and ending all evening entertainments. . . . The ladies may remove their wraps, second floor rear; gentlemen, second floor front. . . . Buffet supper served in the dining room at seven. Help yourself. After the entertainment, or between numbers, late comers may go below and partake of what's left. Smoking material and some mild fluids for the gentlemen in the "den"—second floor front. Smoking is also endured in the library after eight, but not elsewhere. . . . Every guest is required to "register" in one or more of the albums in the library—and to write something besides a mere name. There will be a clock in every room. Curfew shall not ring, but eleven o'clock is late enough. We should all be in bed by twelve—Eugene V. Brewster, Vice-President, pro tem.

Eleven o'clock is late enough, wild spirits though we be! Some of us have to go all the way to Pineapple street, through the hurly-burly of Brooklyn's night life, of a Sunday evening when the churches are letting out, so let us take our wraps from the second floor, rear and front, put them over our semiformal dress, write our *mot* in the album and sally forth . . . these are mad nights, these nights in Brooklyn's Bohemia, but we must not overdo them!

But let us not be overly careful as we pass Borough

548

Hall . . . let us be jovial, and chant whimsically as we go, with a wicked thought that it will be twelve by the clock on the Eagle Building before we retire, a stanza or two from "Curfew Shall Not Ring To-night!" And, as that Bohemian, F. P. A., used to say, "so home and to bed."

William Marion Reedy, we understand, is to come all the way from St. Louis to Brooklyn to recite the entire poem, "Curfew Shall Not Ring To-night," for this new La Bohème Club some evening.

Ah, this is the *vie!*

Preface to a Volume of Poetry

We have often been asked to read the poems in the following collection at teas and similar soul and culture fights. We have always refused. It is not, as some of our friends believe, because of any excess of timidity that we consistently refuse.

It is because no one wants to pay us what it is worth to us. We are perfectly willing, if we get enough money for it, to read poems at Teas, Dinners, Pugilistic Contests, Clam-bakes, Football Games, Prayer Meetings of Any Denomination, Clinics, Divorce Trials, Balls, Dedications, Lynchings, Launchings, Luncheons, Weddings, Jail Deliveries, Tonsil Removals, Ice Cream Socials,

Legal Executions, Wrestling Matches, Tooth Pull-
ings, Commencement Exercises, Operations for
Appendicitis, Coming Out Parties, Taffy Pulls,
Better Baby Contests, Dog Shows, Gambling House
Raids, Sunday School Picnics, Pool Tournaments,
Spelling Bees, Adenoid Unveilings, Murders,
Church Suppers and Cremations. But money we
must have.

For while reading one's own poems to a gang of
strangers need not, of course, be absolutely degrad-
ing, yet it is bound to be a silly sort of performance.

And it is worth money. Poetry, with us, is a business; it takes time, muscular effort, nervous energy
and, sometimes, thought, to produce a poem.

People do not ask painters to go to places and paint
pictures for nothing, but they are forever trying to
graft entertainment off of poets.

Our rates, henceforth, are as follows:

For reading small, blond, romantic poems, thirty-
five dollars per poem. Blond, dove-colored or pink
lyrics prominently featuring the Soul, thirty-five
dollars each.

Humorous poems, not really very funny, twenty-
five dollars each.

Humorous poems, with slightly sentimental flavor,
forty dollars each.

Humorous poems, really quite funny, seventy-
five dollars each.

Dialect poems mentioning persons called "Bill,"
"Jim," "Si," etc., Southern dialect, fifty dollars each;
middle Western, fifty-five dollars.

Pathetic dialect verse charged for according to

the quantity and quality of pathos desired. (See rates on Mother and Old Sweetheart poems.)

Sonnets, ten dollars each. Not less than five sonnets served with any one order.

Pash poems, one hundred dollars each. Pash poems, however, will only be read from the interior of a heavy wire cage.

Free verse, any kind, one dollar a line.

No matter how long or how short the lines actually are, for business purposes a line of free verse is to be considered as containing seven words.

Serious poems, melancholy tone, fifty dollars each.

For ten dollars additional persons not to exceed twelve in number will be permitted to file by and feel the poet's heart beat after reading sad poems; persons in excess of twelve in number charged for at the rate of two dollars each.

Serious poems, optimistic in nature, fifty dollars each.

Old Sweetheart poems, in which she dies, one hundred dollars each. Old Folks at Home poems, sad, fifty dollars each; each reference to angels five dollars additional; father killed, mother left living, sixty-five dollars; both parents killed, seventy-five dollars; with dialect, one hundred dollars. Both parents killed during Christmas holidays, any dialect wanted, angels, toys, etc., two hundred dollars. Auditors' tears guaranteed, and for thirty-five dollars additional poet also will cry while reading this old reliable line of family poetry.

Religious poems, not more than five stanzas, one hundred dollars each.

Agnostic poems, latest cut, one hundred thirty-five to one hundred seventy-five dollars each.

These agnostic goods are for very exclusive circles, as are our radical and anarchistic poems, which come at two hundred dollars each.

Tame revolutionary poems, usual Greenwich Village sort of thing, fifty dollars each; if read in Flatbush, sixty-five dollars each.

Really quite shocking revolutionary poems, two hundred dollars each. A very modern line of goods.

Write for special combination offers and rates on limericks. We have limericks listed in three categories:

Limericks Where Ladies Are Present.

Limericks Where Ladies Are Absent but Clergymen Are Present.

Limericks.

In the event that we are expected to Be Nice and Meet People, 20 per cent added to above rates.

If expected to Meet People, and Being Nice is left optional with us, only 5 per cent added to above rates.

Conversation on poetry or related topics charged for at rate of $75 an hour in addition to reading charges.

Conversation on Rabindranath Tagore: Listened To, $750 an hour. Participated In, $1,000 the first hour and $350 for every additional ten minutes thereafter.

Limericks composed on spot (discreet) twenty-five dollars each. Impromptu couplets, good, twenty dollars each; medium, twelve dollars and fifty cents each; quite bad impromptu couplets, five dollars each.

Poetry written by host, hostess or any guest, listened to at rate of one hundred dollars per quarter hour.

Compliments on same to author, ten dollars each additional.

Compliments spoken so as to be overheard by more than eight persons, twenty dollars each.

Compliments dashed off in little informal notes, forty dollars each if notes are initialed, one hundred dollars each if notes are signed with full name.

For pretending to like Amy Lowell's work our rate is $1,000 an hour or any fraction thereof.

No orders filled amounting to less than two hundred dollars for ninety minutes' work. Certified check must be mailed with orders.

Prices quoted are f. o. b. Pennsylvania Station, N. Y. City.

Patrons will always confer a favor by reporting any inattention on the part of the audience.

Foreword to a Literary Censor's Autobiography

The gentleman who has written the tale of his life at length in this volume is employed by a Vice Commission to ferret out obscenities in works of art. In our estimation he is doing a most important work.

Censors are necessary, increasingly necessary, if America is to avoid having a vital literature. There is a knocking at the gate. The artist is knocking at the gate. If he gets in he will report to us what we already know—that Duncan has been murdered. And if the artist reports life to us as it is, and as we all know it to be . . . well, that would be too frightful to contemplate!

If we are to continue entirely comfortable we must escape the truth by crucifying all those who come bearing witness to it.

The gentleman whose book we introduce has a charming mind. Thoroughly to appreciate it, one must read the entire volume which he has produced. But he has a kind of prologue and epitome of his own, which gives a glimpse of it; our note and his prologue (which follows) are sufficient introduction:

I showed an inclination towards my Life Work at a very early age.

I could not have been more than ten years old when I reported to my Teacher at School that Myrtle Snodgrass, a little girl who sat in the next seat to me, had written a naughty word upon her slate.

"How do you know it is a naughty word?" asked Teacher.

"Because," I answered, "Myrtle Snodgrass jerked her slate away and would not let me read it."

"Then you did not see it?"

"No, ma'am." I have always been truthful.

"Perhaps," said Teacher, "it was not a word at all. You have accused Myrtle of something that you cannot prove. It is you who have been naughty, Harold! You have no right to look at Myrtle's slate if she does not wish you to. And you have reported something you do not know to be true."

I have always been persecuted in my efforts to safeguard the public morals.

"Teacher," I said, "if it wasn't a naughty word, then it must have been a naughty picture."

"Why do you say that, Harold?"

"Teacher, she had been showing her slate to Willie Simms and they had been laughing over it. And when I tried to see too she jerked it away."

I still think my logic was unassailable, child though I was. I still believe that my deductions were quite justified by the circumstances. For in the years since then I have had it borne in upon me, on many, many occasions, that words, phrases, allusions, which I cannot readily understand or which are deliberately hidden from me, are usually capable of some construction not altogether proper. It is always safe to infer, when people refuse to explain to one, that their real and secret meanings will not bear explanation.

I told my father, who was a member of the school board, that the Teacher had scolded me for reporting something so naughty about a little girl that I did not like to go into details, and he took the matter up officially.

Perhaps even then the Teacher would not have lost her position, but I was able to supply supplementary evidence which (my instinct told me even at that early age) tended to prove that this teacher was no fit person to form the minds of ingenuous little children. Arriving at the schoolhouse earlier than any of the other pupils one morning, and earlier than the Teacher herself, I found her desk unlocked. It was usually locked—a suspicious thing in itself, I felt. Naturally, finding it unlocked, I ransacked it, in the interests of the public welfare . . . and, I may add, my father had suggested something of the sort.

I found two damning photographs. Abominable pictures! One was the picture of Teacher herself, surrounded by several other young women, all in the abbreviated costume of the basket-ball team of a girls' college. This might not have been so bad in itself . . . though it is a sort of thing I do not approve . . . but near by was the photograph of a young man partially nude. He had on the costume of a college sprinter . . . nothing else!

The Teacher later told the school board that it was a picture of her brother. But, as my father pointed out, it might just as readily have been the photograph of some one to whom she was not related. And the relationship itself, my father justly said, counted for little against the impropriety of leaving such things where they were likely to fall into the hands of innocent children such as his little son.

Even then the majority of the school board were

556

unwilling to dismiss Teacher on an out and out charge of improper conduct; but my father and some of his right thinking friends were strong enough in the community to get rid of her on another charge. It was generally understood, however, that her services were really dispensed with because of some unnamed immorality . . . my father and his friends were too just and too merciful to relate the details publicly. I am proud and happy to testify that, because of the cloud under which she left our godly little city, this perverter of the morals of childhood was never afterward able to obtain a position as a teacher. There was nothing definite ever published against her . . . but people generally seemed to feel, even as I, child that I was, had felt, that there must be something wrong somewhere . . . something wrong.

Something wrong!

How often I have felt that! How unerringly my soul has reacted to the aroma of evil! I say it (not with worldly pride, for that is sinful, but with the satisfaction of the used and useful weapon in the holy war against iniquity)—I say with satisfaction that I have a sixth sense which directs me infallibly to the detection of obscenity.

Authors may talk of art, and chatter of its relation to life—they may prattle of truth and duty—but they cannot hide from me the carnal thought and the lascivious intention behind their specious innocence!

A thing is either pure or it is impure. My sixth sense informs me at once. No argument is necessary. My spirit is either shocked or it is not shocked.

It is not necessary to understand art in order to condemn it.

I love to sit in my library with the hundreds of books and pictures I have condemned about me and think that I have been of some use to my generation. In my mind's eye, as I run my physical eye over the book bindings, I can see the improper passages quivering and glowing inside the volumes. I know them all by heart!

And I thrill again to each one of them, with the same thrill I felt when I first discovered it and realized that I was about to render another service to society. I tremble, and at times my eyes fill with tears, as I repeat them aloud.

And when I am gone my son will take up the work, I am proud to say. Only last night, as I crept down the basement stairs to the kitchen to listen at the door and make sure the housemaid was conducting herself properly with her young man, I stumbled over my son. He was already at the keyhole. I patted his head in the darkness and thanked heaven that I had been rewarded in such a child. I patted his head and kissed him on his white, young brow, his pure young brow, and we knelt together there.

VI Hermione and Her Little Group of Serious Thinkers

Aren't the Russians Wonderful?

Aren't the Russians marvelous people!

We've been taking up Diaghileff in a serious way—our little group, you know—and, really, he's wonderful!

Who else but Diaghileff could give those lovely Russian things the proper accent?

And accent—if you know what I mean—accent is everything!

Accent! Accent! What would art be without accent?

Accent is coming in—if you get what I mean—and what they call "punch" is going out. I always thought it was a frightfully vulgar sort of thing, anyhow—punch!

The thing I love about the Russians is their Orientalism.

You know, there's an old saying that if you find a Russian you catch a Tartar . . . or something like that.

I'm sure that is wrong. . . . I get so *mixed* on

561

quotations. But I always know where I can find them, if you know what I mean.

But the Russian *verve* isn't Oriental, is it?

Don't you just dote on *verve*?

That's what makes Bakst so fascinating, don't you think?—his *verve!*

Though they do say that the Russian operas don't analyze as well as the German or the Italian ones— if you get what I mean.

Though for that matter, who analyzes them?

One may not know how to an analyze an opera, and yet one may know what one likes!

I suppose there will be a frightful lot of imitations of Russian music and ballet now. Don't you just hate imitators?

One finds it everywhere—imitation! It's the sincerest flattery, they say. But that doesn't excuse it, do you think?

There's a girl—one of my friends, she says she is—who is always trying to imitate me. My expressions, you know, and the way I talk and walk, and all that sort of thing.

She gets some of my superficial mannerisms . . . but she can't quite do my things as if they were her own, you know . . . there is where the accent comes in again!

How Suffering Purifies One!

Oh, to go through fire and come out purified!

Suffering is wonderful, isn't it? Simply *wonderful!*

The loveliest man talked to us the other night—to our Little Group of Serious Thinkers, you know—about social ideals and suffering.

The reason so many attempts to improve things fail, you know, is because the people who try them out haven't suffered personally.

He had the loveliest eyes, this man.

He made me think. I said to myself, "After all, have I suffered? Have I been purified by fire?"

And I decided that I had—that is spiritually, you know.

The suffering—the spiritual suffering—that I undergo through being misunderstood is something *frightful!*

Mamma discourages every Cause I take up. So does Papa. I get no sympathy in my devotion to my ideals. Only opposition!

And from a child I have had such a high-strung, sensitive nervous organization that opposition of any sort has made me ill.

There are some temperaments like that.

Once when I was quite small and Mamma threatened to spank me, I had convulsions.

And nothing but opposition, opposition, opposition now!

Only we advanced thinkers know what it is to suffer! To go through fire for our ideals!

And what is physical suffering by the side of spiritual suffering?

I so often think of that when I am engaged in sociological work. Only the other night—it was raining and chilly, you know—some of us went down in the auto to one of the missions and looked at the sufferers who were being cared for.

And the thought came to me all of a sudden:

"Yes, physical suffering may be relieved—but what is there to relieve spiritual suffering like mine?"

Though, of course, it improves one.

I think it is beginning to show in my eyes.

I looked at them for nearly two hours in the mirror last evening, trying to be quite certain.

And, you know, there's a kind of look in them that's never been there until recently. A kind of a—a——

Well, it's an *intangible* look, if you get what I mean.

Not exactly a *hungry* look, more of a *yearning* look!

Thank heaven, though, I can control it—one should always be the captain of one's soul, shouldn't one?

I hide it at times. Because one must hide one's suffering from the world, mustn't one?

But at other times I let it show.

And, really, with practice, I think I am going to manage it so that I can turn it off and on—if you get what I mean—almost at will.

Because, you know, in certain costumes that look would be *quite* unbecoming.

Quite out of Harmony. And Inner Beauty only comes through Inner Harmony, doesn't it?

Harmony! Harmony! Oh, to be in accord with the Infinite! Nearly every night before I go to bed I ask myself, "Have I vibrated in tune with the Infinite today, or have I failed?"

Soul Mates

I'm taking up Bergson this week.

Next week I'm going to take up Etruscan vases and the Montessori system.

Oh, no, I haven't lost my interest in sociology.

Only the other night we went down in the auto and watched the bread line.

Of course, one can take up *too many* things.

It's the spirit in which you take a thing up that counts.

Sometimes I think the spirit in which you take a thing up counts more than the thing itself—counts in its effect on you, you know.

Of course, the way to get the real meaning out of any thing is to put yourself in a receptive attitude.

In serious things the attitude counts for everything. One mustn't scoff.

If you look at it seriously and scientifically you'll see there's a great deal more than you suspected in all this affinity and soul mate craze, for instance.

Not that I care much for the words "soul mate" and "affinity" particularly; they have been so *vulgarized,* somehow.

The Best People don't use those terms any more. Psychic harmony is the new term.

The loveliest man explained all about it to us the other day. I belong to a Little Group of Thinkers, who take a serious interest in these things, you know.

We are trying to find out how to make our psychic powers count for the betterment of the world. I am very psychic. Some are not.

This man had the most interesting eyes and the silkiest beard, and he said his aura was pink.

If he should meet a girl, you know, with an aura just the shade of pink that his aura is, why then they would know they were in psychic harmony.

Simple, isn't it? But then all truly great ideas *are* simple, aren't they?

But if his aura was blue, and her aura was yellow, then, of course, they would quarrel. That's what makes so much domestic unhappiness.

But he said something that gave me the most frightfully insecure feeling.

He said the aura *changes* its color as the soul progresses.

Two people may be in harmony today, and both have pink auras, and in a year hers may be green and his golden.

What desperate chances a woman takes when she marries, doesn't she?

I sometimes think life must have been a much more comfortable thing before the world got to be so terribly advanced.

But, of course, it is our duty to sacrifice personal comfort for the future of the race and the betterment of the world.

As I was looking at the bread line the thought came to me that the chief difference between this advanced age and other ages was in the fact that people today are willing to take a serious interest in such things.

People are willing to sacrifice themselves today, you know.

It is food for optimism, don't you think?

Not that I was really so uncomfortable in the auto, you know. I had on my new mink coat.

Citronella and Stegomyia

We were talking about famous love affairs the other evening, and Fothergil Finch said he was thinking of writing a ballad about Citronella and Stegomyia.

And, of course, everybody pretended they knew who Citronella and Stegomyia were. Mrs. Voke Easeley—you've heard about Voke Easeley and his New Art, haven't you?—Mrs. Voke Easeley said:

"But don't you think those old Italian love affairs have been done to death?"

"Italian?" said Fothy, raising his eyebrows at Mrs. Voke Easeley.

You know, really, there wasn't a one of them knew who Citronella and Stegomyia were; but they were all pretending, and they saw Mrs. Voke Easeley was in bad. And she saw it, too, and tried to save herself.

"Of course," she said, "Citronella and Stegomyia weren't Italian lovers *themselves*. But so many of the old Italian poets have written about them that I always think of them as glowing stars in that wonderful, wonderful galaxy of Italian romance!"

Fothy can be very mean when he wants to. So he said:

"I don't read Italian, Mrs. Easeley. I have been forced to get all my information about Citronella and Stegomyia from English writers. Maybe you would be good enough to tell me what Italian poet it is who has turned out the most recent version of Citronella and Stegomyia?"

Mrs. Voke Easeley answered without a moment's hesitation: "Why, D'Annunzio, of course."

That made everybody waver again. And Aurelia Dart said—she's that girl with the beautiful arms, you know, who plays the harp and always has a man or two to carry it about wherever she goes—somebody else's husband, if she can manage it—Aurelia said:

"D'Annunzio, of course! Passages of it have been set to music."

"Won't you play some of it?" asked Fothy, very politely.

"It has never been arranged for the harp," said Aurelia. "But if Mrs. Easeley can remember some of the lines, and will be good enough to repeat them, I will improvise for it."

That put it up to Mrs. Easeley again, you know. She hates Aurelia, and Aurelia knows it. Voke Easeley carried Aurelia's harp around almost all last winter. And the only way Mrs. Easeley could break Voke of it was to bring their little girl along—the one that has convulsions so easily, you know. And then when Voke was getting Aurelia's harp ready for her the little girl would have a convulsion, and Mrs. Easeley would turn her over to Voke, and Voke would have to take the little girl home, and Mrs. Easeley would stay and say what a family man and what a devoted husband Voke was, for an artist.

Well, Mrs. Easeley wasn't stumped at all. She got up and repeated something. I took up Italian poetry one winter, and we made a special study of D'Annunzio; but I didn't remember what Mrs. Easeley recited. But Aurelia harped to it. Improvising is one of the best things she does.

And everybody said how lovely it was and how

much soul there was in it, and, "Poor Stegomyia! Poor Citronella!"

The Swami said it reminded him of some passages in Tagore that hadn't been translated into English yet.

Voke Easeley said: "The plaint of Citronella is full of a passion of dream that only the Italian poets have found the language for."

Fothy winked at me and I made an excuse and slipped into the library and looked them up—and, well, would you believe it!—they weren't lovers at all! And I might have known it from the first, for I always use citronella for mosquitoes in the country.

They were still pretending when I got back, all of them, and Aurelia was saying: "Citronella differs psychologically from Juliet—she is more like poor, dear Francesca in her feeling of the cosmic inevitability of tragedy. But Stegomyia had a strain of Hamlet in him."

"Yes, a strain of Hamlet," said Voke Easeley. "A strain of Hamlet in his nature, Aurelia—and more than a strain of Tristram!"

"It is a thing that Maeterlinck should have written, in his earlier manner," said Mrs. Voke Easeley.

"The story has its Irish counterpart, too," said Leila Brown, who rather specializes, you know, on all those lovely Lady Gregory things. "I have always wondered why Yeats or Synge hasn't used it."

"The essential story is older than Ireland," said the Swami. "It is older than Buddha. There are three versions of it in Sanskrit, and the young men sing it to this day in Benares."

Affectation! Affectation! Oh, how I abhor affectation!

It was perfectly *horrid* of Fothy just the same.

Anyone might have been fooled.

I might have been myself, if I were not too intellectually honest, and Fothy hadn't tipped me the wink.

The Exotic and the Unemployed

We've been taking up the Exotic this week—in poetry and painting, you know, and all that sort of thing—and its influence on our civilization.

Really, it's wonderful—simply *wonderful!* Quite different from the Erotic, you know, and from the Esoteric, too—though they're all mixed up with it sometimes.

Odd, isn't it, how all these new movements seem to be connected with one another?

One of the chief differences between the Exotic in art and other things—such as the Esoteric, for instance—is that nearly everything Exotic seems to have crept into our art from abroad.

Don't you think some of those foreign ideas are apt to be—well, dangerous? That is, to the untrained mind?

You can carry them too far, you know—and if you do they work into your subconsciousness.

One of the girls—she belongs to the same Little Group of Advanced Thinkers that I do—has been so taken with the Exotic that she wears orchids all the time and just simply *craves* Chinese food. "My love," she said to me only yesterday, "I feel that I must have chop suey or I'll *die!*" The Exotic has worked into her subliminal being, you know.

She has an intense and passionate nature, and I'm sure I don't know what would become of her if it were not for the spiritual discipline she gets out of modern thought.

Next week we're taking up Syndicalism—it's frightfully interesting, they say, and awfully advanced.

I suppose it's a new kind of philosophy or socialism, or maybe anarchy—or something like that. Most of these new things that come along nowadays *are* something like that, aren't they?

I'm sure the world owes a debt to its advanced thinkers which it can never repay for always keeping abreast of topics like that.

Not that I've lost my interest in any of the older forms of sociology, you know, just because I am keeping up with the newer phases of it.

Only yesterday I rode about town in the car and had the chauffeur stop a while every place where they were shoveling snow.

The nicest man was with me—he is connected with a settlement, and has given his life to sociology and all that sort of thing.

"Just think," I said to him, "how much real practical sociology we have right here before us—all these men shoveling snow—and how little they realize, most of them, that their work is taking them into sociology at all."

He didn't say anything, but he seemed impressed.

And I'm sure the unemployed should be grateful to the serious thinkers for the careful study we give them. Don't you think so?

The Spirit of Christmas

Isn't the Christmas festival just simply *wonderful*?

For days beforehand I feel so uplifted—so, well, *other-worldly*—if you know what I mean.

Isn't it just dreadful that any *material* considerations have to spoil such a sacred time?

It does seem to me that somehow we might free ourselves of *worldliness* and *greediness* and just rise to the spiritual significance of the day. If only we could!

And what a blessing it would be to the poor, tired shop girls if we could!

Though, of course, they, the shop girls, I mean, must be upheld even in their weariest moments by the thought that they are helping on the beautiful impulse of giving!

When they reflect that every article they sell is to be a gift from one thoughtful and loving heart to another they must forget the mere fatigue of the flesh and just feel the stimulus, the inspiration, the vibration!

There are gifts, I admit, that haven't the divine spark of love to hallow them, but after all there aren't so many of that sort. Love one another *is* the spirit of Christmas—and it prevails, whatever the skeptics may say to the contrary. And though it's a pity there has to be a *material* side to Christmas at all, it's so comforting, so ennobling to realize that back of the material gifts is Brotherly Love.

It quite reassures one about the state of the world; it certainly isn't getting worse with Brotherly Love and the Spirit of Giving animating everybody.

Of course, Christmas giving *is* a problem sometimes. It is *so* embarrassing when somebody you'd forgotten entirely sends you a present.

I always buy several extra things just for that emergency. Then, when an unexpected gift arrives, I can rush off a return gift so promptly that nobody'd ever *dream* I hadn't meant to send it all along.

And I always buy things I'd like to have myself, so that if they aren't needed for unexpected people they're still not wasted.

With all my spirituality, I have a practical side, you see.

All well *balanced* natures have both the spiritual and the practical side. It's so essential, nowadays, to be well balanced, and it's a great relief to me to find I *can* be practical. It saves me a lot of trouble, too, especially about this problem of Christmas giving.

I know the value of material things, for instance. And I never waste money giving more expensive presents to my friends than I receive from them. That's one of the advantages of having a well balanced nature, a *practical* side.

And, anyway, the value of a gift is not in the *cost* of it. Quite cheap things, when they represent true thought and affection, are above rubies.

Mamma and Papa are going to get me a pearl necklace, just to circle the throat, but beautifully matched pearls. I wouldn't care for an ostentatiously long string of pearls anyway.

Poor, dear Papa says he really can't afford it—with times so hard, and those dear, pathetic Europeans on everybody's hands, you know—but Mamma made him understand how necessary *beauty* is to me, and he finally gave in.

Isn't it just *wonderful* how love rules us all at Christmas time?

Prison Reform and Poise

Aren't you just crazy about prison reform? The most wonderful man talked to us—to our Little Group of Advanced Thinkers, you know—about it the other evening.

It made me feel that I'd be willing to do anything
—simply *anything!*—to help those poor, unfortunate
convicts. Collect money, you know, or give talks,
or read books about them, or make any other sacrifice.

Even get them jobs. One ought to help them to
start over again, you know.

Though as for hiring one of them myself, or
rather getting Papa to—well, really, you know, one
must draw the line somewhere!

But it's a perfectly fascinating subject to take up,
prison reform is.

It gives one such a sense of brotherhood—and of
service—it's so broadening, don't you think?—taking
up things like that?

And one must be broad. I ask myself every night
before I go to bed: "Have I been *broad* today? Or
have I failed?"

Though of course, one can be *too* broad, don't you
think?

What I mean is, one must not be so broad that
one loses one's poise in the midst of things.

Poise! That is what this age needs!

I suppose you've heard wide-brimmed hats are
coming in again?

Taking up the Liquor Problem

We're thinking of taking up the Liquor Problem —our little group, you know—in quite a serious way.

The Working Classes would be so much better off without liquor. And we who are the leaders in thought should set them an example.

So a number of us have decided to set our faces very sternly against drinking in public.

Of course, a cocktail or two and an occasional stinger is something no one can well avoid taking, if one is dining out or having supper after the theater with one's own particular crowd.

But all the members of my own particular little group have entered into a solemn agreement not to take even so much as a cocktail or a glass of wine if any of the working classes happen to be about where they can see us and become corrupted by our example.

The Best People owe these sacrifices to the Masses, don't you think?

Of course, the waiters, and people like that, really belong to the working classes too, I suppose.

But, as Fothergil Finch says, very often one wouldn't know it. And who could expect a waiter to be influenced one way or another by anything?

And it's the home life of the working classes that counts, anyhow.

When we took up Sociology—we gave several evenings to Sociological Discussion, you know, besides doing a lot of practical Welfare Work—it was impressed upon me very strongly that if one is to do anything at all for the Masses one must first *sweeten* their Home Life.

Though Papa made me stop poking around into the horrid places where they live for fear I might catch some dreadful disease.

And the people we visited weren't at all grateful. So *very often* the Masses are not.

One dreadful woman, you know, claimed that she couldn't keep her rooms—she had two rooms, and she cooked and washed and slept and sewed in them and there were five in the family—claimed that she couldn't keep her rooms in any better shape because they were so out of repair and the plumbing was bad and the windows leaked and all that sort of thing, you know, and one of the rooms was *entirely* dark.

I preached the doctrine of fresh air and sunshine and cleanliness to her, you know, and the impudent thing told me Papa owned the building and it wasn't true at all—Papa only belonged to the company that owned the building. One can't do much for people who will not be truthful with one, can one?

Besides, it is the Silent Influence that counts more than arguments and visiting.

If one makes one's life what it should be Good will Radiate.

Vibrations from one's Ego will permeate all classes of society.

And that is the way we intend to make ourselves felt with regard to the Liquor Problem. We will inculcate abstemiousness by example.

Abstemiousness, Fothy Finch says, should be our motto, rather than Abstinence. We shall be *quite* careful not to identify ourselves with the *more vulgar* aspects of the propaganda.

And of course at social functions in our private homes total abstinence is quite out of the question.

The working classes wouldn't get any example from our homes, anyhow; for of course we never come into contact with them there.

But the working classes must be saved from themselves, even if all the employers of labor have to write out a list of just what they shall eat and drink and make them buy only those things. They simply *must* be saved.

Not that they'll appreciate it. They never do. If I were not an incorrigible idealist I would be inclined to give them up.

But someone must give up his life to leading them onward and upward. And who is there to do it if not we leaders of Modern Thought?

Sympathy

Of course, we're out of town for the summer—
everybody's out of town, now—but I motor in once
or twice a week to keep in touch with some of my
committees.

Sociological work, for instance, keeps right up the
year around.

Of course, it's not so interesting as in the winter.
You see more striking contrasts in the winter, don't
you think?

A couple of girl cousins of mine from Cincinnati
have been here. They're interested in welfare work
of all sorts.

"Hermione," they said, "we want to see the bread
line."

"My dears," I said, "I don't mind showing it to
you, but it's nothing much to see in summer. It's in
the winter that it arouses one's deepest sympathies."

And one must keep one's sympathies aroused.
Often I say to myself at night: "Have I been sympathetic today, or have I *failed?*"

Mamma often lacks sympathy. She objects to having me reopen my Salon this winter.

"Hermione," she said, "I don't mind the subjects
you take up—or the people you take up with—if you

only take them up one at a time. And I am glad when your own little group meets here, because it keeps you at home. But I will *not* have all the different kinds of freaks here at the *same time,* sitting around discussing free love and sex education."

I was indignant. "Mamma," I said, "what right have you to say they would discuss that all the time?"

"Because," she said, "I have noticed that no matter whether they start with sociology or psychology, they always get around to Sex in the end."

Isn't it funny about pure-minded people?—in the generation before this anything that shocked a pure-minded person like Mamma was sure to be bad.

But now it's only the evil-minded people who ever get shocked at all, it seems.

The really *purest* of the pure-minded people don't get shocked by anything at all these days.

I think Mamma is either getting purer-minded all the time or losing some of it—I can't tell which—for she isn't shocked as easily as she was a few months ago.

But I got a shock myself recently.

I found out that plants have Sex, you know.

Just think of it—carrots, onions, turnips, potatoes, and everything!

Isn't it frightful to think that this agitation has spread to the vegetable kingdom?

I vowed I would never eat another potato as long as I lived!

And, after all, what *good* does it do—letting the vegetable kingdom have Sex, I mean?

Even a good thing, you know, can be carried too far.

"Mamma," I told her, "you are hopelessly behind the times. Sex is a Great Fact. Someone must discuss it. And who but the Leaders of Thought are worthy to?"

I intend to say nothing more about it now—but when the time comes I *will* reopen my Salon.

And as far as talking about Sex is concerned—the right sort of a mind will get *good* out of it, and the wrong sort will get *harm*.

I don't really *like* discussions of Sex any more than Mamma does. No really nice girl does.

But we advanced thinkers owe a duty to the race.

Not that the race is grateful. Especially the lower classes.

It was only last week that I was endeavoring to introduce the cook to some advanced ideas—for her own good, you know, and because one owes a spiritual duty to one's servants—and she got angry and gave notice.

The servant problem is frightful. It will have to be taken up seriously.

Envoy

HERMIONE, THE DEATHLESS

She will not die!—in Brainstorm Slum
   Fake, Nut and Freak Psychologist
Eternally shall buzz and hum,
   And Spook and Swami keep their tryst
   With Thinkers in a Mental Mist.
You threaten her with Night and Sorrow?
   Out of the Silences, I wist,
More Little Groups will rise tomorrow!

The lips of Patter ne'er are dumb,
   The Futile Mills shall grind their grist
Of sand from now till Kingdom Come;
   The Winds of Bunk are never whist.
   You scowl and shake an honest fist—
You threaten her with Night and Sorrow?
   Go slay one Pseudo-Scientist,
More Little Groups will rise tomorrow!

With Fudge to feed the Hungry Bum
   She plays the Girl Philanthropist—
Each pinchbeck, toy Millennium
   She swings, a Bangle, at her wrist—

Blithe Parrot and Pert Egoist,
You threaten her with Night and Sorrow?
    Hermiones will aye persist!
More Little Groups will rise tomorrow!

She, whom Prince Platitude has kissed,
    You threaten her with Night and Sorrow?
Slay her by thousands, friend—but list:
    More Little Groups will rise tomorrow!

VII   The Almost Perfect State

Chapter VIII

Before we can proceed to an exposition of the Almost Perfect State we must consider in this Work (or this Opus—for Opus is the more learned-sounding word) the several forms of government that have failed and inquire why they have failed.

SUGGESTION

Every government should ask itself each night before going to bed, "Have I governed well to-day or have I failed?"

Let us first dispose of the Benevolent Despotism since there are many persons in the world who still believe that a Benevolent Despotism would be the best sort of government—if Despots would only *be* Benevolent. In the first place, we do not believe it possible for any Despot to remain Benevolent, even should he begin so; and in the second place, any intelligent and self-respecting population would get so tired of having benevolence handed down to them from above, that they would do as Milton's Satan did, and revolt, regardless of the consequences.

OBSERVATION

Benevolence is all very well for those who practise it, for it is more blessed to give than to receive, but it confirms in those who have no opportunity of returning it a feeling of inferiority, which results in their deterioration.

But we need only to look at some of the Despots of the past to see that Despotism will not do—where it is possible, let us be Pragmatic, for Pragmatism is the easiest sort of Philosophy to apply to human affairs.

Where, then, are the Despots that once flourished and their Despotisms?

Where, we ask, is Nebuchadnezzar?

ANSWER

Gone to grass, gone to grass!
He roared like a bull, he brayed like an ass,
He fed on beans and garden sass,
And he's gone to grass, he's gone to grass!

QUERY

Where is Nimrod?

ANSWER

There are bats within his garret, there are beetles
*   in his dome,*
And should you call at Nineveh, you'll find he's not
*   at home.*

QUERY

And then there was Cheops or Khufu, who was so important and felt so important. Where is Cheops and all his glory?

ANSWER

He lies in his sarcophagus, with sand in his esophagus,
Which isn't much to quench a thirst and isn't much to eat;
Neither thoughts nor slippery ellum in his arid cerebellum,
And his shoes are full of cobwebs, and the spiders bite his feet.

As one of the authors of "Quotations, Words, Phrases, Proverbs, and Colloquial Expressions from the Greek, the Latin, and Modern Foreign Languages" remarks very learnedly, in the back part of the dictionary, *"Sic transit gloria mundi!"*

QUERY

Where is Cleopatra?

ANSWER

Handsome Marcus Antony he sat beside the Nile,
With Cleopatra Ptolemy swapping smile for happy smile,
And they fished with little Coptics for to get a crocodile;
But where is gay Miss Ptolemy now? The Echoes answer, Where?

The dear component parts of her are dusted through
the air—
As an individual Despot, she's scarcely anywhere!

We could multiply instances, did we think it necessary, but our readers have no doubt already grasped the main idea: the universe is not friendly to Despots and they all perish sooner or later.

It may be objected that the contemporaries of these personages have also perished. Such is indeed the fact, but it is a fact that does not help this Opus any, and so we disregard it in the argument, although we are fair enough to admit it as a fact.

Chapter XV

Sometimes, when we sit down to write another installment of this Opus, we are appalled by the time that must necessarily elapse before the Almost Perfect State can come into existence. Sometimes we wonder if it is worth while to go on with the work. We are anything but free from the greed for praise and recognition, and we are planning and building the Almost Perfect State for a race that will give us neither pay nor credit for our pains. Our ideas will get abroad into the world and the Almost Perfect State will break as a dawn over humanity; but we will never see that dawn. We will have been long forgotten; not only will the matter which composes our body have experienced a thousand transmutations, but even our very soul will have changed in a million years from now.

At least we hope it will have changed. When one tries to think of eternity, and of the possibility of being the same person all through it, and *knowing* that one is the same person, the idea of the immortality of the soul assumes a terrible aspect. It is all very well to say, as some persons do, that we will be interested and occupied, so that we will scarcely feel eternity passing. But personally we are sure that we shall have a heavy time getting through with it. We may have to take up chess or Wordsworth's poems.

It was probably this feeling that there was a great deal of eternity to get through somehow that led to the revolt of Satan. We do not remember whether Milton mentions it. The thought came to Satan and for a while he was able to fight it off, but presently all he could do was to sit with his head in his hands and his wings hunched up and brood and brood and brood.

Lucifer and Mulciber and some of the rest of the gang would stroll by and see him sitting that way.
"What is the trouble?" they would ask him, kindly.
"Eternity!" Satan would reply in a hollow voice.

"Don't think of it!" Lucifer would urge him. "I've had spells like that myself—you don't *dare* think of it, or it will get you!"

"I can't think of anything else," Satan would groan.

And the thought spread among numbers of the angels, until all over Paradise they were sitting in little dejected groups, with quivering and contorted pinions, moaning, "Eternity."

"Just think," Satan would say, "we've not only got to *be* all that time, but we've got to be *good*."

And this would get on their nerves to such an extent that dozens of them would arise, all over Paradise, and stamp their feet and shout in chorus: "We *won't* be good!"

"We can't help it," Lucifer would say, "we're angels!"

Which led directly to Satan's resolve.

"Look here," he said one day, "if we try hard enough, we can *quit* being angels!"

It was a novel idea in Paradise, but it spread, leading directly to the Revolt with consequences which are too well known, we feel sure, to need recapitulation by us.

It is possible that when the Revolt did occur it was welcomed in other quarters—that is by the good angels who wished to remain good—and who now found it possible to be good and at the same time occupy themselves in a struggle which took their minds off the thought of eternity.

Chapter XIX

This world, we are told by the men of science, is gradually growing cooler; in some millions of years (just exactly how many no one seems to know) the tropics will be as cool as the so-called temperate zones are now. And it will be at least two or three millions of years (supposing progress to continue at the rate we perceive when we look about us) before the population of the earth has developed sufficiently to make our Almost Perfect State possible. Will humanity or the species which succeeds and inherits from humanity be able to meet these colder conditions and survive?

We are optimistic, we see no cause for alarm, the character of the animal will be modified to meet the conditions of mundane environment. Man will either heat the entire planet artificially or he will grow fur.

And we think he will do the latter. It has not been so many millions of years since his ancestors had fur, and he can grow it again when he needs it. Indeed, some men are able to face the cold partially unclothed, without fur, even now. It has only been a short time since the Highland Scots went generally bare-legged through the snows, and to this day thousands of Scotsmen, while they have their coats, vests, and trousers made of cloth that is all one colour and pattern, nevertheless insist that their trousers be constructed of material very much thinner and more open in weave than the coats and vests. They can scarcely bear to have their legs covered at all, and even in the bitterest weather wear no underclothing over these portions of their anatomy. It is possible that the Highland Scots really have fur covering the parts of the leg which their grandfathers exposed, but that it is invisible because it grows under the skin instead of on the outside. Unfortunately, there is no authentic information on hand to determine the truth of this supposition. But the immunity from cold which the Highland Scot enjoys as to his legs can certainly be acquired by a whole species, if necessary.

And when man no longer feels wintry weather, think of the businesses that will expire almost automatically! Much less coal will be mined; fewer houses need be builded; tailors, shoe shops, clothing factories, dye works, etc., will close forever. Scores of industries will be wiped out.

And this will be well!

MAXIM

One way to avoid having industrial troubles is to avoid having industries.

A MOTTO FOR THE WALL

WHO LOVES TO SOIL

HIS HANDS WITH TOIL

LET HIM STRAIGHTWAY GO TO IT!

MYSELF, I CAN'T ADMIRE THE ANT,

AND SHALL NOT TRY

TO DO IT!

I WILL NOT DRUDGE!

INDEED, I GRUDGE

THE TIME WORK TAKES—'TIS SILLY!

I WILL NOT SHIRK MY NOBLER WORK

OF BEING JUST A LILY!

PRINCIPLE

Economic problems that cannot be otherwise solved should be abolished.

In the Almost Perfect State there will be as little business as possible.

The enormous complicated industries which men seem to think necessary to-day (and which really may be necessary in an overcrowded world, for all we know) will disappear; and with them will go a great deal of strife and biliousness and perplexity.

Strikers, reformers, plutocrats, and sociologists will be no more, and the world will be delivered from the Idle Poor and the Busy Rich.

Everyone in existence will have enough leisure and enough wealth so that the entire population of the globe will be able to call itself, if it chooses, the Idle Rich.

REFLECTION

Programmes which start out with fulminations against the Idle Rich will always fail. For nearly everyone wishes to be idle and rich. And more idleness and more riches for everyone are precisely what the world needs.

We have suggested how the solution of one set of industrial problems may arrive by abolishing the industries which give rise to the problems; we may assume that it is scarcely necessary to take up all the industries in turn.

Let the world apply the principle we have given it.

Chapter XXIV

THE UNIVERSE AND THE PHILOSOPHER

The Universe and the Philosopher sat and looked at each other satirically.

"You know so many things about me that aren't true," said the Universe to the Philosopher.

"There are so many things about you that you seem to be unconscious of," said the Philosopher to the Universe.

"I contain a number of things that I am trying to forget," said the Universe.

"Such as what?" asked the Philosopher.

"Such as Philosophers," said the Universe.

"You are wrong," said the Philosopher to the Universe, "for it is only by working up the most important part of yourself into the form of Philosophers that you get a product capable of understanding you at all."

"You Philosophers always were able to get the better of me in argument," smiled the Universe, "and I think that is one thing that is the matter with you."

"If you object to our intellects," said the Philosopher, "we can only reply that we got them, as well as everything else, from you."

"That should make you more humble," said the Universe. "If I quit letting you have intellect, where would you be then?"

"Where would *you* be," asked the Philosopher, "if you quit letting me have intellect? If I quit thinking you out as you are, and must be, you would cease to exist as you are; for I am a part of you; and if I were to change, your total effect would be changed also."

Then the Philosopher reflected a long moment and, warming to his work, put over this one: "The greater part of you, for all I know, exists in my brain anyhow; and if I should cease to think of that part, that part would cease to be."

"You make me feel so helpless, somehow," complained the Universe hypocritically. "I beg your pardon for asking you to be humble a moment ago.

I see now, very plainly, that it is I who should be more humble in your presence."

"I am glad," said the Philosopher, "that we have been able to arrive at something like an understanding."

"Understanding," echoed the Universe. "It's *so* important, isn't it?" And then: "Come! We have argued enough for one day! There is something terribly fatiguing to me about Profound Thought. Can't we just lie down in the shade the rest of the afternoon and watch the wheels go round?"

"Watch the wheels go round?" puzzled the Philosopher.

"Uh-huh!—the planets and solar systems, and stuff like that. The nicest thing in life, as I have lived it, is just to lie about and drowse and watch the wheels go round—I made nearly everything spherical in the beginning so it would roll when I kicked it. I'd rather play than think."

"You are a Lowbrow!" said the Philosopher.

"Uh-huh," said the Universe. "At times. I suppose that's the reason some of the children neglect the old parent these days."

And then, after a nap, during which the Philosopher contemplated the Universe with a tinge of superiority, the Universe rumbled sleepily: "I know what I am going to do with this intellect stuff. I'm going to take it away from you Philosophers and give it to fish or trees or something of that sort!"

"How frightfully grotesque!" said the Philosopher, turning pale.

"Or to giraffes," continued the Universe. "Giraffes are naturally dignified. And they aren't meddlesome. I'd like to see thousands of Giraffes walking along in a row, with their heads in the air, thinking, thinking, thinking—with tail coats and horn-rimmed goggles!"

"You are absurd!" cried the Philosopher.

"Uh-huh," said the Universe. And, reaching over, the Universe picked up the Philosopher, not ungently, by the scruff of the neck, tossed him into the air, caught him tenderly as he came down, spun him around, and set him right side up on the ground.

"You," said the Universe, grinning at the breathless Philosopher pleasantly, "are sort of damned funny yourself, sometimes!"

Chapter XXXIII

Will there be wars when the Almost Perfect State comes into existence?

There will not be any wars between nations because, as we explained some time ago, when we begin to lay down the basic laws for the Almost

Perfect State, there will be but one nation, if you want to call it a nation. Any wars there are must be civil wars.

But we have a suggestion with regard to war, which the League of Nations is welcome to, if it wishes to take it up in a serious way. (It will be some time before the Almost Perfect State is ready to function; in the meantime, if there is anything that the League of Nations can use in these articles, the League is welcome to the idea.)

Our idea with regard to preventing war came to us the other day while we were playing Kelly Pool. At the place—at one of the places where we play Kelly Pool—the genial custom obtains of hanging drinks for the bunch on each double-header. The winner of the double-header has to buy, if you get what we mean. The price of booze being what it is, and the stakes at Kelly Pool being what they have always been, the winner of a double-header gets a lot of glory, but frequently faces a financial loss.

The League of Nations should adopt this principle as one of its first 1400 points—make the winner the loser, and there will be fewer wars.

That is to say, provide that the nation victorious in any war must not only pay all its own expenses, direct and incidental, but must also pay all the expenses, direct and incidental, of the nation defeated and all the indirect expenses of all neutrals injured as well.

It might also be a good thing to add all these sums together, and assess the victor nation a further amount, equal to the aggregate, to be paid into a fund for the purpose of propagating peaceful thoughts the world around.

We think that this would work out practically. A nation that sort o' wanted to go to war, and felt confident that it would be the victor, would say to itself: "Gee! what's the use? If I win I lose!"

Some little nations, of course, might start wars just to get licked and make the victors pay for it; but when any nation showed that sort of spirit, made it very evident to the world that such spirit actually and unmistakably ruled, the League should blot that nation out of existence entirely. The expense of blotting such nations entirely out of existence should be paid from the fund indicated.

This idea would work better for the League of Nations, perhaps, than for the Almost Perfect State. In the Almost Perfect State the wars will have to be civil wars, since there will be but one nation in the world. But there cannot be civil wars without partisans and organizations. And the victorious party should be made to bear the whole expense.

Our researches into the game of Kelly Pool, we feel, will have been amply justified if this idea of ours is adopted by the League of Nations. Very often we have been asked *why* we play Kelly Pool.

A friend suggested recently that it must be "to forget." We have sometimes been at a loss for an answer. But we have all along felt, in a dim mystical sort of way, that something good, sometime, somehow, would come out of our addiction to Kelly Pool. And here is our triumphant vindication.

Chapter XXXVI

The chief obstacle to the progress of the human race is the human race.

> *For him that seeks to help the world,*
> *The world holds death in fee—*
> *For Socrates the hemlock cup,*
> *For Jesus, Calvary.*

Some weeks ago, in despair over the traits which make the human race so human, we told it to go to hell in its own hand-basket. We left it flat on its miserable back. We gave it notice that we were through giving it advice. There would be, we said, no more of the Almost Perfect State.

But now we resume the series. It is not that the human race has shown any signs of repentance in the interim. The truth is, we have discovered that, greatly as we hate human beings, we love them more. So, we resume. We no longer hope to reform the world in a mere million years. We intend to give it three million years and be more patient with it when it fails.

We shall continue giving precious counsel, because—well, because we can't help it. Like all other zealous reformers, we do what we do because we like doing it better than anything else.

We approach the midmost secret that squirms in the most inward inwards of life—*individually we do what we do because we like doing it better than anything else*. So with all the rest of the human animals upon this travelling planet. Well, then, the rest is easy. To reform the world, to deliver from the womb of time the Almost Perfect State, induce the human race to like what it should like, and presto! the deed is done! It's as simple as that!

Of course, there are a couple of points still to be considered—there always are.

(1) How are we to induce the human race to like what it should like?

(2) What should the human race like?

The reason we have decided to give the human race three million years instead of one million is that we think it will be obliged to devote a million and a half years to question one, and an equal length of time to question two.

603

But there is plenty of time ahead of the universe, or plenty of eternity. It is better to devote three million years to finding the right answer, than to think it over for only a million years or so, get the wrong answer, and have to start at the beginning again. In the meantime, of course, systems and constellations all over the cosmos, from Arcturus to South Ferry, are plunging to Gehenna unsaved for the lack of the right answer.

LET'S ALL GO TO HELL

But that is something we must learn to view with a certain placidity. And after all, this thing of a planet going to Hades may be a good thing. It is so with individuals. A man never appreciates heaven unless he has been to hell. A man who has gone to heaven by way of hell is more likely to stick there. Let him go straight to heaven without a taste of hell and his curiosity about hell is aroused; he gets to wanting a change; he wishes to experiment and fuss around. We often used to think, when we were younger, that if we were running Things in General we should abolish hell. But we are beginning to perceive the reason for its existence.

PLEDGE

There will be in the Almost Perfect State a chance for everyone to go to hell. This is a promise.

Let us all try and be more cheerful about going to hell, and life will be easier for us.

Too many philosophers have made it seem like the end of everything. And that has depressed many of us who felt sure that we were bound there.

If we can only get the slant that hell is a halfway station on the road to heaven, we can face it better.

A STAVE TO TROLL ON THE WAY

> *Cheerily, cheerily, mellow companions!*
> *Sweet gentlemen and ladies,*
> *We'll meet again in heaven,*
> *In six years or seven—*
> *Or else we'll meet in Hades!*

Chapter XXXVII

In creating the Almost Perfect State men must depend upon themselves. The gods do not make men better. And when men have made themselves better, the Almost Perfect State will be here—just like that.

Jove at one time became so disgusted with the human race that he was almost on the point of wiping it out of existence, says an early Latin poet. Men worried him. They wouldn't behave properly. It seemed to him he couldn't make them better.

Then he got the idea of *making them make them-selves better*—but a free translation of part of the poem follows:

"'Twas Monday on Mount Olympus,
And Jove had a regal Peeve;
'I'm sorry,' says he, 'I made these men,'
And he wiped his mouth with his sleeve.
'They shimmy and jazz and murder,
They lie and steal and souse;
There isn't a fellow in twenty stars
That has the soul of a louse.'
From his beard he blew the nectar,
With a gust of the Jovian breath,
And 'To Hell,' says he, 'with the human race—
I hope it chokes to death!
They starve each other's children,
They steal each other's wives,
They take their swords in their bloody fists
To spill each other's lives;
They bore me stiff when they worship,
They bore me when they doubt,
And I'm gonna make me a flock of worlds
With the human Bean left out!
Hebe,' says he, 'some nectar!
And mend your slatternly pace!—
Be damned to 'em all,' says he to his drink,
'I'm sick of the human race!'
Then up spake Aphrodite,
And a proper wench was she—
A lively vamp with a lovely lamp
As blue as the glancing sea—

'O Pater,' says she, 'and Deus!
August Olympian Dad!
Well hast thou said, " 'Tis a low-live bunch"—
Yet not entirely bad!
They have their frolic habits,
But give 'm another chance!
There must be something good in a gang
So nutty about Romance!'
Then up spake wise Minerva,
And she was a high-browed dame
(Latin verbs ate out of her hand,
And Thought was her middle name)—
'I am no sentimental
Sofa snake, I hope,
But I'll say that the Cytherean simp,
For once, has the proper dope:
This romantic stuff, so widely
Sung and advertised,
Might be the means of improving the breed
If properly supervised.'
Jove, he thundered mildly,
As a man might say: 'Go on!'
(And a star or two dropped out of view,
Between the dusk and dawn.)
Jove, he bellowed gently,
And said to the learned dame,
'Slip us the exposition, Kid!
Just what is the little game?'
And the owlets perked and hearkened,
The Bacchian panther purred,
And the Triton hushed himself in the deep
To hear Minerva's word. . . .

Minerva's word—we would translate the rest of it but we have mislaid our grammar—Minerva's word, as you have guessed, was Eugenics, Genetics. Regulate romance, and lure the breed into becoming the parents of a better breed. If men as they exist to-day were handed the most perfect system imaginable, they would gum the cards inside of a century. The men first, then the system will come—or maybe they won't need any system of government at all. But you gotta improve the breed. It will take some time—to show results in a million years, don't wait until to-morrow, start to-day, or start yesterday.

There's no use talking, people will have to be good if they want to realize the Almost Perfect State, and they will have to do the hard work themselves. As Calvin Coolidge once said—we think it was Calvin Coolidge—"*Be good, sweet maid, and let who will be clever!*"

Chapter XXXVIII

I have seen Beauty as a morning star,
  Too exquisite to stay the garish dawn,
But moving the dim way that the shadows are—
  Shining, and soon withdrawn.

I have seen Beauty as a valiant wing
  That strikes one blow against a stormy sky;—
Ever a moving thing, a transient thing,
  That gleams and turns to die.

Interplanetary communication is one of the persistent dreams of the inhabitants of this oblate spheroid on which we move, breathe, and suffer for lack of beer. There seems to be a feeling in many quarters that if we could get speech with the Martians, let us say, we might learn from them something to our advantage.

There is a disposition to concede the superiority of the fellows Out There—just as some Americans capitulate without a struggle to poets from England, rugs from Constantinople, song and sausage from Germany, religious enthusiasts from Hindustan, and cheese from Switzerland, although they have not tested the goods offered which may really lack quality. Almost the only foreign importations that were ever sneezed at in this country were Swedish matches and Spanish influenza.

But are the Martians—if Martians there be—any more capable than the persons dwelling between the Woolworth Building and the Golden Horn, between the Shwe Dagon and the First Church, Scientist, in Boston, Massachusetts?

Perhaps the Martians yearn toward Earth, romantically, poetically, the Romeos swearing by its light to the Juliets; the idealists and philosophers fabling that already there exists upon it an Almost Perfect State—and now and then a wan prophet lifting his heart to its gleams, as a cup to be filled from heaven with fresh waters of hope and courage!

We know they are wrong about us, the lovers in the far stars, the philosophers, the poets, the prophets . . . or *are* they wrong?

They are both right and wrong, as we are probably both right and wrong about them. If we tumbled into Mars or Arcturus or Sirius this evening we might find the people there discussing the shimmy, the jazz, the inconstancy of cooks, and the iniquity of retail butchers—and they would be equally disappointed by the way we flitter, frivol, flutter, and flivver.

And yet, that other thing would be there too— that thing that made them look at our star as a symbol of grace and beauty.

OPTIMISTIC THOUGHT

Men could not think of the Almost Perfect State if they did not have it in them ultimately to create the Almost Perfect State.

We used sometimes to walk over the Brooklyn Bridge—that song in stone and steel of an engineer who was also a great artist—at dusk, when the tides of shadow flood in from the lower bay to break in a surf of glory and mystery and illusion against the tall towers of Manhattan. Seen from the middle arch of the bridge at twilight, New York with its girdle of shifting waters and its drift of purple cloud and its quick pulsations of unstable light is a miracle of splendour and beauty that lifts up the heart like the laughter of a god.

But, descend. Go down into the city. Mingle with the details. The damned, dirty old shed from which the "L" trains and trolleys pull out with their jammed and mangled thousands for flattest Flatbush and the unknown bourne of ulterior Brooklyn is still the same damned, dirty old shed. On a hot, damp night the pasty streets stink like a paperhanger's overalls; you are trodden and over-ridden by greasy little profiteers and their hopping victims; you are encompassed round about by the ugly and the sordid, and the objectionable is exuded upon you from a myriad candid pores; your elation and your illusion vanish like ingenuous snowflakes that have kissed a hot-dog sandwich on its fiery brow, and you say: "Beauty? Aw, hell! What's the use?"

And yet you *have* seen beauty. And beauty that was created by these people and people such as these . . . You have seen the tall towers of Manhattan, wonderful under the stars! How did it come about that such growths came from such soil—that a breed lawless and sordid and prosaic has written such a mighty hieroglyphic against the sky? This glamour out of a pigstye—how come? How is it that

611

this hideous, half-brute city is also beautiful and a fit habitation for demigods? How come?

It comes about because the wise and subtle deities permit nothing worthy to be lost. It was with no thought of beauty that the builders laboured; no conscious thought; they were masters or slaves in the bitter wars of commerce, and they never saw as a whole what they were making; no *one* of them did. But each one had had his dream. And the baffled dreams and the broken visions and the ruined hopes and the secret desires of each one laboured with him as he laboured; the things that were lost and beaten and trampled down went into the stone and steel and gave it soul; the aspiration denied and the hope abandoned and the vision defeated were the things that lived, and not the apparent purpose for which each one of all the millions sweat and toiled or cheated. The hidden things, the silent things, the winged things, so weak they are easily killed, the unacknowledged things, the rejected beauty, the strangled appreciation, the inchoate art, the submerged spirit—these groped and found one another and gathered themselves together and worked themselves into the tiles and mortar of the edifice and made a town that is a worthy fellow of the sunrise and the sea winds.

Humanity triumphs over its details!

The individual aspiration is always defeated of its perfect fruition and expression, but it is never lost; it passes somehow into the conglomerate being of the race.

The way to encourage yourself about the human race is to look at it first from a distance; look at the lights on the high spots. Coming closer, you will be profoundly discouraged at the number of low spots, not to say two-spots. Coming still closer, you will become encouraged once more by the reflection that the same stuff that is in the high spots is also in the two-spots.

Chapter XLII

There will be more flexibility about the legal systems of the Almost Perfect State than there is in our own legal system. There will be, of course, a great many laws, but no person will be expected to obey a law that someone else has made if he can himself make a law on the spur of the moment that is a better law and more justly applicable to his own case.

Let us suppose, for instance, that A chisels B out of one thousand dollars in a business deal; the deal is crooked, essentially, and yet under the existing laws A is protected and B cannot get his money back. B sits down and thinks it over. Then he breaks into A's house with a gun and takes jewels and silverware amounting to one thousand dollars.

There is a law which permits A to have him arrested and brought into court on a charge of larceny.

"Do you not know," the Judge asks B, "that you broke the law when you robbed A's house?"

"Yes," says B, "I broke that particular law. But, Judge, I passed a law of my own that evening which repealed the laws that A was operating under; and my law is the superior law because it is based on justice. If A can pass any law, right now, here in this courtroom, that is any more just than my law that I passed the night I broke into his house, and if his law convinces me that I should give the goods back I will give them back; for I am a law-abiding person; I do nothing that is contrary to law; my only condition is that the laws which I obey must be just." Under the Almost Perfect State the Court will allow B to keep what he took from A's house until A gives him back the one thousand dollars.

The function of the courts in the Almost Perfect State will be to decide which of the laws brought forward in any cause are the most just laws, and order their enforcement; every citizen can pass as many laws as he wants to at any time, and operate under them until they come into conflict with laws that are determined to be more just. The vast complication and expense of legislative government will be done away with when everyone makes his own laws. The judicial and executive departments will be one.

This flexible system should prove more popular than our present system, for it combines the attractions of anarchy with the attractions of conservatism. There is something in it to please everybody. The fellow who dotes on law and order can have all the law and order he wants. The egoist, who insists on being a law unto himself, can go ahead until he meets an egoism more deeply grounded in verity and more defensible, more in conformity with essential justice.

The system, of course, throws a great burden upon the judge executive. But if you are going to have any sort of government at all, you must have a burden somewhere. Even the Anarchists have to recognize that. It is the Almost Perfect State which we are outlining; we are not so presumptuous as to put forward a scheme for an Absolutely Perfect State. There are bound to be flaws in our system.

The vast responsibility of the judge executive we point to with pride, as one of the greatest flaws we have ever encountered in any system.

But we start with a recognition of that flaw, and how great a flaw it is; we do not kid ourselves about it; and we think it is a great gain to simplify the machinery so that all the flaws centre in one spot. That spot can be watched more carefully. A judge executive who loses his sense of justice or his will to be just will be eliminated by the sentiment of the community. Someone will walk into his court and sit down in front of him and pass a law declaring that he deserves to be fired, imprisoned, or executed, as the case may be, and another judge will be found to sustain the law thus passed—if the sentiment of the community is right.

Our Almost Perfect State, it will be noted, calls for an enlightened and ethical citizenry. So do all other schemes for the uplift of the world, although all of the schemers are not aware of it. Some of them seem to think that the machinery is the thing. They think that if perfect mechanism were presented to man as he is now, man could operate it perfectly. Whereas it is our contention that the machinery, the system, always matters less than the spirit that is brought to its operation.

The Almost Perfect State will get away from all machinery, as far as possible, and put it up to the citizens themselves to behave. The true aristocrat is a person who knows his own rights and the rights of everyone else and observes those rights without external compulsion—that is to say, he passes his own laws and obeys the just laws his neighbours pass.

OBSERVATION

Politeness, rooted in the soul, is the only true politics.

REPETITION

There will be no perfect democracy until every citizen is an aristocrat.

QUERY

But how are we to obtain this citizenry of such a quality that an Almost Perfect State is possible?

ANSWER

Bring up your children to read, reverence, and worship the present writer.

COMMENT

Say, isn't that rather cocky?

ADMISSION

Of course it is! But isn't it also what every projector of an Almost Perfect System consciously, or unconsciously, tells you to do about his work?

QUERY

But what are we to do when all these philosophers tell us different things?

ANSWER

Do what you damned please. Most of us never do anything else anyhow.

And try and not worry too much about things. Somebody will think it all out for you!

from Chapter XLV

LINES FOR A GRAVESTONE

Here the many lives I led,
All my Selves, are lying dead:
All they journeyed far to find
Strawed by the dispersing wind:
You that were my lovers true,
That is neither sad nor new!

Naught that I have been or planned
Sails the seas nor walks the land:
That is not a cause for woe
Where the careless planets go!
Naught that I have dreamed or done
Casts a shadow in the sun:
Not for that shall any Spring
Fail of song or swallow's wing!

Neither change nor sorrow stays
The bright processional of days—
When the hearts that grieved die, too,
Where is then the grief they knew?

Speed, I bid you, speed the earth
Onward with a shout of mirth,

Fill your eager eyes with light,
Put my face and memory
Out of mind and out of sight.
Nothing I have caused or done,
But this gravestone, meets the sun:
Friends, a great simplicity
Comes at last to you and me!

VIII Serious Poetry

April Song

Fleet across the grasses
  Flash the feet of Spring,
Piping, as he passes
Fleet across the grasses,
"Follow, lads and lasses!
  Sing, world, sing!"
Fleet across the grasses
  Flash the feet of Spring!

Idle winds deliver
  Rumours through the town,
Tales of reeds that quiver,
Idle winds deliver,
Where the rapid river
  Drags the willows down—
Idle winds deliver
  Rumours through the town.

In the country places
  By the silver brooks
April airs her graces;
In the country places

623

Wayward April paces,
    Laughter in her looks;
In the country places
    By the silver brooks.

Hints of alien glamour
    Even reach the town;
Urban muses stammer
Hints of alien glamour,
But the city's clamour
    Beats the voices down;
Hints of alien glamour
    Even reach the town.

The Pool

Reach over, my Undine, and clutch me a reed—
Nymph of mine idleness, notch me a pipe—
For I am fulfilled of the silence, and long
For to utter the sense of the silence in song.

Down-stream all the rapids are troubled with peb-
    bles
    That fetter and fret what the water would utter,
And it rushes and splashes in tremulous trebles;
    It makes haste through the shallows, its soul is
        aflutter;

624

But here all the sound is serene and outspread
In the murmurous moods of a slow-swirling pool;
Here all the sounds are unhurried and cool;
Every silence is kith to a sound; they are wed,
They are mated, are mingled, are tangled, are
bound;
Every hush is in love with a sound, every sound
By the law of its life to some silence is bound.

Then here will we hide; idle here and abide,
In the covert here, close by the waterside—
Here, where the slim flattered reeds are aquiver
With the exquisite hints of the reticent river,
Here, where the lips of this pool are the lips
Of all pools, let us listen and question and wait;
Let us hark to the whispers of love and of death,
Let us hark to the lispings of life and of fate—
In this place where pale silences flower into sound
Let us strive for some secret of all the profound
Deep and calm Silence that meshes men 'round!
There's as much of God hinted in one ripple's
plashes—
There's as much of Truth glints in yon dragon-
fly's flight—
There's as much Purpose gleams where yonder trout
flashes
As in—any book else!—could we read things
aright.

October

Cease to call him sad and sober,
Merriest of months, October!
Patron of the bursting bins,
Reveller in wayside inns,
I can nowhere find a trace
Of the pensive in his face;
There is mingled wit and folly,
But the madcap lacks the grace
Of a thoughtful melancholy.
Spendthrift of the seasons' gold,
How he flings and scatters out
Treasure filched from summer-time!—
Never ruffling squire of old
Better loved a tavern bout
When Prince Hal was in his prime.
Doublet slashed with gold and green;
Cloak of crimson; changeful sheen,
Of the dews that gem his breast;
Frosty lace about his throat;
Scarlet plumes that flaunt and float
Backward in a gay unrest—
Where's another gallant drest
With such tricksy gaiety,
Such unlessoned vanity?

With his amber afternoons
And his pendant poets' moons—
With his twilights dashed with rose
From the red-lipped afterglows—
With his vocal airs at dawn
Breathing hints of Helicon—
Bacchanalian bees that sit
Where his cider-presses drip—
With the winding of the horn
Where his huntsmen meet the morn—
With his every piping breeze
Shaking from familiar trees
Apples of Hesperides—
With the chuckle, chirp, and trill
Of his jolly brooks that spill
Mirth in tangled madrigals
Down pebble-dappled waterfalls—
(Brooks that laugh and make escape
Through wild arbours where the grape
Purples with a promise of
Racy vintage rare as love)—
With his merry, wanton air,
Mirth and vanity and folly
Why should he be made to bear
Burden of some melancholy
Song that swoons and sinks with care?
Cease to call him sad or sober,—
He's a jolly dog, October!

Sapphics

Leaps the little river
    and laughs at fetters,
Through the pebbled channel
    it flutes and flutters;—
Dances down the rapids
    where Autumn scatters
Gold on the waters.

Something bends the sedge
    and the rushes over,
Something moves and gleams
    where the grasses waver;—
Can it be a nymph
    that has taken cover,
Couched by the river?—

May it be a naiad
    with breasts that glimmer,
Chased of satyrs, dreading
    their hoofed clamour,
Finding strange delight
    in the fears that claim her,
Joy in the tremour?

Maybe Pan himself
    in the ferny hollow
Peels a wand and notches
    a pipe of willow,
Perks an ear and nods
    as he harks the mellow
Song of the shallow.

Who shall say 'twas only
    the leaves that glinted?—
Gods of eld survive;
    it is faith has fainted—
Some shall see forever
    the forest haunted,
Earth all enchanted;

Some shall heed the lyres
    in the winds that murmur,
Some shall see the Triton
    beneath the comber,
Some shall hear the loom
    of the pagan Summer
Weaving her glamour;

Hearing wings they dream:
    'Tis the mounting pigeon
Bearing Venus home
    to her own Ægean!
They are outcasts, strayed
    from a golden region,
Drunk on old legend.

A Gentleman of Fifty Soliloquizes

I

Some ten or twelve old friends of yours and mine,
If we spoke truly, are not friends at all,
They never were. That accident divine,
A friendship, not so often may befall!

But as the dull years pass with dragging feet
Within them waxes, in us wanes, esteem;
For weakly, and half conscious of deceit,
We gave them cause an equal love to dream.

Could we have told some fool with haggard face
Who bared his soul, so sure we'd understand,
His little tragedy was commonplace? . . .
We lied. We stretched to him a brother's hand;

He loved us for it, and mere ruth has kept
Our jaws from yawning while he drooled and wept.

II

The valour cold to be ourselves we lack;
And so from strands of kindness misconstrued
And lenient moments, careless threads and slack
We're meshed within a web of habitude.

And often these are worthier men than we;
  But that itself, in time, becomes offense;
We're burdened with this damned nobility
  That's forced on us, which we must recompense.

We loathe ourselves for being insincere,
  And lavish generous deeds to hide the fact:
For who could wound these hearts? Thus we appear
  Thrice loyal friends in word and look and act!

And golden lies with which we save them pain
But serve to make their true regard more fain.

III

Should chance strike out of me some human heat,
  Leap not at that and think to grasp my soul!
I flee new bonds. My self must still retreat
  Down devious ways to keep me free and whole.

Give me your mind, and I will give you mine.
  Then should it change no heart will bleed or
  burn.
Give me your wits. I want no heart of thine.
  You'll ask too much of life-blood in return.

There was a golden lad in years long gone. . . .
  We twain together left the ways of men
And roamed the starry heights, the fields of dawn,
  In youth and gladness. This comes not again.

Give me your mirth. It bores me when you weep.
My loves you cannot touch. They're buried deep.

631

The Mystic

Have I not known the sky and sea
Put on a look as hushed and stilled
As if some ancient prophecy
Drew on to be fulfilled?

And would it be so strange a thing,
Among the rainy hills of Spring,
A veritable god to see
In luminous reality?
To see him pass, as bursts of sun
Pass over the valleys and are gone?

Have I not seen the candid street
Grow secret in the blaze of noon,
Swaying before the Paraclete
Who weaves its being through his rune?

And would it be too strange to say
I see a dead man come this way?
Like mist the houses shrink and swell,
Like blood the highways throb and beat,
The sapless stones beneath my feet
Turn foliate with miracle;
And from the crowd my dead men come,
Fragrant with youth . . . and living mirth

Moves lips and eyes that once were dumb
And blinded in the charnel earth.

And I have dwelt with Presences
Behind the veils of Time and Place,
And hearkened to the silences
That guard the courts of grace,
And I have dared the Distances
Where the red planets race—
And I have seen that Near and Far
And God and Man and Avatar
And Life and Death but one thing are—
And I have seen this wingless world
Curst with impermanence and whirled
Like dust across the Summer swirled,
And I have seen this world a star
All wonderful in Space!

Inhibition

I live a hidden life unguessed,
A life of quaint, fantastic schemes;
I dwell with flushed, romantic dreams
And freakish humours unconfessed,

Though I can show the world a mien
As cold as any judge's mask . . .
(The judge, too, lives beyond his task
And traffics with a realm unseen.) . . .

Behind the placid front of use
The baffled whims move to and fro;
We fear to let these genii go,
Their wings grotesque we dare not loose,

But sober-faced in church or mart,
In office, street, or drawing-room,
We carry cagèd to the tomb,
The golden nonsense of the heart.

"They Had No Poet . . ."

"Vain was the chief's, the sage's pride!
  They had no poet and they died."—POPE.

By Tigris, or the streams of Ind,
  Ere Colchis rose, or Babylon,
Forgotten empires dreamed and sinned,
  Setting tall towns against the dawn,

Which, when the proud Sun smote upon,
  Flashed fire for fire and pride for pride;
Their names were . . . Ask oblivion! . . .
  "They had no poet, and they died."

Queens, dusk of hair and tawny-skinned,
  That loll where fellow leopards fawn . . .
Their hearts are dust before the wind,
  Their loves, that shook the world, are wan!

Passion is mighty . . . but, anon,
  Strong Death has Romance for his bride;
Their legends . . . Ask oblivion! . . .
  "They had no poet, and they died."

Heroes, the braggart trumps that dinned
  Their futile triumphs, monarch, pawn,
Wild tribesmen, kingdoms disciplined,
  Passed like a whirlwind and were gone;

They built with bronze and gold and brawn,
  The inner Vision still denied;
Their conquests . . . Ask oblivion! . . .
  "They had no poet, and they died."

Dumb oracles, and priests withdrawn,
  Was it but flesh they deified?
Their gods were . . . Ask oblivion! . . .
  "They had no poet, and they died."

Envoi

A Little While

A little while the tears and laughter,
  The willow and the rose;
A little while, and what comes after
  No man knows.

An hour to sing, to love and linger,
  Then lutanist and lute
Will fall on silence, song and singer
  Both be mute.

Our gods from our desires we fashion,
  Exalt our baffled lives,
And dream their vital bloom and passion
  Still survives;

But when we're done with mirth and weeping,
  With myrtle, rue, and rose,
Shall Death take Life into his keeping?
  No man knows.

What heart hath not, through twilight places,
  Sought for its dead again
To gild with love their pallid faces?
  Sought in vain!

Still mounts the Dream on shining pinion,
  Still broods the dull distrust:
Which shall have ultimate dominion,
  Dream, or dust?

A little while with grief and laughter,
  And then the day will close;
The shadows gather . . . what comes after
  No man knows!

SAVAGE PORTRAITS

Miss Higgs

Miss Higgs is fair, and not long since was young,
But she is unsuccessful in her loves;
I used to wonder (till I saw her gloves)
Was failure due to her too facile tongue?
And then—I saw her gloves! Unto them clung
Brave strips of white, as snow in April groves;
One time, no doubt, they both were white as
   doves . . .
A sudden notion left me quite unstrung. . . .

I wondered if . . . I wondered if . . . but, no!
Her nails are clean, her face is fresh and fair
A daintier ear than hers I never saw——
Let not the impish fancy to and fro
Scamper where suitor swains would scarcely dare;
I'd rather think those gloves her *only* flaw.

Miss Pringle

If you're so weak as to remark, "Miss Pringle,
The day is fine," why, then, Miss Pringle laughs;
At all the words of men Miss Pringle laughs.
If you should say, "There's Central Park, Miss
    Pringle,"
Or else, "I'm bitten by a shark, Miss Pringle!"
Or else, "Twice five is ten," Miss Pringle laughs . . .
Shrill as a guinea-hen, Miss Pringle laughs . . .
She laughed once when I said, "'Tis dark, Miss
    Pringle."

At first I thought, "Poor pretty little ijit!
Some nervous malady has caused this habit;
Her throat, no doubt, is always on the fidget,
Just as his twitchy nose perturbs a rabbit."
And then I saw her teeth, white, even, small . . .
She has fine teeth, and nothing else at all.

Dade

Loathing this world of nettles, sin, and grime,
Dade likewise loathes the thought of bettering

638

The unfortunate planet; *he'll* not fling
His virtue into any fight with crime.
Dade is so nice he itches all the time;
His moral hide's so very thin (poor thing!)
That all his contacts burn the man and sting:—
He's like a boil that nears its golden prime.

When Dade goes up to Heaven—he will; he's pray-
    erful—
I trust no cruder saint will jolly him;
I trust the Lord will say: "Be very careful,
And don't shock Dade, you rough-necked Cheru-
    bim!"
Lay him away in cotton wool, O God!
Eternally, as something rare and odd.

Klung

In Klung I find no faults, nor great nor small,
Except: *I find no faults nor flaws in Klung.*
The faultless accents of his faultless tongue
In faultless cadence rise and float and fall,
Charged with great thoughts acknowledged truth
    by all.
A finished thing, unspecked of life, among
His sweating fellows loud of mood and lung—
And yet, somehow, his presence casts a pall.

Of Klung I dare to murmur nothing ill:
De mortuis nil nisi bonum still
Must stop one's mouth, and Klung is *very* dead,
His body's self, a statue, should have room
As monument above an empty tomb,
Filled with the nothings he has done and said.

IX Humorous Poetry

Reincarnated!

Lovers were we a million years agone;
A dozen moons have fallen from the sky,
A thousand empires laid them down to die,
And still our amorous idyl carries on!
When first we met, the roaring Mastodon
Peered in our Cave and watched me black your
    eye;
To-day the roaring L-train rushes by
Your flat—and I shall black your eye anon!
Reincarnation once again, my Sweet,
Brings us together o'er the waste of years!
And once again I catch you by the ears,
My Love, and slam your head against the door
To show you that I love you as of yore—
A love like ours can never grow effete!

An Ancient Lay

Gaze on this speckled Egg the Dodo laid
Back yonder in her proud and cackling prime:
It has turned flint to blunt the teeth of time,
A Total Loss unto the Poultry Trade!
When thick Behemoths grumbled in the shade,
When coiled Leviathans drowsed in the slime
And yawned and meditated Food and Crime,
Oh, what an Omelet had that Egg made!
But might the stone grow sappy, from this shell
A Beakèd Monster peck his way to life,
How reminiscent were the miracle
To us! 'Twas Dodo Squabs we had to eat
That day I beaned and won you for my wife,
A million years come Martinmas, my Sweet!

A Milder Mood

My Love, I am not always violent!
Sometimes, when gorged with meat, musing I lie
And watch the cloud-beasts crawl along the sky
And ramp as if to claw the firmament. . . .

644

Sometimes I am a most Poetic Gent!
I tire of murder, even fetch a sigh
To think how oft I've punched you in the eye
And gnarlèd bludgeons o'er your bean have bent.
Do you recall how in my milder mood
I tore a Sword-Toothed Tiger quite in two
And made from ringing gut and sounding wood
A joyous lyre to chant the praise of you?
Sometimes, my Sweet, when I'm replete with food,
I only wish to sing and purr and coo!

When One Loves Tensely

When one loves tensely words are naught, my Dear!
You never felt I loved you till that day
I sighed and heaved a chunk of rock your way;
Nor I, until you clutched your father's spear
And coyly clipped the lobe from off my ear,
Guessed the sweet thought you were too shy to
    say—
All mute we listened to the larks of May,
Silent, we harked the laughter of the year.
Later, my Dear, I'll say you spoke enough!
Do you remember how I took you, Sweet,
And banged your head against the frozen rill
Until I broke the ice, and by your feet
Held you submerged until your tongue was still?
When one loves tensely one is sometimes rough.

Reconciliation

It was but yesternight that I came home
And found your fair face streaked with sliding tears;
And when I asked you why, upon my dome
You gouged a furrow with the garden shears.
"What is the sad occasion of your grief,
My Love?" I murmured. "Speak to me, oh, speak!"
And you sobbed through your wetted handkerchief:
"You have not beaten me for nigh a week!
Oh, you are faithless! All your love is dead!
Oh, you are faithless, faithless, cold of heart!"
Then with a roar I grabbed you by the head,
And wried your neck, and burst your ribs apart—
And you were glad again and flushed with pride,
Sweet Wild Cat, as when first I called you Bride!

Noah an' Jonah an' Cap'n John Smith

Noah an' Jonah an' Cap'n John Smith,
Mariners, travelers, magazines of myth,
Settin' up in Heaven, chewin' and a-chawin'
Eatin' their terbaccy, talkin' and a-jawin';
Settin' by a crick, spittin' in the worter,
Talkin' tall an' tactless, as saints hadn't orter,
Lollin' in the shade, baitin' hooks and anglin',
Occasionally friendly, occasionally wranglin'.

Noah took his halo from his old bald head
An' swatted of a hoppergrass an' knocked it dead,
An' he baited of his hook, an' he spoke an' said:
"When I was the Skipper of the tight leetle Ark
I useter fish fer porpus, useter fish fer shark,
Often I have ketched in a single hour on Monday
Sharks enough to feed the fambly till Sunday—
To feed all the sarpints, the tigers an' donkeys,
To feed all the zebras, the insects an' monkeys,
To feed all the varmints, bears an' gorillars,
To feed all the camels, cats an' armadillers,

647

To give all the pelicans stews for their gizzards,
To feed all the owls an' catamounts an' lizards,
To feed all the humans, their babies an' their nusses,
To feed all the houn' dawgs an' hippopotamusses,
To feed all the oxens, feed all the asses,
Feed all the bison an' leetle hoppergrasses—
Always I ketched, in half a hour on Monday
All that the fambly could gormandize till Sunday!"

Jonah took his harp, to strum and to string her,
An' Cap'n John Smith teched his nose with his
    finger.
Cap'n Smith, he hemmed some an' hawed some,
An' he bit off a chaw, an' he chewed some and
    chewed some:—
"When I was to China, when I was to Guinea,
When I was to Java, an' also in Verginney,
I teached all the natives how to be ambitious,
I learned 'em my trick of ketchin' devilfishes.
I've fitten tigers, I've fitten bears,
I have fitten sarpints an' wolves in their lairs,
I have fit with wild men an' hippopotamusses,
But the perilousest varmints is the bloody octopusses!
I'd rub my forehead with phosphorescent light
An' plunge into the ocean an' seek 'em out at night!
I ketched 'em in grottoes, I ketched 'em in caves,
I used fer to strangle 'em underneath the waves!
When they seen the bright light blazin' on my
    forehead
They used ter to rush at me, screamin' something
    horrid!
Tentacles wavin', teeth white an' gnashin',

Hollerin' an' bellerin', wallerin' an' splashin'!
I useter grab 'em as they rushed from their grots,
Ketch all their legs an' tie 'em into knots!"

Noah looked at Jonah, an' said not a word,
But if winks made noises, a wink had been heard.
Jonah took the hook from a mudcat's middle
An' strummed on the strings of his hallelujah fiddle;
Jonah give his whiskers a backhand wipe
An' cut some plug terbaccer an' crammed it in his
    pipe!
—(Noah an' Jonah an' Cap'n John Smith,
Fisherman an' travelers, narreratin' myth,
Settin' up in Heaven all eternity,
Fishin' in the shade, contented as could be!
Spittin' their terbaccer in the little shaded creek,
Stoppin' of their yarns fer ter hear the ripples speak!
I hope fer Heaven, when I think of this—
You folks bound hellward, a lot of fun you'll miss!)

Jonah, he decapitates that mudcat's head,
An' gets his pipe ter drawin'; an' this is what he
    said:
"Excuse me ef your stories don't excite me much!
Excuse me ef I seldom agitate fer such!
You think yer fishermen! I won't argue none!
I won't even tell yer the half o' what I done!
You has careers dangerous an' checkered!
All as I will say is: Go and read my record!
You think yer fishermen! You think yer great!
All I asks is this: Has one of ye been *bait*?
Cap'n Noah, Cap'n John, I heerd when ye hollered;
What I asks is this: Has one of ye been *swallered*?

It's mighty purty fishin' with little hooks an' reels.
It's mighty easy fishin' with little rods an' creels.
It's mighty pleasant ketchin' mudcats fer yer dinners.
But this here is my challenge fer saints an' fer
sinners,
Which one of ye has v'yaged in a varmint's inners?
When I seen a big fish, tough as Methooslum,
I used for to dive into his oozly-goozlum!
When I seen the strong fish, wallopin' like a lum-
micks,
I useter foller 'em, dive into their stummicks!
I could v'yage an' steer 'em, I could understand 'em,
I useter navigate 'em, I useter land 'em!
Don't you pester *me* with any more narration!
Go git famous! Git a reputation!"

—Cap'n John he grinned his hat brim beneath,
Clicked his tongue of silver on his golden teeth;
Noah an' Jonah an' Cap'n John Smith,
Strummin' golden harps, narreratin' myth!
Settin' by the shallows forever an' forever,
Swappin' yarns an' fishin' in a little river!

Improbable Epitaphs

HERE LIES
THE BODY OF
NICHOLAS WAX
WHO LOVED
TO PAY
HIS INCOME TAX.

THERE LIES AT REST
IN THIS EARTHLY BED
THE MORTAL
PART
OF POTIPHAR JEDD
WHO NEVER TOLD
WHAT HIS CHILDREN SAID.

A REMARKABLE MAN
WAS SOLOMON GAY
WHO IS PLANTED
HERE
TILL THE JUDGMENT DAY.
WHEN HE FOUND
HE HAD NOTHING
IMPORTANT TO SAY
HE WOULD KEEP HIS MOUTH
SHUT
AND GO ON HIS WAY.

LEONORA BUTTERFIELD
WAS NEITHER
SAINT NOR SINNER,
GOOD TRAITS
AND BAD TRAITS
BALANCED WERE
WITHIN HER,
BUT SHE NEVER JAWED
HER HUSBAND
WHEN HE
WAS LATE FOR DINNER.

THIS IS THE GRAVE
OF
TIMOTHY TETHER
WHO NEVER KICKED
ABOUT THE WEATHER.

OUT HERE IN THE COLD
AND THE WIND
AND THE RAIN
IS THE GRAVE OF THE WIFE
OF BENJAMIN BAYNE,
BELOVED TO THE LAST,
FOR SHE NEVER SAID:
"BEN,
OF COURSE WHEN I'M DEAD
YOU WILL MARRY AGAIN!"

HERE LIE THE BONES
OF ELIHU FOX
WHO NEVER BRAGGED
OF HIS DEALINGS
IN STOCKS.

HERE BY THE ROOTS
OF THIS OLD
OAK TREE
REPOSES THE BODY
OF
ELINOR LEE,
AS LOVELY A WOMAN
AS WOMAN
COULD BE.
SHE NEVER GOT CROSS,
SHE NEVER SAW RED,
WHEN HER SPOUSE BURNT HOLES
IN THE SHEETS AND SPREAD
ON SUNDAY MORNINGS,
SMOKING IN BED.

Pantoum of the Pilfered Pups

Where, oh, where has my little dog gone?—*Old
song.*

Where has my little dog gone?
Grief is wrecking my reason
(He vanished in the Dawn.)
This is the Sausage Season.

LOST, terrier, pure white, male, four years old,
neighborhood 123d st., 8th ave.; reward.—*Newspaper ad.*

Grief is wrecking my reason.
(I doubt thee, Butcher Man.)
This is the Sausage Season.
(Meat-selling Caliban!)

Provisions are steady.—*Market report.*

I doubt thee, Butcher Man—
His collar with gold was crusted,
Meat-selling Caliban!
He had a heart that trusted.

Boston man loved his dog so that he left it $1,200 a year in his will.—*News story.*

His collar with gold was crusted—
　(O Butcher, whet and smile!)
He had a heart that trusted;
　Thy heart is full of guile!

Coats of black dogskin at $29.75.—*From a department store ad.*

O Butcher, whet and smile,
　My doubt of thee profound is!
Thy heart is full of guile—
　And sausage two shillings a pound is!

Owners of lost dogs . . . may apply to A. S. P. C. A., Ave. A and 24th st.—*Newspaper ad.*

My doubt of thee profound is:
　He oft paused by thy door!
And sausage two shillings a pound is!
　He lingered near thy store!

If the price of meat continues to rise, where are we to look for our food supply?—*From an article on the cost of living.*

He oft paused by thy door—
　O Butcher enterprising!
He lingered near thy store—
　The price of sausage is rising!

655

Strong interests on the buying side and offerings small.—*Market report.*

> O Butcher enterprising,
>   Where has my little dog gone?
> The price of sausage is rising:—
>   He vanished in the Dawn!

An Encyclopedia Affair

The gay BOK-CAN was a gentleman
  In a coat of gold and green, O!
And he loved SIB-SZO from head to toe,
  Though the alphabet stretched between, O!

"SIB-SZO," he would say, "you keep away
  From MOT-ORM and his doings,
Distrust the lip of the glib GOU-HIP,
  And hearken to my wooings!

"BOKHARA goats, dear ma'am, eat oats,
  And BURGUNDY grows good wine, ma'am!
CAMPHOR comes from vegetal gums,
  O say that you'll be mine, ma'am!"

But SIB-SZO sighed as she replied,
  "The SIMOON sweeps the sea, sir,
SPINOZA fought for the freedom of thought,
  I cannot wed with thee, sir!"

656

"Where will you find," he cried, "a mind
    More crowded with information?
Edmund BURKE was an eloquent Turk,
    BRAZIL is quite a nation!

"The BURIAT wears his cheek-bones flat,
    BROWNING wrote *Sordello*,
The BRACHIOPOD is a creature odd,
    Do you love some other fellow?"

She bowed her head and she wept and said,
    "SYZRAN is a city,
SOCRATES scorned luxuries,
    What I feel for you is pity.

"The SUGAR-BIRD is rather absurd,
    And STEAM will raise a blister,
My sweetheart is the bold FAL-FYZ,
    But I will be your sister!"

BOK-CAN did choke, and sadness BROKE
    The heart in his noble BUST, sir,
URA-ZYM found an URN for him
    And DUG-EF claimed his DUST, sir!

The Determined Suicide

Just as I raised a pistol to my head
From somewhere came a voice that said:

"Don't pull that trigger! Let that weapon fall!
Perhaps it is not loaded, after all,
And think how silly one appears
Snapping unloaded firearms at one's ears!"
To be ridiculous I can't abide . . .
I wept, and flung the gun aside . . .
For even should each chamber bear its proper load
How did I know the cartridge would explode?
Sometimes they don't explode, and I
Was firm resolved that I would die;
The hurrying thought that I might fail
Through some miscalculation, turned me pale.
And then there dawned on me the hope
That I might hang myself . . . but as the rope
I looped about my neck the still voice cried:
"Don't take this thoughtless way of suicide!
Some meddling fool may come and cut you down,
And then the crass, unsympathetic town
Will laugh!"
I'm sensitive; I never could stand chaff;
No foolish anti-climax must attend
This thing . . . my end must be a tragic end!
I took my razor from the shelf . . .
The voice said: "Brute, you think of naught but self!
Should you use that your spouse would never care,
Thereafter, of a Sunday morn, to pare
Her corns with that accustomed and familiar blade!"
I had not thought of that . . . I laid
The lethal thing away, and sadly went
Out of the house all choked with manly senti-
    ment . . .
Ah, Brute, indeed!

To rob a woman in her hour of need . . .
How should I kill myself? What certain way
To creep out of the garish light of day?
It must be sure; and I began to see
All swift, traditional ways were barred to me . . .
This was a further earnest of the hate
In which myself was held by Fate . . .
Some sure way it must be; sure way, but slow;
Some gradual way, since Fate had willed it so.
Why not, through all the bitter years,
Of disillusion, balked ambition, tears,
With stern, set face and laboring breath
Eat . . . eat and eat . . . and eat myself to death?
Titanic steak, Gargantuan chop and Brobdingnagian
   pie,
Each one succeeding each, until I die!
Ah, eighty years are not too much to give
To suicide, when one has sworn: "I will not live!"

HAIL AND FAREWELL

Down in a Wine Vault

To Harold Gould

Down in a wine vault underneath the city
  Two old men were sitting; they were drinking
    booze.
Torn were their garments, hair and beards were
    gritty;
  One had an overcoat but hardly any shoes.

Overhead the street cars through the streets were
    running
  Filled with happy people going home to Christ-
    mas;
In the Adirondacks the hunters all were gunning,
  Big ships were sailing down by the Isthmus.

In came a Little Tot for to kiss her granny,
  Such a little totty she could scarcely tottle,
Saying, "Kiss me, Grandpa! Kiss your little Nanny!"
  But the old man beaned her with a whiskey
    bottle!

Outside the snowflakes began for to flutter,
   Far at sea the ships were sailing with the seamen,
Not another word did Angel Nanny utter.
   Her grandsire chuckled and pledged the Whiskey
      Demon!

Up spake the second man; he was worn and weary,
   Tears washed his face, which otherwise was
      pasty;
"She loved her parents, who commuted on the Erie;
   Brother, I'm afraid you struck a trifle hasty!

"She came to see you, all her pretty duds on,
   Bringing Christmas posies from her mother's
      garden,
Riding in the tunnel underneath the Hudson;
   Brother, was it Rum caused your heart to harden?"

Up spake the first man, "Here I sits a thinking
   How the country's drifting to a sad condition;
Here I sits a dreaming, here I sits a drinking,
   Here I sits a dreading, dreading prohibition,

"When in comes Nanny, my little daughter's
      daughter;
   Me she has been begging ever since October
For to sign the pledge! It's ended now in slaughter—
   I never had the courage when she caught me
      sober!

"All around the world little tots are begging
   Grandpas and daddies for to quit their lushing.
Reformers eggs 'em on. I am tired of egging!
   Tired of being cowed, cowering and blushing!

"I struck for freedom! I'm a man of mettle!
　Though I never would 'a' done it had I not been
　　drinking—
From Athabasca south to Popocatapetl
　We must strike for freedom, quit our shrinking!"

Said the second old man, "I beg your pardon!
　Brother, please forgive me, my words were hasty!
I get your viewpoint, our hearts must harden!
　Try this ale, it is bitter, brown and tasty."

Said the first old man, "Hear me sobbing.
　Poor little Nanny, she's gone to Himmel.
Principle must conquer, though hearts be throbbing!
　Just curl your lip around this kimmel!"

Down in a wine vault underneath the city
　They sat drinking while the snow was falling,
Wicked old men with scarcely any pity—
　The moral of my tale is quite appalling!

The Old Brass Railing

To Charley Still

Our minds are schooled to grief and dearth,
　Our lips, too, are aware,
But our feet still seek a railing
　When a railing isn't there.

I went into a druggist's shop
To get some stamps and soap,—
My feet rose up in spite of me
    And pawed the air with hope.

I know that neither East nor West,
    And neither North nor South,
Shall rise a cloud of joy to shed
    Its dampness on my drouth,—

I know that neither here nor there,
    When winds blow to and fro,
Shall any friendly odours find
    The nose they used to know,—

No stein shall greet my straining eyes,
    No matter how they blink,
Mine ears shall never hear again
    The highball glasses clink,—

There is not anywhere a jug
    To cuddle with my wrist,—
But my habituated foot
    Remains an optimist!

It lifts itself, it curls itself,
    It feels the empty air,
It seeks a long brass railing,
    And the railing isn't there!

I do not seek for sympathy
    For stomach nor for throat,
I never liked my liver much—
    'T is such a sulky goat!—

I do not seek your pity for
  My writhen tongue and wried,
I do not ask your tears because
  My lips are shrunk and dried,—

But, oh! my foot! My cheated foot!
  My foot that lives in hope!
It is a piteous sight to see
  It lift itself and grope!

I look at it, I talk to it,
  I lesson it and plead,
But with a humble cheerfulness,
  That makes my heart to bleed,

It lifts itself, it curls itself,
  It searches through the air,
It seeks a long brass railing,
  And the railing isn't there!

I carried it to church one day—
  O foot so fond and frail!
I had to drag it forth in haste:
  It grabbed the chancel rail.

My heart is all resigned and calm,
  So, likewise, is my soul,
But my habituated foot
  Is quite beyond control!

An escalator on the Ell
  Began its upward trip,
My foot reached up and clutched the rail
  And crushed it in its grip.

It grabs the headboard of my bed
  With such determined clasp
That I'm compelled to scald the thing
  To make it loose its grasp.

Sometimes it leaps to clutch the curb
  When I walk down the street—
Oh, how I suffer for the hope
  That lives within my feet!

Myself, I can endure the drouth
  With stoic calm, and prayer—
But my feet still seek a railing
  When a railing isn't there.

I

Comet, shake out your locks and let them flare
Across the startled heaven of my soul!
Pluck out the hairpins, Sue, and let her roll!
Don't be so stingy with your blooming hair,
But let the whole created cosmos share
The glory of its colour, flashed and swirled
Like nets of sunset flung to mesh a world. . . .
Don't wear it in a little wad up there!

And yet, Suzanne, my comet and my star,
At times restrain those locks a little, too. . . .
My First Wife let her hair go quite too far
In culinary ways. I beaned her, Sue. . . .
She looked so wistful as she passed away.
That dear, lost woman, Sue! Ah, welladay!

II

Plunge shaded eyes adown the flaming past
And lamp the locks that set the world afire:—
O wig that touched off Troy! O Dido's Pyre,
Where flame was given back to flame at last!

O love that lashed Ulysses to the mast
What time the red-head Sirens smote the lyre!
O simps that used to simmer and perspire
When Mary Stuart's furnace ran full blast!

My Second Wife would very often say:
"There's nothing—*nothing*—I can do with it
Just after it's been washed!" Ah, welladay!
Sometimes I've thought 'twas almost wrong to hit
A woman *hard* . . . I mention this to you
Merely in pensive reminiscence, Sue.

VII

I saw some bright flowers swaying in the park
And thought how like their life your red locks
    blow. . . .
My Flame! My Sunrise and mine Afterglow!
My genial Hearthfire blazing through the dark!
My Gaudy Kid! Upon life's headlands, stark
And bleak, over the treacherous tides that flow,
A beacon light your Fiery Bean doth throw. . . .
I steer by you and save my giddy bark.

How I should hate it, Lighthouse tall and slim,
If you should cut your hair and dim your fire!
My Seventh Wife did that; she doused her glim,
And dousing it, she damped my soul's desire—
I took a brick and shaved the rest away,
But still her memory stirs me. . . . Welladay!

VIII

There is a freckle just below thine ear
That might have been a theme for Shakespeare's
    art . . .
A fleck of gold out of thy golden heart,
A stain that makes thy stainlessness more dear,
Tossed by thy tidal blood as flotsam here
In its warm voyage through every lovely part . . .
Hang Shakespeare, Sue! And don't let freckles start!
I'd just as lief see optics with a blear.

Your hair's your one best bet. Hold on to that.
My Eighth Wife had that silly freckle notion . . .
I soaked the poor girl in a vat of lotion
So much that presently she pined away. . . .
She never had been very strong nor fat. . . .
These dear dead women, Sue! Ah, welladay!

XII

Sun of my Heaven! Harvest Moon of love!
Bright Planet! Comet! . . . whether earth or sky
I scan, your Pink Bean meets my spirit's eye,
O peer of flowers beneath and stars above!
O Aphrodite's Crimson-Crested Dove,
I love you as New Englanders love pie!
Vesuvius Girl! your fiery head fling high
And give yon leering Zenith's face a shove!

My twelfth wife used to go about with twisters
Of kid upon her hair to keep it curly . . .
I pulled it all out by the roots . . . Poor girlie!
Her baldness rather shocked her aunts and sisters . . .

She died soon after . . . Ah, that's woman's way!
They leave us flat so often! Welladay!

XIII

When I approach the chill Lethean river
And stand, all astral gooseflesh, on the brim,
Will your Red Head shine for me through the dim
Damp shadows where I rub my soul and shiver
As I await old Charon's hydro-flivver?
A Lighthouse on the Other Shore? A Glim
Of warmth and courage o'er the waters grim?
Will you be mine on Earth and mine Forever?

Suzanne, I hope things will not go so far . . .
My Thirteenth Wife would say: "Eternity,
My spouse, is not too long for you and me!"
It made me writhe! I painted her with tar
And touched her off and watched her blaze
    away. . . .
How love's old embers burn! Ah, welladay!

XXI

O lovely Griddle where my Cakes of Song
Are baked! O Gulf Stream of my ocean deep!
O Human Thermos Bottle! will you keep
My love as hot as this our whole lives long?
Or will the slow years moderate the strong
Caloric currents? . . . gradual years that creep
To frost Love's tootsies where he lies asleep . . .
Shall our fate be that of the common throng?

Well, you at least will live in memory;
And that, Suzanne, is more than I can say
Of my Wife Number Twenty-one, for she
Out of my mind has faded quite away.
Too vague to be a ghost! She worshipped me,
No doubt . . . but one forgets! Ah, welladay!

XXVII

Blue is my Beard, Suzanne; my Beard is Blue!
Blue as the nose that graduate drunkards wear . . .
Blue as the tumbled meadows of wide air
Pallas Athene's chariot plunges through . . .
(I don't know why I drag in Pallas, Sue,
Except the name sounds rather flossy there) . . .
With my Blue Beard and with your Crimson Hair,
Affinities predestined, Me and You!

Mayhap I've told you why Wife Twenty-seven
Left me to mourn and climbed the starry way
Up from a thirty-dollar flat to Heaven?—
Suzanne, the woman carelessly turned gray!
I gently slew her one sweet Autumn even . . .
These poignant old regrets! Ah, welladay!